AN INTRODUCTION
TO
CRYSTAL CHEMISTRY

AN INTRODUCTION
TO
CRYSTAL CHEMISTRY

by

R. C. EVANS

*Fellow of St Catharine's College and Lecturer in the
Department of Mineralogy and Petrology,
University of Cambridge*

CAMBRIDGE
AT THE UNIVERSITY PRESS
1952

PUBLISHED BY

THE SYNDICS OF THE CAMBRIDGE UNIVERSITY PRESS

London Office: Bentley House, N.W. I
American Branch: New York

Agents for Canada, India, and Pakistan: Macmillan

548

Evli

First Edition 1939
Reprinted with corrections 1946, 1948, 1952

36 213

March 1958

First printed in Great Britain at The University Press, Cambridge
Reprinted by Spottiswoode, Ballantyne & Co., Ltd., Colchester

PREFACE

The discovery of the diffraction of X-rays by a crystal grating and the subsequent development of the technique of crystal structure analysis have led to the accumulation during the last fifteen years of a great mass of experimental data on the internal structure of a wide range of crystalline materials. Already these data have been summarized and reviewed in several works, but hitherto the summaries have been primarily topographical in their approach and have followed a classification based on composition and morphology alone. Crystal chemistry is not, however, a purely descriptive science, and it is in the interpretation of the observed crystal structures and in their correlation with physical and chemical properties that the chief significance and interest lies. The time has now come when a sufficiently wide and diverse range of compounds has been investigated for some of the general principles of crystal architecture to have emerged, and in this book an attempt is made to survey critically the broad field to which X-ray methods have been applied and to codify some of these principles. The field is indeed a broad one, for there are aspects of crystal chemistry of significance to the chemist, the physicist, the metallurgist, the geologist and even the biologist, while on the theoretical side many of the results have an important bearing on the work of the mathematical physicist. For this reason the approach followed is one which demands little detailed crystallographic knowledge on the part of the reader and which seeks rather to emphasize the applications of the general principles of crystal chemistry in these several fields than to describe the specialized details of the results. It is therefore hardly necessary to remark that no attempt has been made to notice all, or even many, of the vast number of crystal structures which have been analysed, and only those structures which seem most suited to illustrate the principles here advanced have been described: the others, together with much important work which has appeared while the manuscript was in preparation or passing through the press, will serve to fill in the details but not to change the outline of the picture here painted. The reader with more specialized interests will find in the generous provision of references material for the further study of the applications of the subject in his own particular field.

Throughout the book atomic radii and interatomic distances are expressed in terms of the Ångström unit, $1 A. = 10^{-8}$ cm. References are given according to the "Harvard System" in the form recommended in the 2nd edition of the *World List of Scientific Periodicals* (Oxford University Press, 1934).

ACKNOWLEDGMENTS

I have been fortunate during the preparation of this book in enjoying the active interest and encouragement of Professor J. D. Bernal, F.R.S., who not only most generously put at my disposal a considerable amount of his own unpublished material but also read through much of the work in manuscript form. For this valuable assistance and criticism I am deeply indebted to him. It is also a great pleasure to express my thanks to Dr Dorothy Crowfoot of Somerville College, Oxford, with whom I had an opportunity of discussing the chapter on molecular compounds during the early stages of its preparation.

For permission to reproduce figures and a table I gratefully acknowledge my indebtedness to the following learned bodies and publishers: the Council of the Franklin Institute (Figs. 1 and 33); William Heinemann, Ltd. (Figs. 2, 3, 4, 31, 35, 36, 40, 41, 42, 44 and 53); the Council of the Royal Society (Figs. 8, 25, 26, 27, 69, 73, 87, 88, 96, 98, 102, 108 and 111); the Council of the American Institute of Physics (Figs. 9, 10, 13, 14, 72, 77 and 93); Edward Arnold and Co. (Figs. 11 and 12); G. Bell and Sons, Ltd. (Figs. 15 and 88); Georg Lüttke (Figs. 16 and 29); Julius Springer (Figs. 17, 39, 54, 55d, 56 and 57); the Council of the Institute of Metals (Fig. 19); Akademische Verlagsgesellschaft G.m.b.H., Leipzig (Figs. 22, 23, 24, 30, 32, 37, 45, 51, 52, 58, 59, 62, 63, 64, 65, 66, 67, 68, 70 and 71); Verlag Chemie G.m.b.H. (Fig. 28); the Council of the American Society

for Metals (Fig. 34); the Chemical Catalog Co. Inc. (Figs. 47, 81*b*
and 82); the Council of the Chemical Society (Figs. 60*b*, 60*c*,
83, 84, 85, 86, 92, 106, 107, 112 and 113); the Council of the
American Physical Society (Fig. 60*d*); the Council of the
Faraday Society (Fig. 76); the proprietors of *Nature* (Figs. 78
and 89); the Council of the American Chemical Society (Figs. 79
and 94); the Council of the National Academy of Sciences
(Fig. 80); the proprietors of the *Philosophical Magazine*
(Table 4).

R. C. E.

CAMBRIDGE
December, 1938

CONTENTS

Preface   *page* v

PART I. THE CRYSTAL LATTICE

Chapter I. INTRODUCTION
Historical survey   1
Early crystal chemistry   5

Chapter II. INTERATOMIC BINDING FORCES
Introduction   9
The Bohr atom and the periodic classification   11
The ionic bond   18
The homopolar bond   26
The metallic bond   32
The van der Waals bond   36
The classification of crystal structures   41

Chapter III. QUANTITATIVE LATTICE THEORY
The early lattice theory of ionic crystals   44
The quantum theory of the van der Waals bond   50
The later lattice theory of ionic crystals   55
The structural significance of lattice theory   60
The quantum theory of the homopolar bond   65
The theory of the metallic state   74
A general theory of the solid state   84

PART II. SYSTEMATIC CRYSTAL CHEMISTRY

Chapter IV. THE METALLIC ELEMENTS
Introduction   89
The structures of the metallic elements   91
The atomic radii of the metals   101

Chapter V. ALLOY SYSTEMS

Introduction	*page* 106
Alloys of two true metals	109
The order-disorder transformation	116
Alloys of a true metal and a *B* sub-group element	122
Alloys of two *B* sub-group elements	141
General features of alloy systems	144
Interstitial structures	145
The chemistry of metal systems	153

Chapter VI. HOMOPOLAR COMPOUNDS

Introduction	157
Atomic radii in homopolar structures	162

Chapter VII. IONIC COMPOUNDS: ISODESMIC STRUCTURES

Introduction	164
The classification of ionic structures	165
Simple isodesmic structures	168
AX structures	182
AX_2 structures	186
$A_m X_n$ structures	194
The chemistry of simple isodesmic structures	194
Crystal structure and morphology	196
Multiple isodesmic structures	203
'Defect' structures	209

Chapter VIII. IONIC COMPOUNDS: MESODESMIC STRUCTURES

Introduction	215
Borates	220
Silicates	223
Germanates	245

Chapter IX. IONIC COMPOUNDS: ANISODESMIC
    STRUCTURES

Introduction   *page* 246
The structure of complex ions   247
Structures containing complex ions   255
The chemistry of anisodesmic structures   265
Some physical properties of crystals   267
Hydrated anisodesmic structures   274
Hydrates containing co-ordinated water   276
Hydrates containing structural water   283
Complex co-ordination compounds   284

Chapter X. IONIC COMPOUNDS CONTAINING
    HYDROGEN

Introduction   287
The hydrogen bond   287
The hydroxyl bond   291
The structure of liquids, liquid crystals and glasses 301

Chapter XI. MOLECULAR COMPOUNDS

Introduction   310
Compounds with small symmetrical molecules   316
Compounds with long molecules   326
Compounds with flat molecules   332
Compounds with complex three-dimensional mole-   349
    cules
The magnetic properties of molecular crystals   350
Incomplete structure analyses   352
Conclusion   365

Bibliography   367

References   370

Index   383

PART I

THE CRYSTAL LATTICE

—◇—

CHAPTER I

INTRODUCTION

HISTORICAL SURVEY

The systematic investigation of the relationship of crystalline form to chemical constitution may be said to date from the invention of the goniometer by Carangeot in 1780. Important contributions had been made earlier than this, notably by Steno, who remarked in 1669 that quartz crystals, whatever their origin or habit, always preserved the same interfacial angles, and by Guglielmini, who in 1688 extended Steno's observations to many other minerals, and also discovered the constancy of cleavage directions in crystals. In the absence of any quantitative data, however, progress was necessarily slow, and the vast field opened up by the goniometer is revealed by the mass of material which appeared in the years immediately following Carangeot's invention. As early as 1783 de l'Isle (1783) published four volumes of data incorporating his observations on many common minerals, while in the next year Haüy (1784) enunciated the laws which govern crystal symmetry and paved the way for his later discovery of the law of rational indices, which, in 1801, he substantiated by a comprehensive crystallographic survey of the mineral kingdom (Haüy, 1801).

The researches of Haüy may well be said to have laid the foundations of modern crystallography, but it was not until the invention of the reflecting goniometer by Wollaston in 1809 that further progress was possible. The contact goniometer had served to provide the data for Haüy's researches on crystal symmetry, but an instrument of an altogether different order of accuracy was required before crystallography could lay claim to the title of an exact science. The application of the reflecting goniometer to crystallographic research resulted in the rapid accumulation of a great wealth of exact experimental data not only on naturally occurring minerals but also on artificial crystals of chemical importance, and it was these data which provided the material for the discovery of isomorphism by Mitscherlich in 1819. The work of Mitscherlich at once directed attention to the chemical significance of crystal form and habit, and from 1820 onwards crystallographic research for nearly a hundred years was concerned primarily with the relationship of crystalline form to chemical constitution. Here we can mention only a few of the more important contributions. Pre-eminent stands the work of Pasteur on the enantiomorphism of tartaric acid, of the greatest significance in the later developments of chemical theory. Other researches were concerned with the physical and crystallographic properties of substances chemically closely related, and as early as 1840 Kopp observed that the tendency to form mixed crystals increased with increasing similarity in molecular volume. Later in the century Hiortdahl and Groth showed that in a series of organic compounds systematic substitution brought about a progressive change in crystal form, while important observations on the physical properties of substances chemically closely related are associated with the names Retgers, Liebisch, Gossner, Barker and Tutton. The great volume of crystallographic data on both inorganic and organic compounds which accumulated during the period was tabulated in Groth's monumental *Chemische Krystallographie* (Groth, 1906–19).

Although the work of the second half of the nineteenth century provided many data which have been of the greatest value to subsequent investigators, it cannot be said to have led to developments in any way comparable in importance with the discoveries of Mitscherlich and Pasteur in the first half of the century. In part this was due to the fact that most of the substances investigated were of far too great chemical complexity, but more particularly was it an inevitable consequence of the fact that the external crystal form, closely prescribed by rigid rules of symmetry, can necessarily give but a very limited expression of the internal constitution and structure of the crystal. Thus, to take a single example, all crystals belonging to the cubic system must, from a crystallographic point of view, be regarded as isomorphous, and purely crystallographic observations can never lead to an explanation of any differences in properties which such crystals may show.

It must not be supposed that speculations on the internal architecture of crystals had not taken place, and in fact in 1665 Hooke showed that all the forms commonly observed in alum crystals could be simulated by building piles of spheres, while in 1784 Haüy, as a consequence of his studies on cleavage, envisaged calcite crystals, of whatever habit, as formed by the packing together of minute rhombohedral units. In this way he was able to account for the law of rational indices, but such a viewpoint was soon shown to be an essentially artificial one by a study of fluorite, in which the cleavage is octahedral, for it is impossible to fill space by packing together units of that shape. More recently the internal structure of crystal was discussed by Barlow and Pope (1906, 1907), and here, for the first time, we see the conception of a crystal as an essentially *geometrical* entity formed by the packing of spherical *atoms*, each of a definite and characteristic size determined by an equilibrium between the attractive and repulsive forces operating between neighbouring atoms. These speculations, as we shall see later, were extraordinarily close to the truth, but it was not until the discovery by Friedrich, Knipping and Laue (1912) of the diffraction of X-rays by a crystal grating that crystallographers were provided with a means of investigating directly the internal structure of a crystal. If the importance of a discovery is to be measured by the consequences to which it gives rise, the discovery of X-ray diffraction must be ranked as one of the most important in the history of science, for it has provided a tool for the investigation of the solid state of a power altogether transcending any that was previously available. Prior to the development of X-ray methods the internal structure of a solid could be deduced only by argument from its physical properties or from its chemical properties in the liquid or gaseous state. X-ray analysis has removed the determination of crystal structure and molecular configuration from the sphere of speculation to that of measurement, and it is not difficult to see that the consequences of such an advance must be of the greatest significance in all branches of chemical theory.

The year following the discovery of X-ray diffraction saw the publication of the first crystal analysis, that of sodium chloride (W. L. Bragg, 1913), the structure of which is illustrated in Fig. 1, and within a short time many other

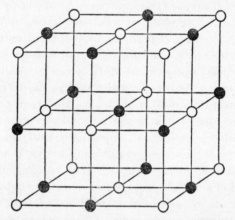

Fig. 1. The structure of sodium chloride, NaCl.

simple structures had been elucidated. In the first few years, however, the interest lay principally on the physical side, in the development of the technique of structure analysis and in the experimental verification of the conclusions of diffraction theory. It was not until after the invention of the X-ray spectrometer (W. H. Bragg and W. L. Bragg, 1913) and the development of the powder- (Debye and Scherrer, 1916; Hull, 1917) and rotation-photograph (Seeman, 1919; Polanyi, 1921; Schiebold, 1923) methods of analysis on the one hand, and the development of a rigid X-ray diffraction theory (Darwin, 1914 a, b; Ewald, 1918; Waller, 1925) on the other, that X-ray methods became firmly established as a tool which has remained substantially unaltered till the present time, and that interest was diverted from the experimental methods to the results to which they gave rise. Once this change in viewpoint had taken place, the science of systematic crystal chemistry became established on a firm foundation, and in the last decade X-ray methods have been applied in almost every branch of chemistry.

EARLY CRYSTAL CHEMISTRY

Crystal chemistry in its widest sense may be defined as the study of the relationship of the internal structure of a body to its physical and chemical properties. It aims at interpreting the properties of any substance in terms of its crystal structure, and, conversely, at associating with any structural characteristic a corresponding set of physical and chemical properties. Ideally crystal chemistry should enable us to predict and synthesize chemical compounds having any desired combination of properties whatsoever.

The foundation of crystal chemistry may be regarded as dating from the observations of W. L. Bragg (1920) on the interatomic distances in series of closely related chemical compounds. If we consider such a series as the alkali halides, all of which except CsCl, CsBr and CsI have the sodium-chloride structure, we find a progressive change in lattice dimensions in passing from a fluoride to an iodide of any metal, or again in passing from a lithium to a caesium salt. This point is illustrated by Table 1, p. 6, in which the half-cell side or interatomic* distance $A-X$† is tabulated for each of the salts. These figures are not those originally employed by Bragg but are based on more recent measurements. A study of this table at once reveals that the change in interatomic distance accompanying a progressive substitution in the series is a regular one, and that, for example, the difference

* The atoms are, of course, ionized in these salts, but for the sake of brevity, where there is no danger of confusion, we shall frequently use the word 'atom' to describe a particle in its ionized as well as in its neutral state.

† Throughout this book we shall use the symbols $ABC...$ to represent atoms or ions of electropositive elements, and the symbols $...XYZ$ the atoms or ions of electronegative elements.

between the interatomic distances in two halides with the same cation is very nearly the same whichever of the alkali metals that cation may be, while conversely, for the halides of a given pair of alkali metals, this difference is nearly independent of the particular halogen in combination. These regularities at once lend weight to the conception of a crystal structure as composed of a set of spherical atoms, each of characteristic size, packed together in contact, and in fact in these data we have the first experimental confirmation of the views earlier expressed by Barlow and Pope.*

TABLE 1

INTERATOMIC DISTANCES IN THE ALKALI HALIDES

	Li	Δ	Na	Δ	K	Δ	Rb	Δ	Cs
F	2·01	0·30	2·31	0·35	2·66	0·16	2·82	0·18	3·00
Δ	0·56	—	0·50	—	0·48	—	0·45	—	(0·57)
Cl	2·57	0·24	2·81	0·33	3·14	0·13	3·27	(0·30)	(3·57)
Δ	0·18	—	0·17	—	0·15	—	0·16	—	(0·14)
Br	2·75	0·23	2·98	0·31	3·29	0·14	3·43	(0·28)	(3·71)
Δ	0·25	—	0·25	—	0·24	—	0·23	—	(0·24)
I	3·00	0·23	3·23	0·30	3·53	0·13	3·66	(0·29)	(3·95)

(Of the caesium salts only CsF has the sodium-chloride structure.)

It is clear that from the observed interatomic distances we can deduce only the sum of two atomic radii and not the individual values of either, since it would be possible to increase the radii of all electropositive and to decrease those of all electronegative elements by an arbitrary amount without altering the A–X distances. By observations on the crystal structures of the elements, or on crystals in which two atoms

* It will be appreciated that the conventional structure diagrams indicate only the positions of the centres of the atoms, and make no attempt to represent either their relative sizes or their mutual contacts. Clearly any attempt to draw the atoms full size would obscure most of the features of the structure.

of the same kind come into contact (Landé, 1920 *a, b*), however, it is possible to deduce unambiguous values for the radii of the elements concerned, and hence of the other elements with which they enter into combination. In this way W. L. Bragg was able to tabulate radii for most of the common elements, but it soon became apparent that the radii thus obtained were not entirely consistent, and that, moreover, they showed several anomalies. Thus, for example, the radius of sodium in sodium chloride appeared to be greater than that of chlorine, a conclusion difficult to reconcile with any accepted picture of atomic structure. Later work, however, soon revealed that the conception of an atom as an entity of characteristic and fixed radius was one which could be entertained only within certain groups of chemical compounds, and, in fact, that a given atom may occur in different bodies in different states of ionization and possessing correspondingly entirely different characteristic radii. Only within a group of 'commensurable' structures, in which the state of ionization is the same, is a comparison of atomic radii of any significance. Thus we now know that the radius of the sodium *atom* in metallic sodium is 1·86 A., but that the radius of the sodium *ion* in the sodium halides has the very different value 0·98 A.

The entirely different character of the interatomic linkage which must occur in sodium on the one hand and sodium chloride on the other introduces the conception of the *metallic* bond as responsible for the coherence of a metal, and the *ionic* or *polar* bond as responsible for that of such a substance as sodium chloride. A study of other crystals shows that there are yet two further types of interatomic force of frequent occurrence, the *homopolar* or *co-ordinate* link which occurs in crystals such as diamond, and the *residual* or *van der Waals* bond which is responsible for the coherence of the inert gases when condensed to solids at low temperatures. These four types of bond all impart characteristic properties to the bodies in which they occur, and in fact provide the most convenient basis for a classification of crystal structures. Crystals, such as the examples just instanced, in which only one type of force occurs, are said to be *homodesmic*, while those, many examples of which will appear later, in which two or more different types of bond are in operation between different parts of the structure are termed *heterodesmic*.

In heterodesmic structures the physical properties such as hardness, mechanical strength and melting point are in general determined by the weakest bond present, that being the first to suffer disruption under increasing mechanical or thermal strain, and accordingly in our classification such structures will be discussed under the heading of the weakest force which occurs. Before, however, passing on to a systematic discussion of crystal structures in terms of such a classification we shall in the next two chapters consider something of the characteristic properties of each of these four types of bond in order to lay the foundation of a more complete understanding of the significance of the structures in which they are found.

CHAPTER II

INTERATOMIC BINDING FORCES

INTRODUCTION

Speculations on the origin and nature of the interatomic forces responsible for the coherence and stability of the chemical molecule date back almost to the foundations of modern chemistry. The electrical character of these forces was suggested tentatively by Desaguliers as early as 1742, and the idea was developed systematically in 1819 by Berzelius, whose views had an important influence on chemistry until the ionic dissociation theory of Arrhenius (1887) was introduced later in the century. By that time, however, the conception had grown up of two essentially different types of binding force to account for the formation, on the one hand, of molecules, such as sodium chloride, containing atoms of essentially different character, and on the other of molecules, such as that of chlorine, composed of similar or identical atoms, and detailed theories of the homopolar bond responsible for the formation of compounds of the latter type were developed simultaneously by Lewis (1916) and by Kossel (1916) in terms of Bohr's then recently published theory of atomic structure.

The development of X-ray crystal analysis immediately threw valuable light on the question of the nature of interatomic forces, for it provided the first means of determining experimentally the atomic configuration of molecules whose form had long been the subject of speculations based on chemical valency theories. One of the earliest, and certainly one of the most important, consequences which followed the first structure analysis was a realization of the fact that no essential distinction exists between the 'chemical' forces responsible for binding together the atoms of the chemical molecule and the 'physical' forces responsible for the coherence of the solid as a whole, and that, in fact, in the great majority of simple compounds the molecule as such has no existence in the solid state. The structural importance of this discovery will be discussed later, but from the point of view of valency theory it was equally important since it opened the way to a physical approach to the interpretation of the chemical bond: physical as well as chemical properties had to be explained in terms of the bond, and, conversely, physical as well as chemical properties threw light on its nature.

This identification of the chemical and the physical bond at once led to the association with the chemist's ionic and homopolar bond of two other types of binding force not previously regarded as chemical in nature at all, namely the metallic bond responsible for the cohesion of a metal, and the very much weaker residual or van der Waals bond, which binds the atoms of the inert gases in the solid state to which they condense at low temperatures. These metallic and residual forces, however, did not lend themselves as readily as did the ionic and the homopolar to any simple explanation in terms of the Bohr theory, and it is only in recent years that the development of the new quantum mechanics has enabled a qualitative and even quantitative description of these bonds to be given. At the same time quantum theory has furnished a more exact description of the properties of the ionic and homopolar bonds, which were previously so successfully described qualitatively in terms of older ideas, so that it is now possible to give a satisfactory theoretical explanation of many of the physical and chemical properties of simple structures.

These applications of the modern quantum theory to the problems of interatomic binding have thrown much light on the nature of the forces involved, and it will undoubtedly be in terms of the quantum mechanics that further advances in the interpretation of chemical forces will be made. From a purely descriptive point of view, however, the rigid treatment of the quantum mechanics has its disadvantages, for many of the conceptions involved do not lend themselves to verbal expression, while a formal mathematical discussion may easily obscure some of the more physical aspects of the problem. Moreover, quantum theory can as yet treat only the very simplest of structure types, whereas the crystal structures which have been experimentally investigated range over the whole field of inorganic, organic and even biological chemistry. It must inevitably be a long time before we can hope for anything approaching a rigid analysis applicable to these more complex structures, but in the meanwhile it is nevertheless possible to give a useful qualitative account of many of their properties in terms of ideas based on the older views of atomic structure. In fact, as Sommerfeld (1928a) has emphasized, for the processes involved in many chemical problems such a description is entirely adequate, and it is often only in more detailed physical problems that we must turn to the newer picture of wave mechanics. Accordingly we give in this chapter an elementary and purely qualitative account of the nature and properties of the several types of interatomic binding force, and defer until Chap. III any discussion of the more recent work on the quantitative description of these forces in simple structures.

THE BOHR ATOM AND THE PERIODIC CLASSIFICATION

The Bohr atom.

The Bohr theory pictures the atom as consisting of a nucleus and an extranuclear structure. The nucleus has a diameter of the order of 10^{-13} cm. and is very small compared with the atom as a whole, the diameter of which is about 10^{-8} cm. In spite of its small size, however, the nucleus contributes practically the whole mass of the atom. It carries a positive charge which (measured in terms of the charge on the electron as unit) is equal to the atomic number Z. Surrounding the nucleus, and conferring electrical neutrality on the atom as a whole, is a set of Z electrons arranged in a series of 'orbits' or 'shells'. The distribution of the extra-nuclear electrons over these orbits determines the chemical properties of the atoms concerned, and is therefore intimately

TABLE 2

The periodic classification of the elements

	1	2	3	4	5	6	7	8	0
1	1 H								2 He
2	3 Li	4 Be	5 B	6 C	7 N	8 O	9 F		10 Ne
3	11 Na	12 Mg	13 Al	14 Si	15 P	16 S	17 Cl		18 A
4	19 K	20 Ca	21 Sc	22 Ti	23 V	24 Cr	25 Mn	26 Fe 27 Co 28 Ni	
4	29 Cu	30 Zn	31 Ga	32 Ge	33 As	34 Se	35 Br		36 Kr
5	37 Rb	38 Sr	39 Y	40 Zr	41 Nb	42 Mo	43 Ma	44 Ru 45 Rh 46 Pd	
5	47 Ag	48 Cd	49 In	50 Sn	51 Sb	52 Te	53 I		54 Xe
6	55 Cs	56 Ba	57 La	58 Ce	59 Pr		60 Nd	61 Il 62 Sm	
6	63 Eu	64 Gd		65 Tb	66 Dy		67 Ho	68 Er 69 Tm	
6	70 Yb	71 Lu		72 Hf	73 Ta	74 W	75 Re	76 Os 77 Ir 78 Pt	
6	79 Au	80 Hg	81 Tl	82 Pb	83 Bi	84 Po	85		86 Rn
7	87	88 Ra	89 Ac	90 Th	91 Pa	92 U			

associated with the position of the elements in the periodic classification in a manner discussed below. A chart of the periodic classification is given in Table 2, and the electronic structure of the elements is summarized in Table 3. Reference may be made to these tables in following the arguments of the next section.

TABLE 3

THE ELECTRONIC STRUCTURE OF THE ELEMENTS

Period	Elements	K	L	M	N	O	P	Q
1	H→He	1→2						
2	Li→Ne	2	1→8					
3	Na→A	2	8	1→8				
4	K→Ca Sc→Ni Cu→Kr	2 2 2	8 8 8	8 8+(1→8) 18	1→2 2 1→8			
5	Rb→Sr Y→Pd Ag→Xe	2 2 2	8 8 8	18 18 18	8 8+(1→8) 18	1→2 2 1→8		
6	Cs→Ba La Ce→Lu Hf→Pt Au→Rn	2 2 2 2 2	8 8 8 8 8	18 18 18 18 18	18 18 18+(1→14) 32 32	8 8+1 8+1 8+(2→8) 18	1→2 2 2 2 1→8	
7	87→Ra Ac→U	2 2	8 8	18 18	32 32	18 18	8 8+(1→4)	1→2 2

The periodic classification.

The short periods. The simplest atom is that of hydrogen of atomic number 1. Here the nucleus carries a single positive charge, and the extranuclear structure consists of a single electron in the innermost K shell of principal quantum number 1. Helium of atomic number 2 has a doubly charged nucleus and two extranuclear electrons in the K shell. In lithium, the third electron added to the extranuclear structure requires the formation of a new L shell, of principal quantum number 2, since the K shell can accommodate not more than two electrons. In passing progressively through the elements beryllium, boron, carbon, nitrogen, oxygen and fluorine of the second period of the table further electrons are added to the L shell, which is finally completed with a complement of eight electrons in neon of atomic number 10. The addition of a further electron again requires the formation of a new shell, and in sodium a single electron occurs in the M shell of quantum number 3. The development of the third period of the table is closely analogous to that of the second, and is completed in argon of atomic number 18 when the M shell also contains eight electrons.

The fourth period: transition metals. Only the electrons in the outermost shell are sufficiently loosely bound to be disturbed by the energies available in any ordinary chemical reaction, and accordingly the chemical properties of an element are largely determined by the number of valency electrons in this outermost shell. In this way we see an immediate explanation of the close chemical relationships between corresponding elements in successive periods of the table, as, for example, between the members of the series lithium to neon in the second period and sodium to argon in the third. This regularity, however, is not displayed in the same way by the elements following argon. The addition of one further electron for the extranuclear structure of potassium results, as with lithium and sodium, in the formation of a new shell, but, whereas in the preceding periods a sequence of eight elements leads from the metallic alkali metal through the non-metallic elements to the inert gas, a sequence of eighteen elements obtains after potassium before the next inert gas, krypton, is reached, and, of these eighteen elements, the first twelve all show a pronouncedly metallic character. This phenomenon finds a ready explanation in terms of our picture of atomic structure, for, after the second electron has been added to the N shell in calcium, further electrons find their place, not in the outermost shell, but in the inner M shell, and in passing through the elements scandium, titanium, vanadium, etc., the number of electrons in this shell grows until finally a new limit is reached in copper, where the M

shell contains eighteen electrons and a single electron occupies the outermost N shell. After copper no further increase in the number of electrons in the M shell takes place, and further electrons enter the N shell giving rise to the series of elements from zinc to krypton closely analogous to the elements in the preceding period of the table.

The elements from scandium to nickel, corresponding to the expansion of the M shell from its original limit of eight to the new limit of eighteen electrons, are termed 'transition metals', and the temporary abeyance in the filling of the N shell, in consequence of which all these elements have only one or two electrons in this outer shell, confers a metallic character on all the members of the series. The fact that it is energetically possible for further electrons to enter the M shell while the N shell remains partially filled reveals that the additional M electrons cannot be very much more tightly bound than those in the N shell, and the variable valency which the transition metals show is indeed an expression of this fact. Thus, while the scandium atom has the electron configuration 2, 8, 9, 2 that of the trivalent scandium ion Sc^{3+} is 2, 8, 8, so that, strictly speaking, trivalent scandium is not a member of the transition series at all. Again, the configuration of copper is 2, 8, 18, 1 and the M shell is complete, but in the ion Cu^{2+} the configuration must be 2, 8, 17, and divalent copper should therefore be regarded as a transition metal. Zinc, however, shows no tendency to occur as a trivalent ion so that by the time this element is reached a stable M shell obtains.

The fifth period. An exactly analogous phenomenon occurs in the fifth period of the classification. After the krypton configuration 2, 8, 18, 8 has been augmented by the addition of successively one and two electrons in a new O shell to give rubidium and strontium, further growth of this shell is temporarily suspended and a second series of transition metals from yttrium to palladium corresponds to the continued 'inner building' of the N shell. Once again, after this shell has reached its limit of eighteen electrons, further building takes place in the outermost shell and a series of elements, silver to xenon, closely resembling the series preceding each of the other rare gases, is formed.

The sixth and seventh periods: the rare earths. In the sixth period the elements caesium and barium correspond, analogously to the other alkali and alkaline earth metals, to the addition of one and two electrons in a new P shell outside the xenon configuration of 2, 8, 18, 18, 8. Once more the further growth of this outermost shell is suspended after the alkaline earth, and a transition group, beginning with lanthanum, is initiated by the addition of a single electron in the O shell. Here, however, a new phenomenon appears, for immediately after lanthanum the further growth of this transition group is in its turn suspended, and the next fourteen electrons added enter the still deeper N shell, giving rise to the group of 'rare earth' elements of atomic numbers 58 to 71. The very close chemical resemblances of all these elements find an immediate explanation in the identity of the electronic configuration of the two outermost shells.

After the completion of the rare earth group, the growth of the transition group, suspended after lanthanum, is resumed and the series of elements hafnium to platinum results.

Following platinum the growth of the P shell continues giving rise to the elements from gold to radium emanation, so that the configuration of this last inert gas is 2, 8, 18, 32, 18, 8. Radium emanation is followed by the as yet undiscovered alkali metal of atomic number 87 and by the alkaline earth radium, corresponding to the addition of one and two electrons in a new Q shell. After radium the growth of the new shell is again suspended, and the remaining four elements of the periodic classification constitute the beginning of an incomplete group of transition metals corresponding to the further growth of the P shell. In uranium of atomic number 92, the last element in the series, the configuration is, therefore, 2, 8, 18, 32, 18, 12, 2.

Table 4 shows an alternative presentation of the periodic classification designed to emphasize the development of the extranuclear structure of the atom and to show the positions of the transition and rare earth elements in the series. The former metals are enclosed in a single and the latter in a double frame. Lines connect analogous elements of similar chemical properties

TABLE 4

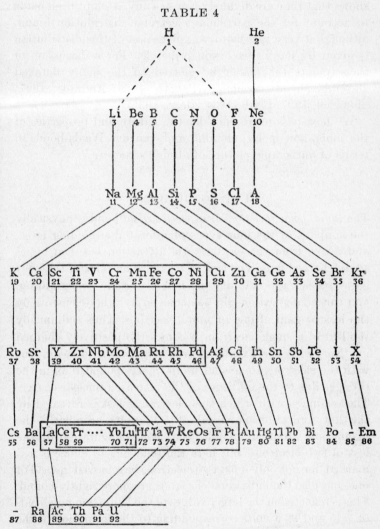

It must be emphasized that in this very brief discussion of the electronic structure of the elements no attempt has been made to consider the mass of data on which this structure is based, and similarly no account has been given of the distribution of the electrons in each shell over the various sub-groups into which magnetic and spectroscopic evidence shows that they are divided. Nor has any attempt been made to account for the particular electronic distribution found, although a very satisfactory explanation of this distribution is given by Pauli's exclusion principle. For a discussion of these points the reader is referred to the many detailed accounts already available (Paneth, 1926; Andrade, 1927; Sidgwick, 1927; Clark, 1934; Born, 1935).

We now pass on to consider the nature and properties of the ionic, homopolar, metallic and van der Waals bonds in terms of our simple picture of atomic structure.

THE IONIC BOND

The *ionic, polar, heteropolar* or *electrovalent* bond is physically the simplest of the four types of interatomic binding force, and arises from the electrostatic attraction between oppositely charged ions. The lack of chemical activity of the inert gases reveals the stability of their electronic configuration, and this configuration can be achieved by other elements by the loss or gain of one or more electrons. Thus sodium, by the loss of a single electron, becomes the positively charged ion Na^+ with the extranuclear configuration of neon, but with the electrons somewhat more tightly bound than in the rare gas due to the influence of the increased nuclear charge. The readiness with which this electron is lost is revealed by the low ionization potential of 5·12 volts. Similarly the magnesium atom can acquire the neon configuration by the loss of two electrons, but here the tendency to ionize is less marked, for not only must two electrons be removed instead of one, but also the individual electrons are more tightly bound. This is reflected in the larger values of the ionization potentials of 7·75 and 22·6 volts corresponding to the formation of the ions Mg^+ and Mg^{2+} respectively.

The tendency to form positive ions thus falls off rapidly in the sequence of elements following each of the inert gases, and practically is mostly limited to the transition and rare earth elements and those of groups 1 to 4 of the periodic table. Elements in the later groups, immediately preceding an inert gas, can attain the configuration of this gas by the addition of one or more electrons to form negative ions. Thus chlorine and sulphur give rise to the ions Cl^- and S^{2-} both having the argon electronic structure. The electrostatic attraction between oppositely charged ions of this kind constitutes the ionic bond, and sodium chloride, NaCl, or magnesium sulphide, MgS, are typically ionic compounds.

It is clearly necessary, in addition to the electrostatic attraction, to postulate the action between the ions of some repulsive force which under equilibrium conditions will be equal to the Coulomb attraction. This force cannot be given any immediate or simple physical explanation, and a discussion of its origin is deferred until Chap. III. Here, however, it is sufficient to say that the low compressibility of all ionic crystals reveals that, whatever its nature, it must be a force varying very rapidly with interatomic distance, and certainly very much more rapidly than the inverse square law of Coulomb attraction. The nearly constant radius of a given ion in all the compounds in which it occurs is another manifestation of this same rapid variation with distance, and to a first approximation we can, for our simple picture, regard the ions in an ionic structure as rigid charged spheres of characteristic constant radius.

Structural characteristics of the ionic bond.

Structurally the characteristic properties of ionic crystals arise immediately from the simple picture of the ionic bond as one which can be exerted between a given ion and an indefinite number of neighbours of the opposite sign, and one which is in no way spatially directed. In consequence, the structure of an ionic crystal is largely determined by purely geometrical considerations, being in fact that in which each ion is surrounded by the largest possible number of oppositely charged neighbours. For a given ion the number of immediate neighbours might be indefinitely large if the radius of the neighbours was small compared with that of the central ion, but such an arrangement would not necessarily be physically possible, since in a structure we must satisfy not only the condition of geometrical packing but also that of electrical neutrality. Thus in sodium chloride the radius of the sodium ion is so much smaller than that of the chlorine ion that there is room round the latter for twelve or more sodium neighbours. Electrical neutrality, however, requires that the number of sodium and chlorine ions shall be equal, and, therefore, that the co-ordination or arrangement of neighbours around each shall be the same. Round the sodium ion only six chlorine neighbours, arranged regularly at the corners of an octahedron, can be accommodated, and this, therefore, is the type of co-ordination not only round the sodium but also round the chlorine ion. In caesium chloride, on the other hand, the two ions are more nearly comparable in size and eight chlorine neighbours can now be packed round the alkali metal. The structure is, therefore, the quite different one illustrated in Fig. 2, in which the ion of each kind is now surrounded by eight neighbours symmetrically disposed at the corners of a cube.

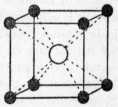

Fig. 2. The structure of caesium chloride, CsCl.

These two quite different structures for substances so closely related emphasize how far more important are geometrical than chemical considerations in determining the structure adopted. They also emphasize certain general features of ionic structures. Thus we see at once that the molecule AX, as such, has no existence in the structure. In sodium chloride each chlorine ion is associated equally with six sodium neighbours and stands in a privileged relation to no one of them. Similarly each sodium is associated equally with six chlorine ions. In no sense is the univalency of chlorine to be interpreted as implying that the chlorine atom is the source of a single bond and such a formula as Na—Cl is misleading. In so far as bonds are to be regarded as originating from the chlorine ion at all, the number of such bonds is six, but that number is a geometrical property of the structure as a whole and not a characteristic of the chlorine ion: in caesium chloride, as we have seen, the number of bonds from each chlorine ion is eight. The univalency of the halogen ions is simply an expression of the unit charge which they carry and is no measure of the number of other ions to which they may be immediately linked.

The structural characteristics of ionic compounds are discussed in detail in Chaps. VII–X.

Physical properties of the ionic bond.

Many of the mechanical, thermal, electrical, optical and other physical properties of ionic crystals may be accounted for qualitatively in terms of our description of the ionic bond.

The strength of the ionic bond is revealed by the mechanical strength, hardness and relatively high melting point of ionic crystals. Quantitatively, however, the mechanical strength is not a valuable criterion, for it is a 'structure sensitive' property very susceptible to the exact physical conditions under which it is measured and one for which it is difficult to obtain significant values.

Hardness. Some data on the hardness of ionic crystals are given below. The hardnesses are expressed in terms of Moh's scale, and the interatomic distance $A–X$ is also given in each case. These data not only show the general order of magnitude of the hardness of ionic crystals but also reveal the change in the strength of the ionic bond in a series of closely related structures. Thus in the series of oxides BeO, MgO, CaO, SrO, BaO the increasing size of the metallic ion brings about an increase in the $A–X$ distance, and this results in a corresponding reduction in bond strength immediately reflected in a rapid decrease in hardness (Goldschmidt, 1928a; Ephraim, 1931):

	BeO	MgO	CaO	SrO	BaO
$A–X$	1·65	2·10	2·40	2·57	2·77
Hardness	9·0	6·5	4·5	3·5	3·3

In exactly the same way the progressive substitution of the anion by one of greater radius causes a decrease in hardness as in the series CaO, CaS, CaSe, CaTe:

	CaO	CaS	CaSe	CaTe
$A-X$	2·40	2·84	2·96	3·17
Hardness	4·5	4·0	3·2	2·9

Equally marked is the change in bond strength due to a change in the charge of the ions. This may be illustrated by such a series as NaF, MgO, ScN and TiC in which the interatomic distance remains nearly constant while the ionic charge increases progressively, or again by such pairs of compounds as LiCl and SrO or LiBr and MgSe:

	NaF	MgO	ScN	TiC
$A-X$	2·31	2·10	2·23	2·23
Hardness	3·2	6·5	7–8	8–9

	LiCl	SrO	LiBr	MgSe
$A-X$	2·57	2·57	2·75	2·73
Hardness	3·0	3·5	2·5	3·5

Melting point. The melting point, or temperature at which the energy of thermal agitation is sufficient to disrupt the interatomic binding forces, is also a rough measure of the strength of these bonds, and, although the problem is here complicated by other phenomena (Pauling, 1928a), the general trend of the melting points of ionic crystals reveals the same variation with interatomic distance and ionic charge shown by the hardness data. Thus in the series of alkali halides NaF, NaCl, NaBr, NaI the melting point falls progressively with increasing interatomic distance:

	NaF	NaCl	NaBr	NaI
$A-X$	2·31	2·79	2·94	3·18
Melting point ° C.	988	801	740	660

and the same effect is shown by the series NaF, KF, RbF and CsF:

	NaF	KF	RbF	CsF
$A-X$	2·31	2·66	2·82	2·98
Melting point ° C.	988	846	775	684

The influence of the ionic charge is revealed by a comparison of the melting points of such a pair of compounds as NaF and CaO:

	NaF	CaO
$A-X$	2·31	2·40
Melting point ° C.	988	2570

Thermal expansion. As a class ionic crystals have relatively small coefficients of thermal expansion corresponding to the strong interatomic binding forces, and the data given below for the coefficient of expansion α of a number of such structures may be later compared with figures for the thermal expansion of structures in which other types of force operate. Within the field of ionic crystals the thermal-expansion data again show the progressive increase in binding force accompanying a decrease in interatomic distance or an increase in ionic charge, so that in the series NaF, NaCl, NaBr and NaI the coefficient of expansion shows a continuous increase:

	NaF	NaCl	NaBr	NaI
$A-X$	2·31	2·79	2·94	3·18
$\alpha \times 10^6$	39	40	43	48

The expansion coefficients of the ionic halides of divalent metals are considerably smaller:

	CaF_2
$A-X$	2·39
$\alpha \times 10^6$	19

Electrical properties. Ionic crystals are non-conductors of electricity since the electrons are all securely bound in the atomic orbitals of the individual ions. They do, however, show an internal photoelectric conductivity with a limiting frequency corresponding to the ionization potential. Since, however, this frequency is normally relatively high, corresponding to wave-lengths in the ultra-violet, the effect is not marked in most ionic crystals. In the molten state conductivity by ion transport occurs, and a relatively high conductivity of the melt is a characteristic property of ionic structures (Biltz, 1924; Biltz and Klemm, 1924; von Hevesy, 1928; Eucken, 1930).

The dielectric constant of ionic crystals is at high frequencies simply the additive effect of the polarizabilities of the separate ions. At low frequencies, however, further polarization may occur, the positive ions as a whole vibrating against the negative and giving rise to a dielectric constant characteristic of the lattice.

The essentially electrical character of the ionic bond is revealed by the dissociation which it experiences in a medium of sufficiently high dielectric constant. Thus most halides are soluble in water while sulphides and oxides, where the binding is stronger, are insoluble: they would probably be soluble with dissociation in a solvent of still higher dielectric constant if one were known. Ionization in solution is not, however, a safe criterion for the ionic bond, for the character of the binding may be affected by the solvent, and many compounds which are soluble with dissociation are probably not ionic in the solid state.

Optical and magnetic properties. The optical and magnetic properties of ionic crystals are to a first approximation those of the aggregate of ions, and refractivities and susceptibilities are additive. The refractivity of the individual ions is a measure of the deformability or polarization of the electronic structure by the electric vector of the incident light, and is therefore largest for ions with a large and loosely bound electron configuration. This is illustrated by the data for the molecular refractivities of the series of ions F^-, Cl^-, Br^-, I^- where the increase in the ionic dimensions is accompanied by a corresponding increase in molecular refraction (Fajans, 1925):

	F⁻	Cl⁻	Br⁻	I⁻
Molecular refraction	2·5	9·0	12·6	19·0

or by the series O^{2-}, F^-, Ne, Na^+, Mg^{2+} in which the influence of an increase in nuclear charge in a series of ions with the same electron configuration is clearly shown:

	O^{2-}	F^-	Ne	Na^+	Mg^{2+}
Molecular refraction	7·0	2·5	1·0	0·5	0·3

These figures emphasize that the overwhelming contribution to the refractivity of any ionic compound is that due to the anion.

In unsymmetrical structures ionic refractivities are no longer additive and the polarization of a given ion is determined not only by the electric vector of the light wave but also by the field due to the polarization of its neighbours. This effect is structurally of great practical importance, for it is only in such cases that the optical properties can give any clue to the crystal structure. The point is discussed more fully later.

The absorption of simple ionic crystals in the high-frequency region is again simply that of the ions, and the crystals are therefore generally transparent and colourless except in the case of the transition and rare earth elements where absorption occurs in the visible. At low frequencies the effect of the lattice begins to be felt, and there is always a characteristic frequency ν, usually far in the infra-red, for which the positive and negative ions vibrate against each other. At this frequency there is heavy absorption and selective reflection giving rise to the *Reststrahlen* of Rubens.

A general account of the physical properties of the ionic bond has been given by Fajans (1925, 1928a).

THE HOMOPOLAR BOND

The electron transfer from the electropositive to the electronegative element which occurs in ionic compounds, and by means of which each atom achieves the stable electron configuration of an inert gas, clearly cannot be responsible for the formation of such a molecule as that of chlorine, Cl_2. The two chlorine atoms in this molecule, each with an outer shell of seven electrons, can, however, both attain the stable argon configuration by a sharing of two electrons in a way which may be represented figuratively thus:

$$\colon \! \overset{\cdot \, \cdot}{\underset{\cdot \, \cdot}{Cl}} \cdot \; + \; \cdot \overset{\cdot \, \cdot}{\underset{\cdot \, \cdot}{Cl}} \colon \; \rightarrow \; \colon \! \overset{\cdot \, \cdot}{\underset{\cdot \, \cdot}{Cl}} \colon \overset{\cdot \, \cdot}{\underset{\cdot \, \cdot}{Cl}} \colon ,$$

where the dots represent the valency electrons of the outermost shell. Such a mechanism of electron sharing as responsible for the formation of the *homopolar* or *covalent* bond was proposed simultaneously by Lewis (1916) and by Kossel (1916), whose work may be regarded as the foundation of modern valency theory. We cannot here discuss the extensive developments of these views or the light which they have thrown on chemical combination in a wide field of inorganic and organic chemistry: for such a discussion the reader is referred to the works of Lewis (1923), Sidgwick (1927, 1933), Ephraim (1928), Noyes (1935), Speakman (1935) and others. We shall, however, give a brief account of the physical properties which the homopolar bond confers on the bodies in which it occurs, and of the structural characteristics which these compounds show.

The conception of a homopolar bond as due to a sharing of electrons between the atoms which it binds together immediately gives rise to an important distinction between it and the ionic bond, for it is clear that the number of homopolar bonds by which a given atom can be linked to others is limited. Thus, in the case of the chlorine molecule, each atom is able to achieve the stable electronic configuration by sharing one of its electrons with the other atom, so that the single chemical bond corresponds to a sharing of two electrons, one provided by each atom, and in forming this chemical bond each atom has effectively increased by one the number of electrons in its valency shell. Once this shell has attained the stable inert gas configuration no further homopolar bonds will be formed, and hence quite generally the number of homopolar bonds which can originate from an atom is equal to the number of electrons required to complete its outermost shell. An element in the nth group of the periodic table can therefore be the source of $(8-n)$ bonds, so that while the halogens are univalent, oxygen in the sixth group is divalent, as in the oxygen molecule

$$: \ddot{O} : \ddot{O} : ,$$

and carbon in the fourth group is tetravalent as in methane or carbon tetrachloride

$$
\begin{array}{cc}
\text{H} & : \ddot{\text{Cl}} : \\
\text{H} : \text{C} : \text{H} \qquad & : \text{Cl} : \text{C} : \text{Cl} : . \\
\text{H} & : \ddot{\text{Cl}} :
\end{array}
$$

A further respect in which the homopolar bond stands in marked contrast to the ionic is in the fact that the several bonds from a polyvalent atom are in general mutually disposed in some characteristic spatial configuration. Thus, for example, in a structure in which the oxygen atom occurs between two atoms A and B to which it is bound by homopolar links, it is found to be displaced from the line AB so that the angle between the two bonds from the oxygen atom is less than 180°. Similarly the four homopolar bonds from a carbon atom are always found to be directed towards the corners of a regular tetrahedron.

Structural characteristics of the homopolar bond.

The characteristic properties of the homopolar bond outlined above have a most profound influence on the type of structure adopted. Primarily the nature of the structure depends upon the number of homopolar bonds in which each of the atoms can take part, so that, considering first the elements, it is clear that the halogens can form only diatomic molecules. The halogens, therefore, can never form homodesmic solids since the individual diatomic molecules, strongly bound within themselves by homopolar forces, can only be linked to each other by residual bonds. With a divalent atom, such as oxygen or sulphur, other alternatives arise. The simplest is the formation of a diatomic molecule linked by a double bond $O=O$, but instead, each atom might be linked by a single bond to two others, each of which in its turn was similarly linked. In this case either closed rings of any number of members or indefinitely extended chains could be formed. Both such arrangements are actually found in crystals and will be considered in the appropriate place, but again the structures cannot be homodesmic since neither arrangement can give rise to a structure coherent in three dimensions. The same remarks apply to the homopolar structures of trivalent elements, and it is only in the fourth group of the periodic table that the quadrivalency of the elements gives rise to the possibility of a three-dimensional homodesmic structure in which every atom is linked to four neighbours.

Diamond. The ideal example of such a homopolar structure is that of diamond illustrated in Fig. 3. Here it will be seen that each carbon atom is surrounded by only four others and that the neighbours are all arranged symmetrically at the corners of a regular tetrahedron. Every carbon atom is similarly co-ordinated.

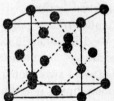

Fig. 3. The structure of diamond, C.

Certain features of the diamond structure call for special notice. In the first place the structure is a very 'open' one. If space is to be filled by a packing together of equal spheres, this may be most economically done if each sphere is surrounded by twelve neighbours, and this arrangement, which is found in the crystal structure of many metals, is an expression of the tendency of each atom to surround itself by the largest number of neighbours geometrically possible. In diamond, although the atoms are all equivalent, there is no such tendency, and each atom is surrounded only by the four neighbours to which it can be linked by its four valency bonds.

A second feature of the diamond arrangement is that the binding throughout the whole structure is essentially 'chemical' in character, a fact which may be represented symbolically by writing the structure in the form proposed by Lewis:

$$: \overset{..}{C} : \overset{..}{C} : \overset{..}{C} : \overset{..}{C} :$$
$$: \overset{..}{C} : \overset{..}{C} : \overset{..}{C} : \overset{..}{C} :$$
$$: \overset{..}{C} : \overset{..}{C} : \overset{..}{C} : \overset{..}{C} :$$
$$: \overset{..}{C} : \overset{..}{C} : \overset{..}{C} : \overset{..}{C} :$$

This representation emphasizes that, just as we regard the unit $: \overset{..}{Cl} : \overset{..}{Cl} :$ as a molecule in chlorine, so must we consider the whole crystal as a single molecule of indefinite extent in diamond. This is yet another example of a structure in which chemical forces are identical with those which determine the physical coherence of the crystal.

Zincblende. Another structure closely related to that of diamond is the zincblende, ZnS, arrangement which is illustrated in Fig. 4. This differs from diamond only in that adjacent atoms are of opposite kind so that each zinc atom is surrounded by four sulphur atoms at the corners of a tetrahedron, and each sulphur atom by four zinc atoms similarly disposed. It would at first sight appear to be impossible for such a structure to be homopolar, and that would indeed be the case if it were necessary that the two electrons constituting a homopolar link should be derived one from

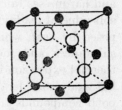

Fig. 4. The structure of zincblende, ZnS.

each of the atoms which they unite. It seems, however, that this condition is not necessary and that in fact the zincblende structure may arise whenever the total number of valency electrons is just four times the total number of atoms. This point will be discussed more fully later but may be illustrated here by the compounds AgI, ZnS and AlP, all of which are homopolar with the zincblende structure.

The zincblende arrangement is another example of a structure in which the molecule as such has no existence, and in this case it is clearly impossible to convey the homopolar character of the binding by any formula representing a single molecule ZnS. The relationship between the zincblende and diamond structures emphasizes again that the bonding in diamond is essentially chemical in nature and that diamond is to be regarded no less as a compound of carbon with carbon than is zincblende as a compound of zinc with sulphur. These points are discussed in more detail in Chap. VI.

Physical properties of the homopolar bond.

Mechanical. The strength of the homopolar bond may be fully as great as that of the ionic, so that mechanically homopolar and ionic crystals have substantially similar properties, and hardness, strength, melting point and thermal expansion are not particularly valuable criteria of the bond type. Homopolar compounds do, however, show considerable variations in their physical properties, and melting points and hardnesses range over wide limits. Thus, zincblende is a soft mineral readily scratched with a knife and easily decomposed by heat, while diamond is the hardest of all known substances and melts above 3000° C. The coefficient of thermal expansion is comparable with that of ionic crystals, but again considerable variations as between different homopolar compounds are found (Klemm, 1928).

Electrical properties. Homopolar compounds differ from ionic electrically in that they are non-conductors in the molten state, and this is often regarded as a criterion of the homopolar bond (Biltz and Klemm, 1924, 1926; von Hevesy, 1928). Homopolar compounds are not soluble in water, but in this respect do not differ from many ionic compounds which are also insoluble. Nor does solution with dissociation necessarily preclude the existence of the homopolar bond in the solid state (Pauling, 1932b), for the presence of the solvent may modify the type of binding. Thus, although hydrogen chloride is dissociated in solution there is considerable evidence that in the gaseous and solid states the binding is homopolar (Pauling, 1932a).

Optical properties. It is in their optical properties that homopolar compounds differ most markedly from compounds of other types, and this difference arises from the character of the binding in which the electrons are linked, not in atomic orbitals of individual ions, but in diatomic orbitals embracing two neighbouring atoms. The tightness of the binding of these electrons may vary between wide limits. In diamond the binding is very secure and the electrons contribute to the absorption only in the ultra-violet, so that the crystal appears colourless. In zincblende or silicon, on the other hand, the binding is less tight so that absorption occurs in the visible spectrum and the substance is coloured or opaque. In tin the binding is so loose that the element has many of the properties of a metal.

Generally the electron levels are so high that they give rise to a very high refractive index, which, together with the colour, produces a resinous lustre very characteristic of homopolar compounds. The high electron levels also give rise to photoelectric conductivity when the crystals are illuminated by light in their absorption bands. With diamond this occurs only in the ultra-violet, but silicon is a photoelectric conductor in the visible while in tin the conductivity approximates to that of a true metal.

The character of the electron binding is also illustrated by the optical properties in solution. In purely ionic compounds the absorption in solution is substantially the same as that in the solid since the electronic distribution in the ions remains unaltered in the dissolved state. In homopolar compounds, on the other hand, the electronic distribution in solution is profoundly altered since the diatomic orbits are no longer possible, and the characteristic absorption is entirely different from that in the solid (Ephraim, 1928).

THE METALLIC BOND

The forces responsible for the coherence of a metal have not usually been regarded as chemical in nature at all, and few attempts have been made to explain them in terms of chemical valency theory, although, somewhat illogically, alloy systems have often been so interpreted. The characteristic physical properties of the metals, however, early gave rise to speculations on the ultimate nature of the metallic state and many of the optical properties, and especially the thermal and electrical conductivity of metals, received a very convincing explanation in terms of the free-electron picture of Drude. On this theory a metal is to be regarded as an assemblage of positive ions immersed in a gas of free electrons. The attraction between the positive ions and the electron gas gives the structure its coherence, and the free mobility of this electron gas under the influence of electrical or thermal stress is responsible for the high conductivity. In terms of this picture many of the physical properties of metals can be given a very satisfactory qualitative and even quantitative description, but there are nevertheless many properties of which no such explanation seems possible. Moreover, the Drude theory gives very little account of the nature and character of the interatomic binding forces in a metal and therefore, from a structural point of view, is obviously of limited application. In the last few years, however, very substantial advances have been made in the theory of the metallic state, and it is now possible to give a theoretical description of the simple metals almost as complete and exact as that which can be given of ionic crystals. Furthermore, these advances have been achieved very largely in terms of the crystal structures of the metals, so that from our present point of view the conclusions reached are particularly significant. We shall not, therefore, give any further account here of the Drude theory, or of its application, for a discussion of which the reader is referred to the comprehensive surveys of Hume-Rothery (1931), Borelius (1935a) and others. In this chapter we shall briefly enumerate some of the properties and characteristics of metals which are of structural significance, and give in Chap. III an account of the more recent work on the theory of the metallic state.

Structural characteristics of the metallic bond.

The attraction between the positive ions and the electron gas which is responsible for the coherence of a metal confers neither spatial nor numerical limitations on the metallic bond: the bonds from any one atom must be regarded as spherically distributed and as being capable of acting on as many neighbours as can be packed round that atom. This picture leads us to expect that in the metallic elements highly co-ordinated structures will obtain, and, in confirmation of this, the structure of the majority of the true metals is found to be one in which the co-ordination is the maximum geometrically possible. The actual structures satisfying this geometrical condition will be described in the chapter devoted to the structures of the metals, and here it is sufficient to emphasize that structurally it is this close aggregation which is the characteristic of the metallic state. This is also shown by liquid metals where the packing, although statistical, is almost as close as in the solid so that a very small volume change occurs on melting true metals.

The metallic bond thus resembles the ionic in giving rise to highly co-ordinated structures, but it differs from the ionic bond in that it is exerted not between two atoms of chemically widely different character but between either identical atoms, as in the metallic elements, or between chemically similar atoms, as in the alloy systems. In ionic structures the necessity for electrical neutrality prescribes the relative number of atoms of each kind which occur, but in metallic systems there is no such condition to be satisfied, and the structure adopted is determined solely by geometrical considerations. The architecture of metallic systems is thus particularly flexible, and it is this flexibility which occasions much of the difficulty and confusion which arises when attempts are made to interpret alloy systems in terms of views of chemical combination based on the properties of ionic or homopolar compounds. The laws of constant composition and of simple proportions arise in ionic compounds through the demands of electrical neutrality: in alloy systems no such demands exist and the composition is often neither constant nor simple.

The crystal chemistry of metallic systems is discussed systematically in Chaps. IV and V.

Physical properties of the metallic bond.

Electrical and optical properties. The majority of the physical properties which distinguish metals from other solids, and which confer on them their 'metallic' character, are due to the free electrons. Thus the characteristic thermal and electrical conductivity and the optical opacity and high reflecting power are all to be explained in terms of the mobility of these electrons. The electrons, although able to move readily throughout the structure, are held within the solid as a whole by potential fields at its surface, so that, corresponding to the binding of the electrons into atomic and molecular orbitals in ionic and homopolar structures, the electrons in a metal may be regarded as bound in macro-crystal orbitals embracing the structure as a whole. The tightness of the binding of these electrons is determined by the height of the surface potential barrier, and physically finds expression as the photoelectric threshold or thermionic work function corresponding to the minimum amount of photo or thermal energy which must be imparted to the electrons before they can be removed from the solid. The photoelectric effect in metals is the precise analogue of the internal photoelectric effect in homopolar structures. In the one case a quantum of light energy exceeding a certain critical value ejects an electron completely from the solid, in the other case the electron is ejected from the molecular orbital in which it is normally bound but remains within the crystal, to which it imparts metallic conductivity until it again becomes bound in a molecular orbital.

The electrical and optical properties of the metals, although throwing much light on the nature of the metallic state, are essentially non-structural properties inasmuch as they persist substantially unmodified in the liquid. They can, therefore, necessarily give only limited information about the constitution of metallic crystals, and it is to other properties, and particularly to mechanical properties, that we must turn for further information in this direction.

Mechanical properties. The pronounced qualitative resemblances which all metals display in their electrical and optical properties have no immediate parallel in their mechanical characteristics, in respect of which the metallic elements show a great diversity of behaviour emphasizing the wide variations in the strength of the metallic binding as between one element and another. Thus, in hardness, they range from the extremely soft alkali metals to the very hard chromium or tungsten, and this range of properties is similarly reflected in a wide diversity of melting points extending from $-39°$ C. for mercury to about $3300°$ C. for tungsten. The coefficients of thermal expansion also show a corresponding variation from values of the order of 80×10^{-6} per $°$ C. for the alkali metals to values of the order of 5×10^{-6} per $°$ C. for the hard metals.

The mechanical property of metals, however, which most strikingly distinguishes them from most other solids, and which gives them much of their technical importance, is their malleability. This property is essentially a structural characteristic and arises from the very simple crystal structures and the undirected nature of the metal bonds, as a result of which the crystal may glide by a relative displacement of closely packed layers in the lattice. In ordinary polycrystalline specimens the phenomenon is complicated, but in single metal crystals gliding occurs under the action of vanishingly small stresses and is found to take place on just those planes and in just those directions in the structure in which the atoms are most closely packed and which in consequence are energetically most favoured. Ionic and homopolar crystals, with their relatively more complex structures, cannot generally deform in this way and so are brittle. Even among the metals, those with complex structures and the alloys in which foreign atoms disturb the regularity of the lattice are markedly less malleable.

THE VAN DER WAALS BOND

The *residual* or *van der Waals* bond differs from the three other types of interatomic binding force which we have discussed in that it is not responsible for the coherence of any solids which lie within the range of normal experience, so that its properties cannot be described in terms of simple and commonly occurring substances. Nevertheless, the residual bond does actually occur as an attraction between the atoms and ions of all solids, but it is so weak compared with the ionic, homopolar and metallic forces that its effect is completely masked in any structure in which it occurs in conjunction with any of these stronger bonds, and in such cases its effect is quantitatively small and qualitatively insignificant in its influence on the properties. The only solids in which the properties of the isolated residual bond can be studied are those in which neither ionic, homopolar nor metallic forces can occur, and homodesmic residual structures are therefore confined to the inert gases in the solid state to which they condense at low temperatures. The very low melting points of all these gases reveal the weakness of the residual link.

The conception of a weak force of attraction between atoms and molecules already chemically saturated was first introduced by van der Waals (1873) to account for the behaviour of actual gases, and has since been invoked in problems of capillarity and adsorption, but in the earlier work no attempt was made to explain the nature of this force or the mechanism in which it had its origin. Later, however (Debye 1920), the force was qualitatively described as due to the polarization of the electronic configuration of each atom by the field of its neighbours, this polarization resulting in an attraction between the dipoles thus created. Recently the nature of the van der Waals force has been the subject of much work, and it is now clear that such a simple picture cannot give an adequate account of the interatomic attraction, and that, in particular, such polarization cannot lead to any attraction at all between atoms or molecules of a symmetrical structure such as that of the inert gases. Once again we defer until Chap. III any discussion of this more recent work and confine ourselves here to an elementary account of the structurally important properties of the residual bond.

Structural characteristics of the van der Waals bond.

Structurally the residual bond bears a close formal resemblance to the metallic bond as one which can link an atom to an indefinite number of neighbours, and one which is spatially undirected. This resemblance finds expression in the close-packed structures of the solid inert gases, and the mechanical properties of these gases in the solid state, if they were systematically investigated, would doubtless be found to be closely parallel to those of the metals. It is even possible to imagine an 'alloy' chemistry based on systems of two or more inert gases at low temperatures.

Although homodesmic residual compounds can occur only with the inert gases, heterodesmic compounds in which the properties are determined largely by residual forces are of common occurrence, for in any structure in which discrete molecules without external field occur the binding between these molecules can only be of the residual type, and the structure is then determined by the shape of the molecules and the way in which they can pack together. Such structures are illustrated in the simplest possible case by solid oxygen or chlorine. Here the diatomic molecule X_2 is tightly bound by strong homopolar forces, but these forces are completely satisfied within the molecule and can contribute nothing to the intermolecular binding, which is therefore residual in type. In consequence the elements are gaseous under normal conditions and condense to the solid only at low temperatures. By far the most important molecular structures in which the molecule as a whole is preserved as a separate entity are, however, those which embrace the whole field of organic chemistry, and, although in some cases the intermolecular forces in organic compounds are not purely residual in character, these compounds do on the whole show the characteristic physical properties associated with a weak binding force. They are discussed in detail in Chap. XI.

Physical properties of the van der Waals bond.

The physical properties of molecular structures fall into two classes according as to whether they arise from the character of the binding or from the electronic configuration in the atoms or molecules concerned. In the former class are the mechanical and closely associated properties, in the latter the electrical and optical properties.

Mechanical properties. The weakness of the residual bond is revealed by the low melting point, softness, high compressibility, high thermal expansion and low heat of sublimation of a molecular structure. The low melting points and softness of molecular substances are facts of such common experience as to need no discussion here. Data on the compressibilities of crystals are summarized by Reis (1920) who gives the following range of values for structures of different types:

Structure type	Compressibility
Metals (excluding alkali metals)	$0 \cdot 3 - 4 \cdot 5 \times 10^{-6}$ cm.²/kg.
Alkali metals	9–61
Refractory oxides	$0 \cdot 5 - 1$
Salts	1– 6
Molecular compounds	20–50

It will be seen from these figures that the compressibilities of molecular compounds are considerably greater than those of other structure types with the exception of the alkali metals.

Data on the coefficient of thermal expansion of molecular

compounds are very meagre, but here again the values found
for the few substances that have been investigated show that
the expansion of these compounds is considerably greater
than that of other structure types. The following summary of
coefficients of cubical expansion is again due to Reis:

Structure type	Coeff. of cubical expansion
Metals (excluding alkali metals)	$2-13 \times 10^{-4}$ per °C.
Alkali metals	18–25
Refractory oxides and sulphides	1– 6
Salts of oxyacids	3–10
Metal halides	6–13
Oxalic acid	26
Urea	29
Naphthalene	32

Once again the values for the molecular compounds are
significantly greater than for the other structures.

The heat of sublimation of molecular structures is a further
indication of the weakness of the residual bond. Thus the
heat of sublimation of solid chlorine is 4·5 kcal./mol., and
this may be contrasted with the heat of dissociation of the
diatomic molecule, which has the much greater value of
58·5 kcal./mol. corresponding to the rupture of the far
stronger homopolar bond. In hydrogen the contrast is still
more marked and the heats of sublimation and dissociation
are 0·5 and 100 kcal./mol. respectively.

Electrical and optical properties. The electrical and optical
properties of molecular crystals are almost entirely those of
the atoms or molecules of which they are composed, and are
substantially the same in the solid as in the liquid and gaseous
states. This is due to the fact that the electronic structure
of the atom contributes little to the weak residual binding,
so that the electron systems do not interpenetrate and the

electrons may still be referred to their atomic or molecular orbitals. The analogy with metal structures here, of course, completely breaks down, and molecular crystals are nearly all transparent, non-conducting, diamagnetic substances. The electrical and optical properties can, therefore, naturally give little information about the nature or structural characteristics of the van der Waals bond.

This concludes our qualitative account of the four types of interatomic binding. For reference, a summary of their principal physical and structural properties is given in Table 5.

TABLE 5

PHYSICAL AND STRUCTURAL PROPERTIES ASSOCIATED
WITH THE FOUR INTERATOMIC BONDS

Property	Ionic	Homopolar	Metallic	van der Waals
Mechanical	Strong, giving hard crystals	Strong, giving hard crystals	Variable strength. Gliding common	Weak, giving soft crystals
Thermal	Fairly high M.P. Low coefficient of expansion. Ions in melt	High M.P. Low coefficient of expansion. Molecules in melt	Variable M.P. Long liquid interval	Low M.P. Large coefficient of expansion
Electrical	Moderate insulators. Conduction by ion transport in melt. Sometimes soluble in liquids of high dielectric constant	Insulators in solid and melt	Conduction by electron transport	Insulators
Optical and magnetic	Absorption and other properties primarily those of the individual ions, and therefore similar in solution	High refractive index. Absorption profoundly different in solution or gas	Opaque. Properties similar in liquid	Properties those of individual molecules, and therefore similar in solution or gas
Structural	Non-directed, giving structures of high co-ordination	Spatially directed and numerically limited, giving structures of low co-ordination and low density	Non-directed, giving structures of very high co-ordination and high density	Formally analogous to metallic bond

THE CLASSIFICATION OF CRYSTAL STRUCTURES

The four types of interatomic binding described in this chapter are the only substantially distinct types of bond which occur in the solid state, and by reason of the characteristic properties, both physical and structural, which they confer on the bodies in which they are found, these four types of bond afford the most convenient basis for a classification of crystal structures. This classification is immediately applicable to homodesmic structures, while heterodesmic compounds will be considered in each case under the heading of the weakest binding present, for, as we have already emphasized, the specifically crystalline character is determined by the weakest binding force. Thus, for example, all organic compounds, as well as a few inorganic bodies, fall into the section devoted to the residual bond.

In certain cases the type of binding cannot be unambiguously determined, for between the homopolar bond and the metallic, on the one hand, and the homopolar and the ionic, on the other, there is no sharp distinction but a gradual transition, which is correspondingly reflected in the crystal structure. In fact, the structural properties illustrate, perhaps more convincingly than any other, the continuous character of this transition. In such cases the section under which the compounds concerned are classified is a matter of arbitrary choice determined by practical convenience. The fact that the metallic structures are in many ways the simplest, while molecular structures are in some respects the most complex, makes it desirable in our systematic discussion to follow an order different from that adopted in this chapter, and our four fundamental sections of crystal chemistry will be:

(1) Metal systems;
(2) Homopolar compounds;
(3) Ionic compounds;
(4) Residual, or molecular, compounds.

The classification within each section will be primarily into homodesmic and heterodesmic compounds, while the heterodesmic structures will be further subdivided according to the general shape of the molecules or atomic aggregates which they contain. Here, however, it is impossible to generalize, and the details of the classification can only be considered in terms of particular cases.

We give in Table 6 a condensed diagrammatic representation of our scheme which serves to illustrate the general lines of the classification. This table will be elaborated and explained in detail as each class of compound is discussed.

Before finally passing on to a systematic account of the structural properties of chemical compounds we give in the next chapter a more quantitative account of the nature and properties of the interatomic binding forces discussed qualitatively above. In recent years the development of the new quantum mechanics, and particularly the results of X-ray structure analysis, have redirected attention to the nature of the chemical bond, and now it is possible, in the case of many simple compounds, to give a very satisfactory quantitative account of their properties in terms of the forces responsible for their formation. These methods are, however, as yet only in their infancy and can be applied only to the very simplest of the compounds which have been surveyed by the X-ray crystallographer. The rapidity with which our knowledge of the cohesive forces in solids has developed gives every reason for believing that it will not be long before this limitation is removed, but it is quite clear that the *quantitative* expression of the several types of interatomic bond must nevertheless experience considerable modification before anything approaching finality is reached. On the other hand we may hope that *qualitatively* little alteration will be necessary, and it therefore seems desirable to separate the qualitative treatment given in this chapter from the more tentative quantitative approach outlined in Chap. III.

TABLE 6

The classification of crystals

	Metallic		Homopolar	
	Homodesmic	Heterodesmic	Homodesmic	Heterodesmic
or less e-packed tals	The true metals Alloys of the true metals with one another	Zn, Cd, Hg, Sn Alloys of the more metallic B sub-group metals with one another or with true metals	Diamond, Si, Ge Compounds of B sub-group elements among themselves, e.g. zincblende, wurtzite, etc.	Compounds of B sub-group metals with P, S, etc., e.g. nickel arsenide and pyrites type structures
crystals	—	Se, Te Sb_2S_3	—	—
crystals	—	As, Sb, Bi Graphite MoS_2	—	—
ework tals	Interstitial structures	—	—	—

	Ionic			van der Waals	
	Isodesmic	Mesodesmic	Anisodesmic	Homodesmic	Heterodesmic
or less e-packed tals	Halides and oxides of metals, of general types AX, AX_2, AX_3 Perovskite and spinel structures	Borates Orthosilicates Ring silicates Germanates	Salts of almost all inorganic acids	The inert gases	Molecular gases, e.g. O_2, N_2, HCl, CO_2, etc., etc. Sulphur All organic compounds with finite molecules
crystals	—	Pyroxenes Amphiboles	—	—	Cellulose Rubber Fibrous proteins
crystals	—	Micas, etc.	Gypsum	—	Layer lattices
ework tals	—	Felspars Zeolites	—	—	'Globular' proteins

CHAPTER III

QUANTITATIVE LATTICE THEORY

THE EARLY LATTICE THEORY OF IONIC CRYSTALS

The elementary picture of the ionic bond discussed in the last chapter, which treats this bond as arising from the electrostatic attraction between oppositely charged ions, is one which readily lends itself to a precise quantitative treatment, and attempts to calculate theoretically the properties of ionic structures have been the subject of much work during the last twenty years. We shall not here discuss any of the work on lattice theory prior to the development of the method of X-ray analysis, for although, as early as the middle of the eighteenth century, speculations on the subject, which are now of the greatest historical interest, were attributed to Boscovich (1763), any work before 1912 was necessarily somewhat artificial, in that it was undertaken without any knowledge of the actual structures of the substances discussed.

The Born-Landé theory.

The foundations of modern lattice theory were laid by Born and Landé (1918), and it is in terms of the ideas originally outlined by these authors that almost all the more recent developments have been expressed. Although the work of these authors has undergone considerable modification and development, not least at the hands of Born himself, the original theory still conveys many of the essential features of the argument and provides a convenient basis on which to discuss its later developments.

The electrostatic potential energy of a pair of ions considered as point charges $z_1 e$ and $z_2 e$ at a distance r apart is given by

$$u = z_1 z_2 e^2 / r,$$

so that if the ions are oppositely charged this is the amount of work which is necessary to separate them to infinity. Such a function clearly cannot express the potential energy of ions in a crystal, since it takes no account of the repulsive forces which must operate at close approach to confer on the ions their characteristic radii. Born and Landé expressed this repulsive force by writing for the potential energy of a pair of ions the expression

$$u = z_1 z_2 e^2/r + b/r^n.$$

In this equation the first term, as before, represents the electrostatic potential energy, and for oppositely charged ions is, of course, negative. The second term is an empirical expression of the repulsive potential and contains the constants b and n, to be experimentally determined. To represent a repulsion b must be numerically positive.

The potential energy per pair of ions in a crystal structure is not the same as that of an isolated pair of ions in free space, and its evaluation necessitates the summation of the mutual potential energies of all the charges in the lattice. When the effect of this mutual interaction is taken into account the energy is found to be given by the equation

$$u = A z_1 z_2 e^2/r + B/r^n, \qquad \ldots\ldots(1)$$

where A is a numerical constant of the order of unity, termed the Madelung constant, and B is a second constant still to be empirically determined. The value of the Madelung constant depends upon the particular structure considered, and its exact calculation is mathematically very difficult. It has, however, been evaluated by Madelung (1918) and by Ewald (1921) for most simple highly symmetrical structures, while W. L. Bragg (1933a) has shown that very elementary arguments can often give a close approximation to the true value.

The greater part of the early work on lattice theory was undertaken with reference to the alkali halides, and it will simplify our discussion if we develop our argument in terms of these salts. For univalent ions equation (1) becomes

$$u = -A e^2/r + B/r^n. \qquad \ldots\ldots(2)$$

From this equation we can immediately find a relation between A and B by expressing the condition that the equilibrium distance r_0 between adjacent ions is that at which the potential energy is a minimum. This condition is

$$\left(\frac{\partial u}{\partial r}\right)_{r=r_0} = Ae^2/r^2 - nB/r^{n+1} = 0,$$

whence
$$B = Ae^2 r_0^{n-1}/n,$$

so that
$$u = -\frac{Ae^2}{r_0}\left(1 - \frac{1}{n}\right),$$

or, for one gram molecule,

$$U = -\frac{NAe^2}{r_0}\left(1 - \frac{1}{n}\right), \qquad \ldots\ldots(3)$$

where N is the number of ion pairs per gram molecule.

The value of n can be deduced from the experimentally observed compressibilities, for we can see in a general way that a large value of n represents a rapid variation of repulsive force with distance and correspondingly a small compressibility. For the detailed calculation the reader is referred to the original papers, but it may be readily shown that the compressibility k is given by

$$k = 18r_0^4/Ae^2(n-1),$$

from which equation n may be determined since all the other quantities are known. In this way Born and Landé derived for a number of alkali halides values for n of the order of 9, indicating a very rapid variation of repulsive force with distance. Attempts to calculate n theoretically gave the much lower value of about 5. It will be seen, however, from equation (3) that the total lattice energy is not greatly altered by small changes in n since the contribution of the repulsive energy is in any case small compared with that of electrostatic attraction.

The Born-Haber cycle. The energy $|U|$ of equation (3) is the amount of work, per gram molecule, which must be expended to disperse the crystal to an assemblage of widely separated ions. As such it cannot immediately be compared with any measurable quantity, and, in particular, is not to be identified

either with the heat of sublimation, which is the energy necessary to disperse the crystal into a molecular gas, or with the
chemical heat of formation. A comparison with experimental
data can, however, be made by means of the cyclical process
first advanced by Born (1919a) and by Haber (1919). This
process may best be illustrated by a concrete example such as
that shown in Fig. 5.

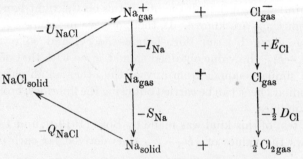

Fig. 5. The Born-Haber cycle applied to sodium chloride.

Consider one gram molecule of sodium chloride in the
crystalline state. By the expenditure of an amount of work
equal to $-U_{\mathrm{NaCl}}$ this may be converted into a gas of ions Na^{+}
and Cl^{-}. The conversion of these ions into neutral atoms
involves the expenditure of an amount of energy E_{Cl}, the
electron affinity of the chlorine atom, and the recovery of
an amount of energy I_{Na}, the ionization energy of sodium.
If the sodium now be allowed to condense to the solid, and
the chlorine atoms to associate to Cl_2, a further amount of
energy $S_{\mathrm{Na}} + \tfrac{1}{2} D_{\mathrm{Cl}}$ is recovered. Here S_{Na} is the heat of
sublimation of sodium and D_{Cl} the heat of dissociation of
chlorine per gram molecule. Finally, if the sodium and
chlorine thus obtained are allowed to combine chemically the
heat of formation Q_{NaCl} is recovered.

In performing this cycle of operations the total energy
interchange must clearly be zero, so that we have

$$- U_{\mathrm{NaCl}} + E_{\mathrm{Cl}} - I_{\mathrm{Na}} - S_{\mathrm{Na}} - \tfrac{1}{2} D_{\mathrm{Cl}} - Q_{\mathrm{NaCl}} = 0. \quad \ldots\ldots(4)$$

In this equation all the quantities are known except U_{NaCl},
which we wish to determine, and E_{Cl}, which cannot be

readily measured physically. In the absence of values for the electron affinity of the halogens it is therefore not possible to use the Born-Haber cycle to provide a direct check on the values of the lattice energy deduced from equation (3). It is possible, however, to obtain an indirect check, for we may transpose equation (4) into the form

$$\tfrac{1}{2}D_{Cl} - E_{Cl} = -U_{NaCl} - I_{Na} - S_{Na} - Q_{NaCl},$$

and in this equation all the quantities on the right-hand side except U_{NaCl} are known. If, therefore, we insert for U_{NaCl} the value given by the Born-Landé theory, and so evaluate $\tfrac{1}{2}D_{Cl} - E_{Cl}$, the value obtained should agree with that derived in a similar manner from any of the other alkali chlorides. A similar check can be carried out using the fluorides, bromides and iodides.

A test of this kind was made by Born (1919a), and Table 7 shows the values of $\tfrac{1}{2}D_X - E_X$ thus derived for each of the

TABLE 7

VALUES OF $(\tfrac{1}{2}D_X - E_X)$ FOR THE HALOGENS DEDUCED
FROM THE ALKALI HALIDES

(After Born, 1919a)

Values in kcal./g. atom

	F	Cl	Br	I
Li	—	(−58)	(−60)	(−58)
Na	−23	−53	−59	−55
K	−28	−63	−65	−63
Rb	—	(−77)	—	—
Cs	—	−61	—	—
Mean	−26	−62	−61	−59

The values in parentheses are less certain.

halogens from data on the various alkali halides. When we remember the number of quantities involved in this comparison, and the fact that the lattice energies are of the order of 200 kcal. per gram molecule, the agreement must be considered very satisfactory. Actual values for the lattice energies are tabulated in Table 8. These values are those deduced on the Born-Landé theory from equation (3) using the empirical value $n = 9$ for the exponent of the repulsive potential.

TABLE 8

LATTICE ENERGIES OF THE ALKALI HALIDES DEDUCED
FROM THE BORN-LANDÉ LATTICE THEORY

(After Born, 1919a)

Values in kcal./g. mol.

	F	Cl	Br	I
Li	−231	−179	−167	−153
Na	−220	−182	−168	−158
K	−210	−163	−155	−144
Rb	—	−144	−140	−138
Cs	—	−156	−150	−141

Application to other physical properties. The Born-Landé theory enables not only the lattice energy but also other physical properties of the structure to be calculated. We have already seen how the compressibility of a crystal may be deduced and have shown that experimental values for this quantity are in fact required to determine the value of n. The theory was early applied by Born (1919b) to calculate other elastic constants and also the characteristic frequency of lattice vibration, corresponding to the infra-red *Reststrahlen* frequency, and was soon extended to deduce coefficients of thermal expansion and breaking strengths of simple ionic crystals. In most cases values in satisfactory agreement with experiment were obtained.

An application of the lattice theory to deduce the physical properties of more complex structures was made by W. L. Bragg and Chapman (1924) and by Chapman, Topping and Morrall (1926). These authors, by regarding certain rhombohedral carbonates and nitrates as purely ionic structures, were able to deduce values for the characteristic rhombohedral angles in close agreement with those experimentally observed. In a similar manner Bollnow (1925) considered the structures of rutile and anatase and explained this dimorphism of TiO_2 as due to the nearly equal lattice energy of these two structures. He was also able to deduce values for the axial ratios in close agreement with experiment. We cannot, however, discuss here these purely physical applications of the early lattice theory since we are primarily concerned with its structural importance, and for them, as well as for a more detailed account of the development of the theory, we refer the reader to the works of Heckmann (1925), Born (1926), Born and Bollnow (1927), Grimm (1927), Herzfeld (1928), Eucken (1930), van Arkel and de Boer (1931), Sherman (1932) and Born and Göppert-Mayer (1933).

THE QUANTUM THEORY OF THE VAN DER WAALS BOND

In the original Born-Landé lattice theory no attempt was made to take account of the van der Waals forces between the ions in the crystal structure. These forces are normally very weak compared with those acting between electrically charged ions, so that in ionic structures their effect is usually qualitatively insignificant. It does not follow, however, that they can be safely ignored in a quantitative treatment, and it is easy to understand, for example, that the van der Waals contribution to the total lattice energy might be the ultimate factor in determining which of two structures, otherwise energetically nearly equivalent, was actually adopted. In any case, for purely molecular structures, a lattice theory analogous to that already discussed for ionic crystals is required.

The London theory.

The earliest attempts to explain the forces of van der Waals attraction were not concerned with these forces in solids but arose from their importance in the kinetic theory of gases. In 1912 Keesom regarded all molecules, although uncharged, as having a dipole moment and attributed the forces to the attraction between these dipoles. This so-called *orientation effect* gave rise to an interaction energy of the form

$$u = -\frac{A}{r^6} \cdot \frac{1}{kT},$$

but such an expression was shown to be inadequate by Debye

on the grounds that the temperature variation which it predicted was not in accordance with experiment. Moreover, it is difficult to understand how the atoms of the inert gases or such molecules as N_2 and O_2 could possess a permanent dipole moment. While the orientation effect may exist in the case of unsymmetrical molecules some further type of force must also occur, and this Debye explained as an *induction effect* in which the attraction occurred between the dipoles induced in each molecule by the field of its neighbours. In this way an interaction energy, again inversely proportional to the sixth power of the distance but now independent of temperature, was obtained.

The development of the wave mechanics revealed that there were difficulties in explaining the van der Waals forces in terms of either of these effects, for it was shown that the atoms of the inert gases must be exactly spherically symmetrical and can show neither permanent nor induced static dipole. Furthermore, in such molecules as H_2, N_2, O_2, etc., although electric moments are permitted (actually the wave mechanics indicates quadripole moments), the forces deduced are only about 1/100 of those experimentally observed. On the other hand, however, the wave mechanics introduces another type of interaction, a so-called *dispersion effect*, which cannot be explained in terms of classical mechanics at all but which arises from a dynamic polarization of the molecules associated with their zero-point motion. It is not easy to explain in physical terms the exact nature of this new type of interaction, but London (1937), in an excellent general review, has expressed it thus:

"If one were to take an instantaneous photograph of a molecule at any time, one would find various configurations of nuclei and electrons, showing in general dipole moments. In a spherically symmetrical rare gas molecule, as well as in our isotropic oscillators, the average over very many of such snap-shots would of course give no preference for any direction. These very quickly varying dipoles, represented by the zero-point motion of a molecule, produce an electric field and act upon the polarizability of the other molecule and produce there induced dipoles, which are in phase and in interaction with the instantaneous dipoles producing them. The zero-point motion is, so to speak, accompanied by a synchronized electric alternating field, but not by a radiation field: the energy of the zero-point motion cannot be dissipated by radiation."

The exact treatment (London, 1930b; Eisenschitz and London, 1930) gives for the dipole-dipole interaction energy due to this dispersion effect the expression

$$u = 3h\nu_0 - \frac{3}{4} \cdot \frac{h\nu_0 \alpha^2}{r^6},$$

where ν_0 is the proper frequency of the two molecules, α their polarizability and h Planck's constant. In this expression the first term is simply the zero-point energy of the two isolated molecules, and the second term the interaction energy corresponding to the van der Waals attractive force.

The wave mechanics treatment leaves unaltered the expressions given by Keesom and by Debye for the orientation and induction effects which obtain with molecules having permanent dipoles, so that in the general case the total contribution to the van der Waals energy is made up of three different constituents, each, however, inversely proportional to the sixth power of the distance. The relative magnitudes of these three contributions are shown in Table 9. It will be

TABLE 9

THE THREE CONSTITUENTS OF THE VAN DER WAALS ENERGY

(After London, 1937)

The values are the contribution to the lattice energy for unit intermolecular distance expressed in ergs $\times 10^{-60}$

	Orientation effect	Induction effect	Dispersion effect
CO	− 0·0034	− 0·057	− 67·5
HI	− 0·35	− 1·68	−382·0
HBr	− 6·2	− 4·05	−176·0
HCl	− 18·6	− 5·4	−105·0
NH_3	− 84·0	−10·0	− 93·0
H_2O	−190·0	−10·0	− 47·0

seen that in all cases the influence of the new dispersion effect is considerable and that in most cases this is by far the largest contribution. Except in very strongly polar molecules, such as H_2O, the orientation effect is negligible, and even in HCl its contribution is not large. The induction effect can be ignored in almost every case.

The repulsive forces. The wave mechanics treatment also throws light on the nature and origin of the repulsive forces which in molecular no less than in ionic structures must exist to confer on the atoms or molecules their characteristic sizes. Here again, in describing qualitatively the character of these forces we may quote the explanation of London (1937):

"Even if a molecule does not show any permanent multipole but has, on an average, an absolutely spherically symmetrical structure, e.g. like the rare gases, quite apart from all the effects due to the internal electronic motion, the mean charge distribution itself gives rise to a strong, so to speak 'static', interaction, simply owing to the fact that by penetrating each other the electronic clouds of two molecules no longer screen the nuclear charges completely and the nuclei repel each other by the electrostatic Coulomb forces. In addition to this, and simultaneously, a second influence is to be considered. Already the penetration of the two electronic clouds is hampered by the Pauli principle: two electrons can only be in the same volume element of space if they have sufficiently different velocities. This means that for the reciprocal penetration of the two clouds of electrons the velocity and therefore also the kinetic energy of the internal electronic motion must be augmented: energy must be supplied with the approach of the molecules and there is consequently a repulsive force between them."

The exact calculation of the repulsive forces presents considerable difficulties and cannot be carried out as readily as that of the forces of van der Waals attraction, so that, so far, the calculations have been made in detail only for the simplest case of helium. The quantum mechanics does, however, indicate that an inverse power law cannot adequately express the potential of these forces, and that an exponential law of the form

$$u = be^{-r/\rho}$$

gives a more appropriate representation (Unsöld, 1927; Brück, 1928). It is not yet, however, possible to calculate the values of the constants b and ρ and these quantities must, therefore, be empirically determined.

If we take into account the several contributions discussed above, the total lattice energy of a molecular structure may be expressed in the form

$$U = 3h\nu_0 + be^{-r/\rho} - c/r^6, \qquad \ldots\ldots(5)$$

where the three terms represent respectively the energy of the zero-point motion, of the repulsive forces, and of the forces of van der Waals attraction. The analogy between the lattice theories of molecular and ionic crystals is emphasized by comparing equation (5) with the corresponding expression (2), p. 45, for the lattice energy of ionic structures.

Application of the theory. The theory thus developed has been applied to the crystal lattices of the inert gases and also to the structures of such gases as H_2, N_2, O_2, Cl_2, CH_4, CO, NO, etc., in all of which the intermolecular forces are purely molecular in type, and values for the heats of sublimation have been obtained in satisfactory accord with experiment. In molecular structures there is no necessity to invoke the Born-Haber cycle in comparing the theory with observation since the lattice energy corresponds to the dispersion of the structure into an assemblage of molecules (as contrasted with an assemblage of ions in the ionic case), and is therefore directly comparable with the heat of sublimation. Table 10 shows a comparison of the calculated and observed heats of sublimation in a few molecular structures and it will be seen that the agreement is quite good. Born and Mayer (1932) have emphasized, however, that this agreement is to some extent illusory in that the calculated energies do not include the contribution of the repulsive term in equation (5) and that this contribution is not necessarily negligible compared with that of the van der Waals attraction. Nevertheless, the comparison shows that the new theory does at least give values for the lattice energy of the right order of magnitude, whereas all the previous treatments gave values some one hundred times too small.

The very small values of the lattice energies shown in Table 10, compared with those of ionic structures (Table 8, p. 49), reveal the weakness of the residual bond.

TABLE 10

LATTICE ENERGIES OF SOME MOLECULAR STRUCTURES

Values in kcal./g.mol.

	Calculated lattice energy	Observed heat of sublimation
Ne	−0·47	0·59
N_2	−1·64	1·86
A	−2·08	2·03
CH_4	−2·42	2·70

General accounts of the lattice theory of molecular structures and of the quantum theory of the residual bond have been given by London (1929, 1937), Lennard-Jones (1931 a, b) and by Slater and Kirkwood (1931), and the reader is referred to these works for a more detailed account of the matters here discussed.

THE LATER LATTICE THEORY OF IONIC CRYSTALS

The Born-Mayer treatment.

The quantum treatment of the van der Waals forces and the development of a lattice theory of molecular structures by London and his co-workers led to further work on ionic crystals and to a lattice theory of these structures in which the van der Waals forces, neglected in the early work of Born and Landé, were taken into account. Although the Born-Landé theory had achieved considerable success in describing the properties of many ionic structures, and especially of those of the alkali halides, it had gradually become clear that it suffered from serious limitations. Thus the lattice energies of divalent ionic compounds, such as the oxides and sulphides of the group 2 metals, were not in very good agreement with the values deduced from the Born-Haber cycle, while Slater (1924) showed, from accurate measurements on the compressibilities of a number of alkali halides, that the value of n could not be regarded as constant and equal to 9, as Born and Landé had proposed, but varied between wide limits. Equally serious was the fact that the value determined from the pressure variation of compressibility was entirely different from that deduced from the compressibility itself, as is shown by the following data:

	LiF	NaCl	KI
n from compressibility	5·9	9·1	10·5
n from pressure variation of compressibility	14·3	9·8	6·8

An extension of the lattice theory by Lennard-Jones and Taylor (1925), Lennard-Jones (1925), and Lennard-Jones and Dent (1926) led to values of n dependent on the types of ions concerned, and a similar general treatment was given by Pauling (1928a), but we shall not discuss this work here as it has since been largely developed and generalized in the later work of Born and Mayer (1932) now to be described.

Born and Mayer write the lattice energy of an ionic crystal in the form

$$u = -Ae^2/r + Be^{-r/\rho} - c/r^6 + \epsilon. \qquad \ldots\ldots(6)$$

This expression may be compared with the corresponding equation (2), p. 45, of the old theory. The first term remains unaltered and is the contribution of the energy of electrostatic attraction. The exponential repulsion term replaces the original empirical term B/r^n. The third term represents the effect of the van der Waals forces, and the last term is the contribution of the zero-point energy. The exponential term for the repulsive energy, although it is to be preferred on the grounds of the quantum theory to the original term, was introduced by Born and Mayer as a purely empirical expression in which the constant ρ was determined as before from compressibility measurements. It was found that the values of ρ thus deduced for all the alkali halides never differed by more than about 6 per cent from their mean: we have already seen that in the original expression n varied between about 5 and 11 for different alkali halides.

A rigid calculation of the contribution of each of the four terms of equation (6) to the lattice energy of all the alkali halides has been made by Mayer and Helmholz (1932) and their results are summarized in Table 11. These values show that the contribution of the zero-point energy is in all cases very small, but that the influence of the repulsive forces and of the van der Waals forces cannot be ignored, and, in fact,

TABLE 11

LATTICE ENERGIES OF THE ALKALI HALIDES DEDUCED FROM THE BORN-MAYER THEORY

(After Mayer and Helmholz, 1932)

(1)	(2)	(3)	(4)	(5)	(6)	(7)	(8)
Salt	Coulomb energy	van der Waals energy	Re-pulsive energy	Zero-point energy	Total energy. Sum (2)–(5)	Lattice energy on Born-Landé theory	Ob-served lattice energy
	Ergs/mol. $\times 10^{-12}$				Kcal./g. mol.		
F	−19·81	−0·09	+3·06	+0·27	−16·57	−240·1	−255·3	—
Cl	−15·51	−0·25	+1·86	+0·17	−13·73	−199·2	−199·9	—
Br	−14·42	−0·23	+1·56	+0·11	−12·98	−188·3	−186·0	—
I	−13·10	−0·26	+1·27	+0·08	−12·01	−174·1	−168·9	—
F	−17·22	−0·14	+2·45	+0·20	−14·71	−213·4	−222·0	—
Cl	−14·18	−0·20	+1·63	+0·12	−12·63	−183·1	−182·7	181·3*
Br	−13·39	−0·19	+1·43	+0·10	−12·05	−174·6	−172·3	—
I	−12·35	−0·22	+1·19	+0·08	−11·30	−163·9	−159·1	—
F	−14·93	−0·24	+1·95	+0·15	−13·06	−189·7	−192·5	—
Cl	−12·71	−0·27	+1·49	+0·10	−11·39	−165·4	−164·0	—
Br	−12·11	−0·25	+1·29	+0·08	−10·99	−159·3	−156·1	—
I	−11·30	−0·26	+1·10	+0·07	−10·39	−150·8	−143·7	153·8
F	−14·14	−0·27	+1·82	+0·10	−12·52	−181·6	−182·1	—
Cl	−12·20	−0·32	+1·38	+0·08	−11·06	−160·7	−157·2	—
Br	−11·60	−0·28	+1·22	+0·06	−10·60	−153·5	−149·4	151·3*
I	−10·86	−0·28	+1·07	+0·05	−10·02	−145·3	−140·0	—
F	−13·26	−0·45	+1·66	+0·08	−11·97	−173·7	−170·9	—
Cl	−11·28	−0·53	+1·23	+0·07	−10·51	−152·2	−145·2	—
Br	−10·81	−0·48	+1·14	+0·06	−10·07	−146·3	−139·4	—
I	−10·19	−0·46	+1·01	+0·05	− 9·59	−139·1	−131·2	141·5

* Helmholz and Mayer (1934).

that the van der Waals contribution is a maximum in just those
structures in which the electrostatic energy is smallest. The
total lattice energy deduced from the Born-Mayer theory does
not for any of the salts differ greatly from that derived in
terms of the old Born-Landé theory, but it will be seen from
the table that in the case of some of the salts, for which direct
measurements of the lattice energy are available (Mayer,
1930; Helmholz and Mayer, 1934), the new treatment does
give slightly better agreement with experiment. Similarly
the new values of the lattice energies, when introduced into
the Born-Haber cycle, give appreciably more consistent values
for the electron affinities of the several halogen atoms, so that,
in fact, the values derived in this way are probably the most
reliable estimates of these quantities yet available.

Similar calculations for the ionic oxides and sulphides of
certain divalent metals have been made by Mayer and
Maltbie (1932) and their results are shown in Table 12. In
this case compressibility data were available for only one of
the bodies considered, namely MgO, and the value of the
constant ρ in the repulsive energy term was therefore assumed
to be the same as that found from the alkali halides. A con-

TABLE 12

LATTICE ENERGIES OF SOME OXIDES AND SULPHIDES

(After Mayer and Maltbie, 1932)

(1)	(2)	(3)	(4)	(5)	(6)	
Salt	Coulomb energy	van der Waals energy	Re-pulsive energy	Zero-point energy	Total energy. Sum (2)–(5)	
	Ergs/mol. × 10^{-12}					Kcal./g. mol.
MgO	− 76·3	− 0·1	+11·5	+0·3	− 64·7	− 939
CaO	− 66·7	− 0·2	+ 9·3	+0·2	− 57·4	− 831
SrO	− 60·6	− 0·2	+ 7·8	+0·1	− 52·9	− 766
BaO	− 57·0	− 0·3	+ 7·0	+0·1	− 50·2	− 727
MgS	− 62·5	− 0·2	+ 7·4	+0·2	− 55·2	− 800
CaS	− 57·5	− 0·2	+ 6·8	+0·1	− 50·9	− 737
SrS	− 55·3	− 0·2	+ 6·0	+0·1	− 47·4	− 686
BaS	− 49·8	− 0·2	+ 5·3	+0·1	− 44·6	− 647

sideration of Table 12 shows, as is naturally to be expected, that the total lattice energy of the oxides and sulphides is considerably greater than that of the alkali halides and that in these structures both the zero-point energy and the contribution due to the van der Waals forces are entirely negligible. An attempt to confirm these values of the lattice energy by employing them in the Born-Haber cycle, equation (4), p. 47, to deduce the electron affinities of the oxygen and sulphur atoms gave the values for these quantities shown in Table 13. The agreement is less good than with the alkali halides, but is nevertheless in this case conspicuously better than that given by the application of the original Born-Landé theory.

TABLE 13

THE BORN-HABER CYCLE APPLIED TO CERTAIN
OXIDES AND SULPHIDES

(After Mayer and Maltbie, 1932)

All energies in kcal./g. mol. of the salt

(1)	(2)	(3)	(4)	(5)	(6)	(7)
Salt	Lattice energy U_{MX}	Heat of formation Q_{MX}	Heat of sublimation of metal S_M	Heat of dissociation of O_2 and S_2 $\frac{1}{2}D_{X_2}$	Ionization energy of metal I_M	Electron affinity of O and S. Sum (2)–(6) E_X
MgO	-939	145	34	59	521	-180
CaO	-831	151	44	59	412	-165
SrO	-766	140	39	59	384	-144
BaO	-727	133	38	59	350	-147
MgS	-800	81	34	66	521	-98
CaS	-737	113	44	66	412	-102
SrS	-686	112	39	66	384	-85
BaS	-647	110	38	66	350	-83

Since its original development the Born-Mayer theory has been applied to a number of structures and it has also undergone modification in detail. Thus Mayer (1933a) has shown that the term c/r^6 introduced by London to express the van der Waals energy is inadequate in the case of the alkali halides, and, by taking into account the dipole-quadripole interaction

ignored by London, has added a further term of the form
D/r^8 to the total lattice energy. In this way a van der Waals
energy contribution is obtained about twice as large as that
deduced by Born and Mayer. The implications of this work,
as well as of the application of the lattice theory to other
simple compounds by Mayer (1933b), Mayer and Levy (1933)
and by Huggins (1937), will be considered in the next section,
where the structural significance of the lattice theory of ionic
and molecular compounds is discussed.

The application of the Born-Mayer theory to the calculation
of the elastic constants and other physical properties of the
alkali halides has been considered by Zdanow, Erschow and
Galachow (1935) and by Jensen (1936).

THE STRUCTURAL SIGNIFICANCE OF LATTICE THEORY

The structural importance of the quantitative lattice theory
discussed in the preceding sections lies in the light which it
throws on the stability of crystal structures, on the types of
binding which occur in different structures, on the conditions
which determine the appearance of different structures in
substances chemically closely related, and, quite generally,
on the problems of polymorphism and morphotropy.* We may
consider these several points separately.

The stability of a crystal structure.

In general, among homodesmic structures the most stable
are those which have the largest lattice energy,† and it is
clear that in determining the stability of a crystal the lattice
energy is as fundamental a quantity as, say, the heat of sublimation or the chemical heat of formation. From equation
(1), p. 45, of the elementary Born-Landé theory we see at
once that the most stable structures are those containing

---

* Morphotropy may be defined as a progressive change in crystal structure brought about by systematic chemical substitution.

† Lattice energy is, of course, negative. In speaking of a large lattice
energy we adopt the conventional usage and imply a numerically large value
of this negative quantity.

small and highly charged ions. This is in accordance with the data given in the last section, where the lattice energies of oxides and sulphides of divalent metals were seen to be much greater than those of the alkali halides, and is also in accordance with the generally greater hardnesses and higher melting points of the former group of compounds. We have already shown in detail in Chap. II that among compounds of ions with a given valency, as for example in the whole series of alkali halides, the highest melting points and greatest hardnesses are associated with the smallest interionic distances. Detailed data illustrating these points have been collected by Fajans (1925).

In heterodesmic structures the stability no longer necessarily bears any immediate relation to the lattice energy since the breakdown of such crystals in general takes place in several stages. The first of these may represent the failure only of some of the weakest bonds in the structure and may leave undissociated stable molecules or complex groups, the energy of which makes a large contribution to the total lattice energy.

The stability of hypothetical compounds. The lattice theory can be applied not only to actual structures but also to imaginary structures or to the structures of chemical compounds which have never been prepared, and in fact as early as 1923 Grimm and Herzfeld (1923) applied the Born-Landé theory to explain the non-existence of such compounds as $NeCl$, $NaCl_2$, $MgCl_3$, etc. If we imagine, say, $NeCl$ to be an ionic crystal with the sodium-chloride structure, the heat of formation of this body is given in terms of the Born-Haber cycle by a relation analogous to equation (4), p. 47, viz.:

$$Q_{NeCl} = -U_{NeCl} + E_{Cl} - I_{Ne} - S_{Ne} - \tfrac{1}{2}D_{Cl_2}.$$

Subtracting from this the corresponding equation for sodium chloride we have, neglecting the heats of sublimation S_{Na} and S_{Ne} which are small compared with the other quantities,

$$Q_{NeCl} - Q_{NaCl} = -(U_{NeCl} - U_{NaCl}) - (I_{Ne} - I_{Na}),$$

so that the difference in heat of formation of the two compounds is equal to the difference in lattice energies less the difference in ionization energies of the cations. The lattice energies of the two structures cannot be very different and, therefore, the difference in heats of formation arises primarily from the difference in ionization energies of neon and sodium. These ionization energies are respectively 496 and 118 kcal. per gram atom and their difference is larger than the heat of formation of sodium chloride. That of neon chloride is therefore necessarily negative and the structure is unstable. In a similar way the heats of formation of other imaginary compounds are found to be very small or negative. The data in Table 14 show the heats of formation of existing and hypothetical chlorides deduced in this way. In most cases the values for the hypothetical salts are negative and in all cases they are substantially smaller than those for the compounds which have a real existence.

TABLE 14

HEATS OF FORMATION OF EXISTING AND
HYPOTHETICAL CHLORIDES

(After Grimm, 1928)

Values in kcal./g. mol.

NeCl −260			
NaCl +95	NaCl$_2$ −210		
CsCl +105	CsCl$_2$ −60		
MgCl +15	MgCl$_2$ +150	MgCl$_3$ −200	
AlCl +45	AlCl$_2$ +80	AlCl$_3$ +160	AlCl$_4$ −840

Lattice theory and morphotropy. The calculation of the relative lattice energies of the several different structures with which a given chemical compound might crystallize, with a view to explaining why one particular structure is actually adopted, presents considerably greater difficulties. These differences in lattice energy as between different structures are generally quite small so that significant conclusions can only be drawn if the individual lattice energies can be calculated with considerable precision. Thus Hund (1925) showed that in terms of the Born-Landé theory the sodium-chloride structure should be more stable than the caesium-chloride arrangement for all the alkali halides, so that this theory was not able to account for the occurrence of the latter structure in the three salts CsCl, CsBr and CsI. On the other hand, Hund also showed that the two structures differed little energetically so that nothing short of a very exact theory could be expected to reveal the difference. In the later work of Born and Mayer (1932) this particular transition was considered in more detail, and it was found that even when the contribution of the van der Waals forces was taken into account the sodium-chloride structure still appeared to be the more stable for all the alkali halides. If, however, the van der Waals contribution was about twice as large as that given by London's theory the occurrence of the caesium-chloride structure for three of the salts could be explained. As we have already mentioned, Mayer (1933a) has since shown that the van der Waals energy given by the London theory is considerably too small, so that the transition may now be satisfactorily regarded as due to the influence of the van der Waals forces.

Lattice theory and chemical binding.

Quantitative lattice theory can give much information about the type of binding force which occurs in a crystal structure. Thus, for example, if the observed lattice energy of a compound differs greatly from that deduced theoretically it is a clear indication that the type of binding which actually occurs is different from that assumed in the calculation. Grimm and Sommerfeld (1926) treated in this way the case of the compound ICl, which they regarded as an imaginary ionic structure I^+Cl^-. The calculated values for the lattice energy and heat of formation deduced on this assumption were found to be entirely different from those experimentally observed.

A less extreme but more important illustration of the application of lattice theory to determine the type of interatomic binding is given by the work of Mayer (1933b) and of

Mayer and Levy (1933) on the lattice energies of silver and cuprous halides. Lattice theory shows that for all the silver salts the rock-salt structure should be the most stable. Actually this arrangement obtains in AgF, AgCl and AgBr, but in AgI the lower co-ordinated zincblende structure is found. No reasonable adjustment of the lattice energy can make this structure the more stable and it is accordingly deduced that in AgI the binding is no longer truly ionic but is instead partially homopolar in character. In agreement with this deduction Franck and Kuhn (1927) have shown spectroscopically that the structure is composed of atoms and not of ions. In the case of the cuprous halides the zincblende structure is to be expected in all the salts and this is indeed the structure actually found. In passing from the chloride to the iodide, however, the observed lattice energies show increasing departures from the calculated values, as is seen from the data in Table 15.

TABLE 15
LATTICE ENERGIES OF CUPROUS HALIDES
(After Mayer and Levy, 1933)

Values in kcal./g. mol.

	CuCl	CuBr	CuI
Observed value	− 222	− 216	− 213
Calculated value	− 216	− 208	− 199
Difference	6	8	14

Again this effect is to be associated with the increasingly homopolar character of the bond as the distortion or 'polarization' of the anion increases.

The brief account which we have given of the structural importance of the lattice theory illustrates in a general way some of the directions in which it may be applied, but it also emphasizes some of the inevitable shortcomings of the quantitative treatment. Thus we have seen that to be of any practical utility the lattice theory must give a very exact expression of the lattice energy, for as between different possible structures the energy differences may be small, and quite trifling contributions to the total energy may ultimately determine which structure actually obtains. When we consider how frequent have been the modifications and developments of the theory of even such simple structures as those of the alkali halides it is clear that it must be a long time before lattice theory can handle adequately the more complex structures to which X-ray methods of analysis have been applied. While every attempt to further the precise quantitative expression of chemical linkage is to be welcomed, we must for the present be content to give a purely qualitative account of the properties of the vast majority of known structures.

In the case of the homopolar and the metallic bonds the difficulties in the way of an exact quantitative treatment are even greater, and, although the theory of metals has recently developed to an extent which promises soon to rival the theory of ionic crystals, the very simplest of homopolar structures still prove to be mathematically very intractable. Nevertheless, the modern theory of these binding forces is of the greatest importance, for it has given rise to many significant developments in the purely qualitative description of them even when a quantitative application is not possible. For this reason we now pass on to consider the more recent work on structures in which homopolar or metallic forces are operative.

THE QUANTUM THEORY OF THE HOMOPOLAR BOND

The Heitler-London theory.

We have already given in Chap. II a general account of the physical properties and structural characteristics of the homopolar bond as well as of its qualitative description by Lewis and by Kossel. The first attempt to apply the new quantum theory to the bond was made by Heitler and London (1927) in a discussion of the hydrogen molecule. We cannot here give any account of the mathematical background of the Heitler-London theory, but physically the homopolar binding

of two atoms appears in this theory as an 'exchange' phenomenon. If two atoms, each containing a single electron, such
as two hydrogen atoms, approach one another, the interaction energy of the two systems may correspond to an
attraction between them. This is the case if the spins of the
two electrons are oppositely directed, and under these conditions the 'resonance' effect between them may be pictured
as an oscillatory interchange of the electrons between the two
atoms in such a way that they can no longer be associated
with either atom in particular but appear instead to be a part
of both atoms. In this treatment we see a more precise expression of the older picture of shared electrons as responsible for
the homopolar bond, and also of the conception of valency
saturation, for in each bond the spins of two electrons neutralize
each other and the two electrons involved are incapable of
forming further bonds. An atom can only take part in a homopolar binding when it contains one or more electrons with
unneutralized spins.

The original Heitler-London theory is mathematically far
too formal to be of great practical utility in any structural
problem and, moreover, even in the simplest cases, is not
quantitatively sufficiently accurate to provide data of any
value in lattice theory. Thus, in the simple case of the hydrogen
molecule, the calculated heat of dissociation is only about
60 per cent of the experimental value, while the many-bodied
problem of a crystal structure eludes treatment altogether.
At the same time the mathematical rigidity of the theory
precludes even its qualitative application in such cases. We
shall therefore not give any further discussion here of the
Heitler-London theory, but pass on instead to consider some
of the later and less formal treatments of the homopolar bond
which have arisen from it and which are of the greatest value
in the interpretation of the crystal structures of homopolar
compounds.

The reader who wishes for a further account of the Heitler-
London theory is referred to the general reviews of Pauling
(1928b), Rodebusch (1928), London (1928, 1929), Heitler
(1930) and of Born (1931).

The Pauling-Slater treatment.

Although the Heitler-London theory has proved to be quantitatively disappointing and although it is, in its rigid form, of very limited applicability, the method of treatment introduced by Heitler and London is nevertheless of general validity, and their theory may be regarded as laying the foundation of much of the more recent work on valency theory. In the hands of Pauling, Slater, Lennard-Jones, Mulliken and others the theory of the homopolar bond has been developed and extended in a semi-empirical and less formal manner which has enabled it to be applied, at least qualitatively, to a far wider field than could ever be covered by the rigid analysis of Heitler and London, and which has brought to light many results of the greatest structural and physical importance. It is entirely outside the scope of this book to attempt to give any account of the detailed features of the work of these various authors and, indeed, it is questionable whether such a treatment would in any case be of much value. The quantum theory of the homopolar bond cannot be regarded as having reached anything approximating to a final stage in its development and, while change is so rapid, its more detailed aspects, and certainly its quantitative treatment, can scarcely be regarded as more than ephemeral. Nevertheless there have emerged certain general features of the theory which have stood the test of time, and here we shall content ourselves with a qualitative discussion of some of the structurally significant aspects of the newer work.

Directed valency. The original Lewis theory of the homopolar bond was able to account for the valencies of the various elements in most of their compounds in terms of the picture of electron sharing. The theory could not, however, offer any explanation of the observed spatial distribution of the valency links which is such a characteristic property of the homopolar bond and which differentiates it so sharply from other types of interatomic binding force. In the newer picture, in which the bond is attributed to a sharing of two electrons of oppositely directed spins, this spatial distribution of valencies receives a more satisfactory explanation. Thus Slater (1931 a, b, c) and Pauling (1931 a) have shown that a complete description of the homopolar bond must include a specification of the state of quantization of the electrons taking part. They conclude that p-electrons give rise to stronger bonds than s-electrons and that if an atom takes part in several p-electron linkages these links tend to be perpendicular to each other. Thus, in ammonia, nitrogen in its normal state has three p-electrons and the three bonds are therefore so directed as to give a pyramidal structure, a conclusion which is in accordance with the observed dipole moment of the molecule. In a similar way the molecule of water is not linear, although here the bond angle differs from 90° owing to interaction between the hydrogen atoms.

When the binding electrons are not all of one kind further complications arise. Thus in its normal state the carbon atom has only two electrons with unshared spin and so can be linked in two single or one double bond as in CO. A very small energy increment, however, is sufficient to bring about a change of quantization by transferring one of the s-electrons to the p state, so producing four electrons with unpaired spins and the possibility of a corresponding number of homopolar bonds. In the vast majority of carbon compounds the atom must be excited in this way, and Pauling (1931 a) has shown that when such a change of quantization occurs all the bonds are symmetrically directed towards the corners of a regular tetrahedron. This conclusion is, of course, in complete accord with all the crystallographic and other evidence on the disposition of the carbon valencies. Even when the number of bonds formed is fewer than four, such bonds as occur are mutually inclined at the characteristic tetrahedral angle of 109° 28′.

With atoms of higher atomic number, in which d- as well as s- and p-electrons may take part in homopolar binding, the possibility of higher and also of less symmetrical co-ordination arises. If the co-ordination round a given atom is 6-fold Pauling's treatment shows that its neighbours may be disposed either at the corners of a regular octahedron or in a less symmetrical arrangement at the corners of a trigonal prism, and this latter type of co-ordination is in fact observed in MoS_2. When the co-ordination is only 4-fold, the four neighbours of an atom may lie either at the corners of a regular tetrahedron or, if certain conditions are satisfied, in a plane at the corners of a square. This latter somewhat unexpected co-ordination is of quite common occurrence in structures of the type ABX_4, such as $K_2Ni(CN)_4$, K_2PtCl_4, etc., in which the B atom is surrounded by four X neighbours, and it is also found in simpler structures such as PtS and PdO. Its explanation must be regarded as a considerable achievement of the new quantum theory.

Resonance structures. One of the most significant deductions of the quantum theory of homopolar binding is the fact that in many structures a single electronic configuration corresponding to a certain static distribution of bonds does not obtain, but that rather several alternative configurations, corresponding to different possible bond distributions, may simultaneously co-exist. The actual structure cannot, therefore, be represented by a unique molecular formula, but only by a combination of several possible formulae. In such cases the molecule or crystal is said to 'resonate' between these various structures. This resonance phenomenon can occur whenever the several individual structures are comparable in energy, but the particularly important point which emerges from the treatment is that in such cases the influence of resonance confers additional stability on the structure, so that it becomes energetically more favoured than any of the single structures of which it is built up.

One of the most important resonance structures, and the one which has been discussed in the greatest detail, is that of benzene. The familiar Kekulé theory treated this molecule as an equilibrium between the two arrangements

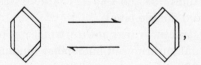

and in fact these are two of the possible structures of the ring.

The Dewar formula

although it has never been regarded as of great chemical significance, is also another possible structure, and Pauling and Wheland (1933) have now shown that the actual arrangement must be regarded as a resonance between the five canonical structures

By far the greatest contribution to the structure, however, is made by the two Kekulé formulae, resonance between which stabilizes the molecule to the extent of about 1·35 electron volts as compared with a single ring of three double bonds. Similarly, in naphthalene the observed arrangement is a resonance between no fewer than forty-two canonical structures, and again it is this resonance which confers stability on the molecule.

From a structural point of view these deductions from the quantum theory are of the greatest importance in that they often provide a far more successful interpretation of the observed crystal structures than was possible in terms of older ideas. Thus, to revert to the case of benzene, the precise equivalence of all six carbon atoms arising from the resonance interpretation of this molecule is in exact accordance with the X-ray evidence, which reveals the molecule as a perfectly regular plane hexagon. Moreover, the characteristic carbon-carbon distance of 1·43 A. is very nearly the arithmetic mean between the values 1·54 and 1·35 A., characteristic respectively of the single and double bonds.

Many other structures are known in which resonance between two or more configurations of homopolar binding must occur. Thus Slater (1931a) has suggested that many examples of polymerization may be cases in which valency bonds formerly

operative within the molecule have partly changed over to
the rôle of intermolecular forces, while Pauling and Wheland
(1933) have attributed the stability of certain free radicals to
the existence of resonance among several possible structures.
Pauling and Sherman (1933a) have considered a number of
complex organic compounds and shown on energetic grounds
that resonance must take place. A simple example is the
complete degeneracy which exists in the anion of a carboxylic
acid between the structures

$$R-C\diagdown\!\!\!\!\diagup{\overset{O}{\underset{O^-}{}}} \quad \text{and} \quad R-C\diagup\!\!\!\!\diagdown{\overset{O^-}{\underset{O}{}}} ,$$

a degeneracy that results in a crystal structure in which the
cation appears equally bound to the two oxygen atoms. Many
other examples of resonance which have important structural
implications are best considered when the individual crystal
structures are under discussion.

The purely chemical implications of resonance have been
discussed by Sidgwick (1936, 1937).

Resonance between homopolar and ionic structures. Resonance between different structures is not confined to purely
homopolar compounds, but can also occur between a homopolar and a corresponding ionic configuration. In fact, such
a possibility has already been adumbrated in our discussion of
the lattice energies of silver and cuprous halides, where we
saw that in certain salts the binding was partially ionic and
partially homopolar in character. This wider conception of
resonance opens up the possibility of a completely continuous
transition from the homopolar to the ionic bond. Thus, the
halogen acids can all be regarded as resonance structures
between the configurations

$$H^+ \; \overset{..}{\underset{..}{:}}X\overset{}{:}{}^- \quad \text{and} \quad H\overset{..}{:}X\overset{..}{:} ,$$

but there can be no doubt that in HF the former configuration
makes the larger contribution while in HI the effect of the
polarization of the iodine atom makes the latter configuration
increasingly important.

Such a resonance between ionic and homopolar configurations undoubtedly occurs in a very great number of simple crystal structures. In many silicates, for example, although the binding can generally be regarded as purely ionic, Slater (1931a) has shown that certain of the bond angles depart from those to be expected in a typically ionic structure and imply some measure of homopolar binding. In such cases the ionic and homopolar descriptions do not, however, differ fundamentally and it is of little consequence whether we describe the binding as homopolar, or as ionic with strong polarization of the anions. In the ionic picture a transfer of electrons from cation to anion is supposed to take place but increasing polarization attracts them back again, reducing the dipole moment of the link until ultimately a typically homopolar bond results. The purely homopolar bond is probably an idealized abstraction except between two atoms of the same element.

We shall find many other examples of resonance between homopolar and ionic bindings and of the continuous nature of the transition between them when we consider individual structures in detail.

One- and three-electron bonds. The possibility of a homopolar bond being formed not by two electrons but by one or by three has occasionally been somewhat arbitrarily advanced to account for the formation of various individual compounds which could not be explained in terms of the ordinary valency theory, and it is one of the most successful achievements of the new quantum treatment that it can account for the occurrence of such bonds and at the same time explain their rarity. Pauling (1931b) has shown that a single electron bond can exist between two atoms A and B only if the two states $A^{\cdot} + B$ and $A + {^{\cdot}}B$ can exist with substantially the same energy. In the same way a three-electron bond between the atoms is possible only if the configurations $A : + . B$ and $A . + : B$ are energetically approximately equivalent. In terms of the one-electron bond Pauling (1931b) has been able to explain the anomalous behaviour of boron trihydride which occurs only in the associated form B_2H_6. This substance Pauling writes

$$\text{H} \quad \text{H}$$
$$\text{H} : \text{B} \vdots \text{B} \vdots \text{H}$$
$$\text{H} \quad \text{H}$$

with two hydrogen atoms attached by one-electron bonds. The formula must not, however, be interpreted as implying that any particular pair of hydrogen atoms is singled out for this type of binding. Instead, the various configurations with different pairs of atoms attached in this way are all included in the final structure and this additional degeneracy provides further resonance energy, thus increasing the stability of the molecule.

The bond energy associated with one- and three-electron linkages is roughly one-half of that of the normal two-electron bond.

Physical properties of the homopolar bond. The new quantum treatment has enabled certain of the physical properties associated with the homopolar bond to be theoretically explained. Bond energies and the spatial disposition of valencies have already been briefly discussed. Pauling (1931 *a*) has considered the question of rotation about the homopolar bond and shown theoretically that there must be free rotation about a single bond but no rotation about a double bond, a conclusion in agreement with common chemical experience. The magnetic properties of homopolar compounds have also been discussed by Pauling (1931 *a*) who has shown that these properties may be of value in identifying the type of binding in any structure. Paired electrons contribute nothing to the magnetic moment of a molecule or complex ion so that the observed moments determine the number of unpaired electrons present.

For a detailed account of the quantum theory of the homopolar bond the reader is referred to the papers of Pauling (1931 *a, b*, 1932 *a, b*), Pauling and Wheland (1933), Pauling and Sherman (1933 *a, b*), Pauling and Huggins (1934) and of Slater (1931 *a, b, c*). Summaries and general reviews have been published by Mulliken (1931, 1932), Pauling and Huggins

(1934), van Vleck and Sherman (1935) and by Dushman and Seitz (1937).

THE THEORY OF THE METALLIC STATE

The simple Drude-Lorentz free-electron theory of metals, briefly described in the last chapter, was developed primarily to account for the thermal and electrical conductivities of metals and for the Wiedemann-Franz Law connecting these quantities. It is well known that in its original form this theory encountered difficulties in explaining the specific heats of metals, to which the free electrons appeared to make no contribution. This difficulty was resolved by Sommerfeld (1928b), who showed that, as a consequence of the exclusion principle, the great majority of the electrons in a metal must have energies far exceeding those of thermal agitation, all the low energy states being completely occupied by the maximum number of electrons which they are allowed to accommodate. Only at very high temperatures does the electronic energy change appreciably with temperature, and it is, therefore, only at very high temperatures that the electrons make any considerable contribution to the specific heat. In spite of this success, however, the Sommerfeld treatment still handled only a very arbitrary selection of metallic characteristics, and in particular threw no light on many of those properties which are structurally the most important. Thus the theory could give no picture of the metallic bond sufficiently rigid for any quantitative discussion of the cohesion of metals. Nor could it account for the various characteristic metal crystal structures or explain the difference between them, and still less could it provide any systematic basis for the co-ordination of the great mass of empirical material on alloy systems which had been collected.

The Bloch theory.

The first attempt to represent the essentially crystalline character of a metal was due to Bloch (1929), who extended Sommerfeld's treatment by taking into account the wave nature of the electrons and by regarding the electrons, not as perfectly free, but as moving under the influence of the periodic field of the crystal lattice. For a free electron the energy is given by

$$E = \tfrac{1}{2}mv^2 = \frac{1}{2m} \cdot k^2,$$

and is proportional to the square of the momentum k, so that these two quantities are related by a parabolic law of the type shown in Fig. 6. The exclusion principle forbids any two electrons to have the same set of quantum numbers, and in consequence all the energy states up to some maximum energy

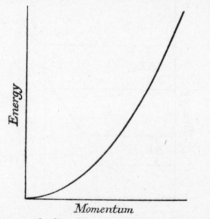

Fig. 6. The energy of a free electron as a function of its momentum.

E_m are practically completely filled, while only at very high temperatures do many electrons have an energy greater than E_m. This may be expressed in a slightly different way if we represent the state of each electron by a point whose position is determined by the three components k_x, k_y and k_z of its momentum k. The energy of the electron is then proportional to the square of the vector joining its representative point to the origin of the momentum space thus defined. The exclusion principle now requires that each electron shall have to itself a spherical shell in this momentum space, so that the whole assemblage of the many electrons in the crystal will occupy a spherical domain whose size is determined by the total number of electrons. This is the picture which arises from Sommerfeld's treatment of the electrons as entirely free.

When the periodic field of the lattice is taken into account Bloch showed that the energy of the electron no longer varies continuously with momentum but experiences discontinuous changes at certain critical momentum values in a way shown diagrammatically in Fig. 7. At some distance from these critical momentum values the energy approximates to that of a free electron, but just below these values the energy is abnormally depressed and just above them it is abnormally raised. Corresponding to each of these discontinuities there

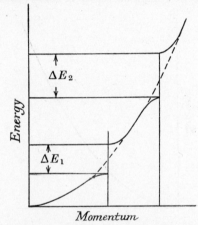

Fig. 7. The energy of an electron in a crystal lattice as a function of its momentum. Energy values lying in the ranges ΔE_1, ΔE_2, etc. are completely forbidden.

is a range of energy ΔE_1, ΔE_2, etc., which is completely forbidden. The whole assemblage of electrons now no longer occupies a continuous range of energies but is, instead, divided into a series of discrete so-called 'Brillouin zones'.

In the one-dimensional illustration just discussed, a range of forbidden energy must always occur at the zone boundary, but it can be shown that this is not necessarily so when the problem is considered in terms of the three-dimensional momentum space. In this case the energy discontinuities are found to take place when the representative point describing the state of an electron crosses one of a number of sets of planes, and it can be shown that these planes are, in fact, parallel to all the geometrically possible crystal faces, so that the Brillouin zones now become a series of concentric polyhedral figures. For different directions of the vector *k* the energy discontinuities do, in general, leave different energy ranges forbidden. It may, therefore, happen that a forbidden range for one direction of *k* is completely covered by allowed ranges for other directions, and in this case, although an energy increase

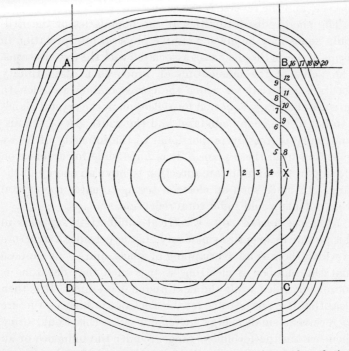

Fig. 8. Two-dimensional representation of the zone system in some hypothetical metal. The curves are contours of equal energy and the straight lines the zone boundaries across which energy discontinuities occur.

always occurs in crossing a zone boundary at a given point, there may nevertheless be electrons at certain places in an outer zone with energies less than those of other electrons in an inner zone. This point is made clear by the two-dimensional example illustrated in Fig. 8. Here the first zone boundary is the square *ABCD* and the curves are contours of equal energy. At some distance from the boundary of the zone these contours are nearly circular, as would be the case for free electrons, but near the boundary they are considerably distorted. In the inner zone the points of maximum energy are the corners A, B, C and D and the energy at these points may be greater or less than that at a point such as X in the outer zone. If it is greater there is an 'overlap' of the zones and no range of forbidden energy; if it is smaller the zones are discrete and the reverse is the case.

The energy discontinuities at the boundaries of the Brillouin zones may be given a simple physical interpretation in terms of the de Broglie waves associated with the free electrons. The value of the momentum at which each discontinuity occurs is just that for which the corresponding wave-length satisfies the Bragg equation for reflection in the crystal planes parallel to the zone boundary, and the width ΔE of the discontinuity is roughly proportional to the intensity of X-ray reflection from these planes. It is impossible for an electron moving in the appropriate direction to have an energy in the range ΔE since such an electron trying to enter the crystal from outside would suffer total reflection.

Electrical conductivity. Electrical conductivity appears in this picture in an entirely new way. Let us consider a structure in which there is no overlapping of zones, and let us suppose that the number of electrons is just such that one zone is completely filled while the next above it is empty. It is then clear that it is not possible for the electrons in such a structure to receive a small energy increment since this would bring them within the forbidden range. Under the influence of an electric field the electrons can acquire no drift velocity and the substance is an insulator. In this way we see that a free electron does not necessarily give rise to conductivity: only if a zone is incompletely filled or overlaps a higher zone can conduction occur.

Different possible zonal configurations are shown diagrammatically in Fig. 9. The shading represents possible energy states while those actually occupied are shown in black. In Fig. 9*a* the condition is that of an insulator since one zone is completely filled and the one next above it is empty. If the energy gap between the two zones is very small, as in Fig. 9b, the crystal will still be an insulator at the absolute zero but may acquire conductivity at higher temperatures if the energy of thermal agitation is sufficient to lift some electrons into the empty zone. In this case the conductivity increases with temperature and the substance behaves as a semi-conductor. The energy state of a normal conductor is represented in Fig. 9c and 9d. In the former case the zones are discrete but the lowest zone is only partly filled, while in the latter an overlap takes place and the crystal is a conductor whether the lowest zone is completely filled or not.

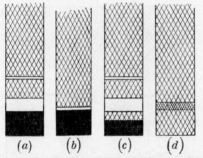

Fig. 9. Zonal configurations in different solids:
(a) an insulator; (b) a semi-conductor; (c) and (d) a conductor.

The Brillouin zones of permitted energy values may be regarded from a somewhat different point of view by considering the relationship which they bear to the energy levels of the individual atoms of the metal concerned. It is clear that if we imagine a metal lattice to be continuously expanded the zone system must experience profound modification, and must ultimately degenerate into the atomic energy levels of an isolated atom when the interatomic distances become sufficiently large. Fig. 10, p. 80 (Seitz and Johnson, 1937b), shows schematically the behaviour of the atomic energy levels of an alkali metal as the lattice is contracted. The individual levels are seen gradually to broaden out and ultimately to overlap in such a way that at the equilibrium spacing represented by A the overlapping is complete, filled and unfilled zones are

brought together and the metal becomes a conductor. If the
equilibrium spacing were somewhat greater, corresponding
to a point such as B at which the lowest zone does not overlap
the one next above it, conductivity could occur only if this
zone was incompletely filled.

This intricate broadening and overlapping of the zones is
a characteristic of practically all metals and arises from the
profound influence which the formation of the lattice exercises
on the electronic orbits of the individual atoms. In such a
case the association of the zones with the individual atomic
states becomes more symbolical than real, but, as we shall
see below, in non-metals, where the atomic orbits are less

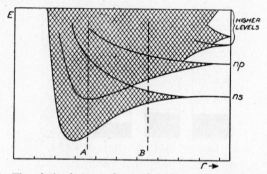

Fig. 10. The relation between the zonal configuration and atomic energy
levels in an alkali metal.

radically modified, it is still possible to correlate particular
zones with particular atomic energy levels. The overlapping
of zones which occurs in the metals becomes increasingly
probable as the atomic states become more densely packed,
and for this reason conductivity is much more common among
heavy elements than among those of low atomic number.
Similarly, in a given group of the periodic classification conductivity tends to increase with increasing atomic number, as
for example in the elements diamond, silicon, germanium, tin
and lead.

Structural properties. From a structural point of view the
most important applications of metal theory are concerned
with the character of the metallic bond and with the lattice

energetics and stability of different structures. These problems have been discussed by Wigner and Seitz (1933, 1934) who have considered in particular the cubic body-centred arrangement of sodium. If we imagine in such a structure that a set of planes is constructed bisecting the lines joining each atom to its nearest and next nearest neighbours, the whole lattice is divided into a series of polyhedra, of the form shown in Fig. 11, one surrounding each atom. Since the free electrons in the metal will tend to be dispersed as widely as possible, there is a large probability that in each such polyhedron one, and only one, electron will be found. The potential energy of the crystal can then be treated as made up of the energy of the charges within the individual polyhedra together with the mutual

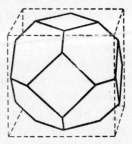

Fig. 11. The polyhedral domain surrounding each atom in a cubic body-centred structure.

energy of the polyhedra themselves. The former contribution is simply that of an electron in the field of the ion, while the latter is negligible since the separate polyhedra are electrically neutral and very nearly spherical, so that the crystal is therefore held together primarily by the attraction between each ion and the electron in its own polyhedron. This attraction is also responsible for the coherence of the separate polyhedra, since any expansion of the metal is accompanied by an increase in their size and a corresponding increase in the mutual potential energy of the positive ion and electron which each contains.

It is not so immediately evident why the ions in the metal maintain their characteristic separation, corresponding to an effective radius considerably greater than that of the same ion in polar crystals, but this point is made clear when the kinetic energy of the free electrons is taken into account. An electron moving with a velocity v is associated with a de Broglie wave of wave-length h/mv, and if such an electron is bound in a block of metal of linear dimensions L only discrete velocities corresponding to standing waves of wave-lengths $2L$, $2L/2$,

$2L/3, \ldots, 2L/n, \ldots$ are permitted. These velocities are, therefore, $nh/2mL$ and correspond to the energies $n^2h^2/8mL^2$. By the exclusion principle not more than two electrons can have the same energy so that in the whole block all possible energy states up to very high values of n must be occupied, and since the energy of each electron is proportional to L^{-2} the total kinetic energy is also proportional to this quantity. It follows that a compression of the metal results in an increase in the kinetic energy of the free electrons.

The total contribution of the free electrons is therefore, on this picture, made up of two components: (1) the kinetic energy, just discussed, which is proportional to L^{-2} or to $V^{-2/3}$, where V is the volume of the metal, and (2) the potential energy of the electron in each polyhedron in the field of the positive ion, which is, of course, proportional to $-V^{-1/3}$. The sum of these two components gives a function of the form shown in Fig. 12, in which the position of the minimum determines the equilibrium conditions and actual interatomic distances in the crystal.

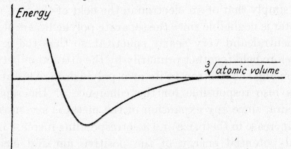

Fig. 12. The energy of the electrons in metallic sodium as a function of the atomic volume.

When applied to the alkali metals this treatment gives values for the cell dimensions, compressibility and other physical properties in satisfactory agreement with experiment (Wigner and Seitz, 1933, 1934; Slater, 1934b; Millman, 1935; Seitz, 1935; Fuchs, 1936a, b), but for copper, silver and gold similar calculations yield far too large values for the compressibilities, so that these metals are much harder than the theory demands (Fuchs, 1935; Krutter, 1935). The explanation of this discrepancy appears to lie in the fact that in these elements the ionic radii are relatively much larger than in the alkali metals and approach much more nearly to one-half the actual interatomic distances. Before the equilibrium condition represented by the minimum in the energy function of Fig. 12 is reached the positive ions come into contact so that the structure is determined primarily by the stacking of these ions in geometrically the most compact way. For this reason the elements copper, silver and gold have a cubic close-packed structure whereas that of the soft alkali metals is the less highly co-ordinated cubic body-centred arrangement.

The stability of metal structures may be regarded from a somewhat different point of view in terms of the Brillouin zones of the lattice, for, as we have seen, the energy of states just below the surface of a Brillouin zone is abnormally low, and that of states just above the surface abnormally high. It follows that, other things being equal, those structures will be most stable in which a given zone is as nearly full as possible and yet in which there is a minimum of overlapping into another zone. This viewpoint has been extensively applied to the metallic elements to explain their observed structures, and Jones (1934 b) has been able to account for the structure of bismuth in this way. It is, however, in the interpretation of alloy systems that the method has achieved its most striking success, and we accordingly postpone any further account of it until these systems are considered in detail.

Other physical properties. The application of the Bloch theory to many other physical properties of metals has also been considered and a lattice theory of the metallic state has now been built up scarcely less complete than that which Born and his co-workers have developed for ionic crystals. Some of these applications have already been adumbrated, and others include the work of Mott (1935) on the magnetic properties of the transition metals, and, from a somewhat different point of view, that of Gombás (1935 a, b, 1936 a, b, c) on the lattice theory of the alkali metals. We cannot, however, here discuss these applications of the theory: an adequate discussion would occupy a disproportionate amount of space, and in any case admirable accounts are readily available in the works of Mott and Jones (1936), and of A. H. Wilson (1936), and in the excellent review of Seitz and Johnson (1937 a, b, c). The particular features of the Bloch theory which are of structural significance are discussed in the reviews of Evans (1936) and of Mott (1937). Less up-to-date but more comprehensive accounts of the theory of metals have been given by Hume-Rothery (1931), Slater (1934 a) and Borelius (1935 b).

A GENERAL THEORY OF THE SOLID STATE

The account which has been given in this chapter of the quantitative theories of the several types of interatomic binding represents a very considerable advance in our understanding of the solid state. At the same time, however, it is difficult to escape the conclusion that the series of *ad hoc* treatments so lacking in co-ordination, which appear to be necessary to describe the various types of solid, must ultimately undergo some measure of unification before anything approaching finality can be reached. Thus most of the earlier work on metal theory was developed primarily to explain the conductivity of the metals, in respect of which property they differ from the best insulators by a factor of the order of 10^{22}, and this somewhat arbitrary concentration of attention on certain particular properties has tended to conceal the fact that in many other respects metals and non-metals are qualitatively very closely alike. We have already seen that between the metallic and the homopolar bonds, on the one hand, and between the ionic and the homopolar on the other, there is no sharp distinction, but instead a smooth and continuous transition. Any theory of the solid state, to be aesthetically satisfying or physically significant, must ultimately embrace within a single unified framework these three principal manifestations of interatomic cohesion.

In the zone theory, applied so successfully by Bloch and others to the metallic state, we see what promises to be the beginning of such a unification. In this theory, as we have seen, conductivity no longer appears as a particularly significant property of the metallic state but instead as an almost fortuitous property determined by the accidental configuration of the zones. The distinction between metals and non-conductors is no longer a fundamental distinction between free and bound electrons (for even an insulator may contain free electrons), but rather a relatively trivial distinction between different possible zonal configurations. It is as yet far too early to give any detailed account of the application of zone theory to ionic and homopolar structures, but already it has yielded promising results in the case of the few simple structures to which it has been applied.

The alkali halides have been discussed along these lines by Shockley (1936) and by Ewing and Seitz (1936) who have traced the development of the zones from the energy levels of

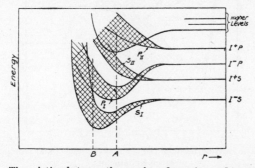

Fig. 13. The relation between the zonal configuration and atomic energy levels in lithium fluoride.

the isolated ions concerned. Fig. 13 (Seitz and Johnson, 1937 b) illustrates the formation of the zones in the case of LiF, and a comparison with the corresponding diagram for a metal (Fig. 10, p. 80) shows that here the zones preserve their identity in a much more definite manner. At the equilibrium spacing represented by A the zones are narrow, so that the ionic character of the orbits is largely preserved, and the zones do not overlap. No partially filled zones exist and the substance is an insulator.

The application of the zone theory to homopolar compounds has been discussed by Kimball (1935) who has considered the structure of diamond. In this case, where the atomic energy states are well separated, the zones which develop as the lattice spacing is diminished intermingle and then separate again into groups in a manner illustrated in Fig. 14. At the equilibrium spacing the filled zones extend up to the edge of the forbidden region, by which they are widely separated from the unoccupied levels, so that diamond must be an insulator, as is indeed the case. At the same time, the behaviour of the zones suggests an explanation of the conductivity of carbon in the form of graphite. In this structure the distance between certain neighbouring carbon atoms is considerably greater than in diamond. The detailed form of the zone development must of course be different from that illustrated in Fig. 14, but

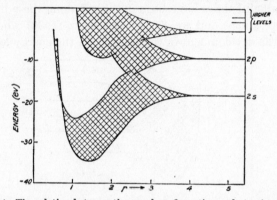

Fig. 14. The relation between the zonal configuration and atomic energy levels in diamond.

if the same type of intermingling and subsequent separation occurs it may happen that the large carbon-carbon distance corresponds to the point of overlap, in which case conductivity could freely take place. If this is indeed so the conductivity of graphite arises as an immediate consequence of the large spacing between the layers in the structure.

A general account of the zone theory of solids, including a description of its application to many physical properties outside the scope of our present discussion, has been given by Seitz and Johnson (1937 a, b, c).

This concludes our general discussion of the several types of interatomic binding force which occur in crystal structures and of the properties associated with each of them. We now pass on in the remaining chapters of this book to a systematic account of the same field, but considered this time from a detailed structural point of view. The classification of chemical elements and compounds in terms of the binding forces which are responsible for their existence, and therefore indirectly in terms of the crystal structures which they possess, necessarily diverges widely from the more conventional classifications, but that does not mean that such a classification is in any way more artificial or less significant. The solid state is a forbidden field in chemistry and its nature can only be determined by extrapolation from the behaviour of substances as liquids and gases. Such an approach has tended both to conceal many of the essential characteristics of the solid state and to confer on solids, quite erroneously, many of the properties of liquids and gases. Thus the conception of the molecule has come to play far too great a part in chemistry, for while the molecule is a very real entity in the gaseous state, this is by no means necessarily so in solids: here it is the exception rather than the rule for the molecule to have a discrete existence. In its turn this picture of the sanctity of the molecule has created a quite false impression of the importance of the classical laws of chemistry. The laws of constancy of composition and of simple proportions now appear as trivial and insignificant consequences of geometrical requirements rather than as profound and fundamental expressions of the laws of nature. The conception of valency, too, so successful in organic chemistry, has been widely, and sometimes blindly, applied in fields altogether outside its scope, until, on chemical grounds alone, it has become clear that certain classes of compound refuse resolutely to conform to accepted chemical principles. This is notably the case with intermetallic systems, but we shall find that it is also true of other types of compound, including many which have been revealed, and which could only have been revealed, by X-ray methods. If the classification to be followed here is unconventional it is certainly not arbitrary, and it must be increasingly from a structural viewpoint that chemistry in the future will be written.

The reader who wishes to remind himself of the details of our classification should refer back to the last section of Chap. II, p. 41.

PART II
SYSTEMATIC CRYSTAL CHEMISTRY

—◇—

CHAPTER IV

THE METALLIC ELEMENTS

INTRODUCTION

It is the aim of our discussion of systematic crystal chemistry, to which the rest of this book is devoted, to investigate the relationships which exist between the structure and the chemical constitution of crystalline substances. In this way we may hope to be able to interpret as many as possible of the physical and chemical properties of these substances in terms of their crystal structure, and, quite generally, to establish a correlation between particular properties and individual structural characteristics. Ideally, we should be able, on the one hand, to give a very comprehensive account of the properties of any given body knowing only its structure and the types of binding force in operation, and, on the other, to propose, and even to synthesize, structures having any desired combination of properties whatsoever. We are as yet a long way from this idealized goal, but X-ray methods have now been applied to a sufficiently wide range of bodies, representative of inorganic, organic and even biological chemistry, for a number of general principles to have emerged, and we have already learned to recognize the structural significance of many of the properties of these substances.

We shall here make no attempt to describe the detailed features of all, or even of many, of the known structures. Such descriptions are already available in the works to be mentioned below, and in any case it is not our desire to present crystal chemistry in the form of a purely descriptive science. Here our interest in the structures lies only in the general principles which they illuminate, and in so far as detailed descriptions are necessary they will be confined to structures of common occurrence and general interest. Frequently the detailed features of a structure are unimportant or insignificant, and then an idealized or simplified description will serve our purpose. Sometimes a purely qualitative account of only certain aspects of the structure will suffice to illustrate the general principles involved.

At this stage it is convenient to refer briefly to two works which review in a purely descriptive way the whole field of published structure analyses. The more comprehensive and detailed of these is the *Strukturbericht* published as a supplement to the *Zeitschrift für Kristallographie*. The first volume of this work describes, with references, all the structures published in the period 1913–28. Six further volumes cover the periods 1928–32, 1932–35, 1936, 1937, 1938 and 1939 respectively. A less comprehensive but more readily accessible work covering much the same field is Wyckoff's *The Structure of Crystals*, the second edition of which, together with its supplement, describes all the important structures published up to the end of 1934. Wyckoff's book is particularly valuable for its critical apprizal of the reliability of the published structures and for the excellence of its diagrams. In both of these works the treatment is purely descriptive and no attempt is made to discuss the chemical significance of the structures observed or to classify these structures along the lines to be followed here. Instead, the classification is designed solely for convenience of reference and is made in terms of the chemical formulae of the bodies concerned. In either work the reader will find full descriptions of most of the structures mentioned here, and also references to the original structure analyses. In this book we shall in general refer explicitly only to papers in which the chemical implications of the observed structures are discussed, and not quote works of purely structural interest.

We now proceed to our systematic survey of crystal chemistry following the classification outlined in Chap. II. In this chapter we shall illustrate some of the general features of metal structures by reference to those of the metallic elements, and in Chap. v exemplify these features in greater detail by a study of alloy systems. Such a distinction, as we shall see, is in many respects artificial, but it offers the practical advantage of enabling the structural characteristics of the metallic bond to be discussed in the first instance in terms of relatively simple systems.

THE STRUCTURES OF THE METALLIC ELEMENTS

Classification.

The crystal structures of the metals make it convenient to divide these elements into the two groups shown in Table 16, p. 92. The metals in the larger of these groups may be termed *true metals* and include the alkali and alkaline earth metals, beryllium, magnesium, copper, silver, gold and the transition elements. All of these metals have simple crystal structures and exhibit to a more or less marked extent the properties generally characteristic of the metallic state. The remaining metallic elements, those of the *B sub-groups*, have more complex structures and show to a greater or lesser extent significant departures from typically metallic properties.

The true metals.

All the true metals so far studied, with the exceptions of manganese and uranium, have one or more of three typical structures:

A_1. The cubic close-packed structure.
A_3. The hexagonal close-packed structure.
A_2. The cubic body-centred structure.

The first two structures are alternative ways of packing equal spheres as tightly as possible in space. A single layer of spheres can be tightly packed in only one way, namely that which obtains when the spheres occupy the corners of an equilateral triangular network as shown by the circles marked 1 in Fig. 15. In this arrangement each sphere is in contact with six neighbours at the corners of a regular hexagon. If a second similar close-packed layer is superposed upon the first, the spheres in this second layer occupy the positions 2, and each sphere is in contact with three spheres in the layer below. (The second layer could, of course, equally well occupy the positions 3, but it is clear that in an indefinitely extended structure no difference between these two arrange-

TABLE 16

THE CLASSIFICATION OF THE METALLIC ELEMENTS

True metals											B sub-groups				
		Transition metals									2	3	4	5	6
Li A_2	Be A_3														
Na A_2	Mg A_3											Al A_1	Si		
K A_2	Ca A_1 A_3	Sc	Ti A_3	V A_2	Cr A_2 A_3	Mn	Fe A_1 A_2	Co A_1 A_3	Ni A_1 A_3	Cu A_1	Zn	Ga	Ge	As	Se
Rb A_2	Sr A_1	Y A_3	Zr A_2 A_3	Nb A_2	Mo A_2	Ma	Ru A_3	Rh A_1 A_2	Pd A_1	Ag A_1	Cd	In	Sn	Sb	Te
Cs A_2	Ba A_2	La A_1 A_3	Ce* A_1 A_3												
			Hf A_3	Ta A_2	W A_2	Re A_3	Os A_3	Ir A_1	Pt A_1	Au A_1	Hg	Tl A_1 A_3	Pb A_1	Bi	
	Ra	Ac	Th A_1	Pa	U										

* And the other rare earth elements. Only Ce (A_1, A_3), Pr (A_3), Nd (A_3) and Er (A_3) have been studied.

A_1 = cubic close-packing.
A_2 = cubic body-centred structure.
A_3 = hexagonal close-packing.

Several of the elements are polymorphous and have other more complex structures in addition to those indicated.

ments exists.) A third layer may be added in one of two ways, for either it may be so disposed that it lies vertically above the first layer, or alternatively it may occupy the positions 3, in which case all three layers are different. The former arrangement, which is that illustrated in Fig. 15b, is hexa-

gonal close-packing and the sequence of layers is 121212...
continued indefinitely. A unit cell is shown by dotted lines
in Fig. 15b, and is illustrated separately in perspective and
plan* in Fig. 16. The second arrangement is cubic close-
packing. Here the layers repeat 123123123..., for it can
readily be seen that if a fourth layer is added to the first three
in such a way as to occupy neither the positions 2 nor 3 it

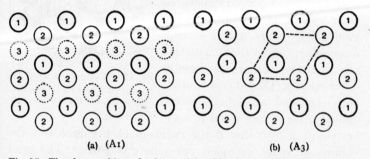

(a) (A₁)   (b) (A₃)

Fig. 15. The close-packing of spheres: (a) cubic close-packing; (b) hexagonal
close-packing. In (b) the hexagonal unit cell is outlined. The numbers
correspond to the successive layers of the structures. In both arrangements each sphere is surrounded by 12 equidistant neighbours.

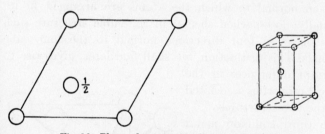

Fig. 16. Plan and perspective diagram of the unit cell
of hexagonal close-packing.

must fall above the layer 1. It is not, perhaps, immediately
apparent that this arrangement has cubic symmetry and is,
in fact, an arrangement of spheres at the corners and face

* In plans of structures the positions of atoms not in the plane of the
diagram are shown by expressing their distance above that plane as a fraction of the height of the unit cell. The reader should, if possible, accustom
himself to envisaging any structure and its co-ordination from the plan
alone; with all but the simplest structures a perspective diagram is generally
too complex to be of much value.

centres of a cubic unit cell. The point, however, is made clear by Fig. 17, which represents eight unit cells of cubic close-packing. Here the face-centring of the unit cell is evident but the close-packed nature of the layers normal to the cube diagonals is also emphasized.

Fig. 17. Cubic close-packing. The diagram illustrates the relationship between Fig. 15a and the cubic cell.

In both close-packed structures each sphere is in contact with twelve neighbours, and it is clear on general grounds that energetically the two structures cannot differ greatly. They do, of course, both represent an equally economical filling of space, and it may be readily shown that if the radius of each sphere is a the volume of space occupied per sphere is $5.66\,a^3$. The most important practical difference between the two structures arises from the way in which the close-packed layers are disposed. In hexagonal close-packing there is only one direction normal to which the atoms are arranged in individually close-packed sheets; in the cubic structure such sheets occur in four directions normal to the four cube diagonals. This distinction, we shall find later, gives rise to important differences in the physical properties associated with the two structures.

The third common metal structure is the body-centred cubic, the unit cell of which is shown in Fig. 18. Here each atom is surrounded by only eight neighbours arranged at the corners of a cube, and the structure is a somewhat less tightly-packed one. The volume of space occupied per atom is $6.16\,a^3$.

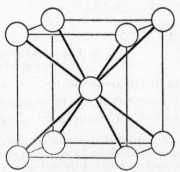

Fig. 18. The cubic body-centred structure. Each sphere is surrounded by eight equidistant neighbours.

The cubic close-packed, the body-centred cubic and the hexagonal close-packed structures are conventionally represented by the symbols A_1, A_2 and A_3 respectively, and the structures of the true metals are indicated in Table 16, p. 92, by these symbols. A few of the elements are polymorphous and manganese is quite exceptional in that it is polymorphous and in all its forms has very complex structures. Even so, the anomaly is more apparent than real, and in β-Mn, for example, the complexity of the arrangement arises from the position which it occupies intermediate between the body-centred and face-centred cubic structures.

The high co-ordination characteristic of the structures of all the true metals emphasizes the general properties of the metallic bond described in detail in Chap. II, where we found that the bond was spatially undirected and could operate between a given atom and an indefinite number of neighbours. Physically the most important purely structural characteristics of metals are the mechanical properties, and these arise from the ease with which a metal can deform by gliding. In a single crystal a vanishingly small stress is sufficient to start a glide deformation, and this is found always to take place on those planes in the structure which are most tightly packed, and, in these planes, along the lines of closest packing. In the polycrystalline aggregates of normal occurrence the phenomenon is more complicated but, even so, malleability and ductility are intimately bound up with the ease with which gliding can occur, and are, therefore, in practice confined to metals of simple structure. In metals with complex structures, and in alloys in which the regularity of the lattice is interrupted by foreign atoms, malleability is rare and the metal is commonly hard and brittle.

Even among the true metals the ability to deform by gliding is not shown equally by all the members of the group, but is in fact much more marked in those having a cubic close-packed structure owing to the greater number of planes on which gliding can take place. This distinction leads us to a further sub-division of the true metals which is technically of the greatest importance, for these elements include practically all the metals of value in the arts and, with the exception of aluminium, zinc and lead, all those of any considerable commercial importance as well. In the one group we have all those metals with the cubic close-packed structure, and these include Cu, Ag, Au, Ni, α-Co and γ-Fe, together with a few other elements of less importance. All these metals are markedly ductile and malleable and fairly soft. In the other group are the metals with a hexagonal close-packed or a cubic body-centred structure. The most important of these are Cr, V, Mo, W, β-Co and α- and β-Fe. All these elements are decidedly less malleable, harder and more brittle than those in the first group. It is the special position of iron as a member of both groups which gives it much of its metallurgical importance, for according to the heat treatment which it receives it may be made to assume the properties characteristic of either group.

The B sub-group metals.

The B sub-group elements are as a class structurally far more complicated and show a far greater diversity of properties than the true metals. None of the elements is homodesmic, and in fact these metals demonstrate more convincingly than any other series of structures the continuous and gradual nature of the transition from the metallic to the homopolar bond. The character of this transition may be most conveniently illustrated by describing a series of typical structures.

Iodine. Iodine has a typically molecular structure in which I_2 molecules, strongly bound within themselves by homopolar forces, occur relatively widely separated in the lattice and are linked to each other only by feeble residual bonds. We have already remarked that an element in the nth group of the periodic classification can give rise to only $(8-n)$ homopolar bonds, and the structure of iodine with each atom so linked to one other is in complete accord with this rule.

Selenium and tellurium. The structure of selenium and tellurium is illustrated in Fig. 19. The structure consists of a series of infinite helical chains of atoms running parallel to the vertical axis of the hexagonal unit cell. Within the chain each atom is strongly bound by homopolar forces to its immediate neighbours, but between the chains the forces are far less strong and the interatomic distances are correspondingly considerably greater than those within the chains. The essentially homopolar character of the binding in the chains is illustrated not only by the fact that the $(8-n)$ rule is obeyed but also by the characteristic helical nature of the chain itself. The helical formation arises from the mutual disposition of the two bonds from each atom at an angle of about 100°: if the binding were polar or metallic they would be oppositely directed and the chains would be straight. In so far as there is any significance in speaking of the molecule

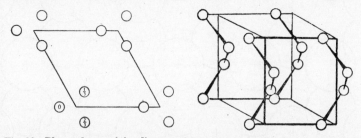

Fig. 19. Plan and perspective diagram of the hexagonal unit cell of the structure of selenium and tellurium. The helical chains extend indefinitely through the crystal in the vertical direction.

in such a structure each helical chain must be considered as constituting a single molecule infinitely extended in one dimension.

Arsenic, antimony and bismuth. The structure of these elements is formed by the superposition of a series of puckered sheets of atoms, each of the type shown in Fig. 20, p. 98. Within each sheet the binding is purely homopolar and each atom is so linked to three neighbours. One such sheet may therefore be regarded as a two-dimensional molecule of indefinite extent analogous to the one-dimensional molecule in the structure of selenium. The characteristic intervalency angle of about 100° results in the puckering of the sheets since all three neighbours of any one atom lie on the same side of it. Each atom has in addition three neighbours on the other side belonging to the adjacent sheet, but these atoms are considerably more remote and less tightly bound than those in its own sheet. The structure again illustrates the $(8 - n)$ rule since each atom is the source of three homopolar bonds. It is clear, however, that in antimony and bismuth, if not in arsenic, the binding must also be partially metallic in character, for neither the electrical conductivity nor the high melting point of these elements can be reconciled with a purely homopolar or molecular linkage.

Germanium and tin. The elements germanium and tin in the fourth group both have the diamond structure character-

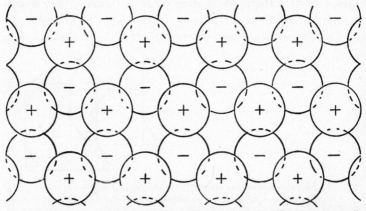

Fig. 20. Plan of a single sheet of the structure of arsenic. The atoms are all at one of two heights indicated by the signs $+$ and $-$. Successive sheets are so arranged that the lower atoms in one sheet fall vertically above the 'holes' in the sheet below.

istic of a typically homopolar body, but here again the electrical conductivity is sufficient to show that the electrons must be very loosely bound and that the linkage is partially metallic in character. The structures are, however, homogeneous in that the type of binding is the same in all directions, and if we are still to look for the molecule in such a structure we must regard the whole crystal as comprising one single three-dimensional molecule.

Gallium and indium. The structures of gallium and indium are quite anomalous and not only differ from each other but also fail to satisfy the $(8 - n)$ rule, although, in the case of gallium, the actual structure may be formed by the slight distortion of an idealized structure in which this rule is obeyed. The structures are of considerable complexity and will not be described here.

Cadmium, zinc and mercury. In cadmium and zinc the tendency towards purely metallic binding is yet more marked but the influence of the homopolar binding is nevertheless still felt. In spite of their pronouncedly metallic character the hexagonal structure of these elements is not exactly hexagonal close-packing, but, instead, a structure which differs from it only in that of the twelve neighbours of a given atom the six in its own plane are somewhat closer than the remaining six. As a result of this difference the axial ratio $c:a$ is $1\cdot9$ instead of $1\cdot63$, the value corresponding to true close-packing. The particularly close binding of six of the twelve neighbours may be regarded as a further example of the $(8-n)$ rule, and we can picture the binding of these neighbours as being partially homopolar in character while the more remote neighbours are linked by purely metallic forces. Mercury, in the same group as cadmium and zinc, has a simple structure in which the atoms are disposed at the points of a rhombohedral lattice, and each atom has, therefore, only six neighbours.

In the elements of the first group all trace of homopolar binding has disappeared, and copper, silver and gold have truly metallic cubic close-packed structures.

Aluminium, thallium and lead. The structures of these elements have not yet been specifically mentioned. Although they appear in our classification as members of the B sub-group, they all have close-packed structures characteristic of true metals. In thallium and lead this is due to the formation of a moderately stable 20-electron O shell corresponding to the partially ionized ions Tl^+ and Pb^{2+} (see Table 3, p. 13). The relative stability of this 20-electron configuration and the resultant incomplete ionization in the structure cause thallium and lead to simulate in many of their properties the alkali and alkaline earth metals respectively. In aluminium, too, in the elementary state there are indications that the ionization may be incomplete and the close-packed structure may be due to this cause. The anomalous position of these elements, which confers on them some of the properties of both the true and B sub-group metals, must be borne in mind when alloy systems in which they occur are discussed.

Physical properties. The gradual and continuous nature of the transition from metallic to homopolar binding which takes place in the B sub-group elements, and which is so clearly reflected in their structures, also has an influence on their physical properties. Most obvious of these is the mechanical behaviour, for the increasing complexity of the structures makes glide deformation difficult and the elements therefore tend to be hard and brittle when compared with the true metals. The complex and relatively 'open' nature of the structures leads to a contraction in volume when the solid melts to a statistically close-packed liquid and so explains the expansion on solidification which gives several of these elements their technical importance. The magnetic properties also reveal the partially homopolar character of the binding. Many elements are diamagnetic because they consist of diamagnetic atoms, but homopolar crystals show a far larger structural diamagnetism which is a characteristic of the crystal and cannot be attributed to the individual atoms. This structural diamagnetism, moreover, decreases rapidly with increasing temperature and vanishes on melting. Just such a behaviour is found in the elements Ge, Sn, As, Sb, Bi, Se and Te, all of which are strongly diamagnetic and lose their diamagnetism on melting. The anisotropy of thermal expansion and compressibility of certain of these elements also reveal the distinction between the types of force operating in different directions in the structure.

In the case of bismuth the magnetic properties have been discussed in detail in terms of the Brillouin zone system of the metal by Jones (1934b) who has shown that a large structural diamagnetism is to be expected whenever those zones occupied by electrons are very nearly filled.

The conception of the transition from the metallic to the homopolar binding here introduced, and the picture of the forces in certain structures as possessing in part the properties of each type of bond, are further examples of the resonance phenomenon discussed generally in Chap. III. The particular application of resonance to some of the B sub-group elements has been discussed by Slater (1931 a).

THE ATOMIC RADII OF THE METALS

The atomic radii of some of the metallic elements are shown graphically in Fig. 21, p. 102. The values there given call for some explanation and qualification before their full significance can be discussed. In the case of true metals with close-packed structures the atomic radius is clearly half the closest distance of approach. In structures of lower co-ordination, such as the cubic body-centred arrangement of the alkali metals or the rhombohedral structure of mercury, a similar definition of atomic radius is applicable, but the values so deduced are not immediately comparable with those derived from structures of higher co-ordination. It is found, both from a study of polymorphous metals having several structures of different co-ordination, and from alloy systems in which metal atoms often occur in a state of co-ordination different from that which obtains in the pure element, that a small but systematic decrease of atomic radius takes place with decreasing co-ordination. The extent of this change of radius has been studied by Goldschmidt (1928b) who has summarized observations on a series of elements and alloy systems by expressing the radius in 8-, 6- and 4-fold co-ordination corresponding to unit radius in a close-packed structure. He gives the following values:

Co-ordination	Radius
12	1·00
8	0·97
6	0·96
4	0·88

It will be seen from these figures that the change in radius may be considerable and that a comparison of radii of different elements is only of significance when the state of co-ordination is known. Especially is this true in alloy systems where the

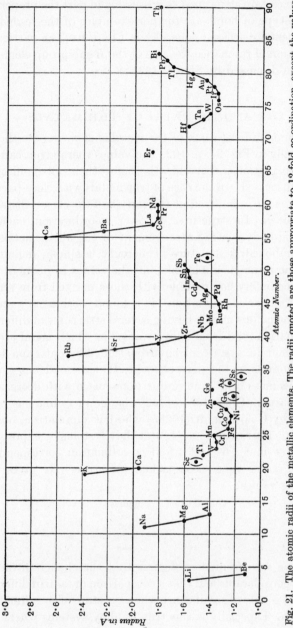

Fig. 21. The atomic radii of the metallic elements. The radii quoted are those appropriate to 12-fold co-ordination, except the values in parentheses which are one-half the distance of closest approach in the structure of the element.

atomic radius is of the greatest importance in determining the structure and where atoms frequently occur in a state of co-ordination different from that in the elementary state. For this reason the atomic radii given in Fig. 21 are not necessarily those directly observed in the several elements but are the values appropriate to 12-fold co-ordinated structures.

A further difficulty arises in discussing the radii of the B sub-group metals, for in these elements the co-ordination is so irregular that the conception of a precise radius ceases to have any very definite meaning. Even in these cases, however, we can define the radius as half the distance of closest approach, but the values thus obtained will be of significance only in the structure of the element and will have no immediate influence on its behaviour in alloy systems. Values of the radius derived from a study of alloys are therefore often of more general utility than those deduced from the elements themselves, and values can, moreover, be so obtained corresponding to degrees of co-ordination not found in the pure metal. As an example of this we may quote a germanium-copper alloy having a hexagonal close-packed structure, which enables the radius of germanium in 12-fold co-ordination to be deduced although no structure with such high co-ordination exists for the pure element. The values of the radii of B sub-group metals included in Fig. 21 are all indirectly determined in a similar manner and are appropriate to 12-fold co-ordination. In order to emphasize the difference between these radii and those obtaining in the structures of the elements themselves the two sets of values are summarized in Table 17, p. 104.

Certain general features of Fig. 21 call for emphasis. In the first place it will be noticed that the radii of all the elements are of the same order of magnitude, and that the increasingly complex extranuclear structure of the elements of high atomic number does not give rise to any very large increase in radius owing to the compensating influence of the greater nuclear charge. In each period the alkali metal has by far the largest radius, and with increasing valency in the *A* groups the addition of electrons to the extranuclear structure is accompanied by a marked decrease in radius due to the increased nuclear charge. This decrease in radius is arrested in the middle of each family of transition metals so that all these elements within each period have very roughly the same radius. In each of the families of *B* sub-group elements a pronounced increase in radius takes place.

Hume-Rothery (1930) has attempted to express the radii of all the metals by a general empirical formula. He has shown that within any one given group the radii of the elements of

TABLE 17

THE ATOMIC RADII OF THE METALS

The upper value is half the distance of closest approach, the lower the value corresponding to 12-fold co-ordination

True metals											*B* sub-group			
		Transition metals									2	3	4	5
Li 1·52 / 1·56	Be 1·12 / 1·12													
Na 1·86 / 1·91	Mg 1·60 / 1·60											Al 1·43 / 1·43	Si 1·17 / —	
K 2·31 / 2·38	Ca 1·96 / 1·96	Sc 1·51 / —	Ti 1·46 / 1·46	V 1·30 / 1·35	Cr 1·25 / 1·28	Mn 1·18 / 1·37	Fe 1·24 / 1·26	Co 1·25 / 1·25	Ni 1·24 / 1·24	Cu 1·28 / 1·28	Zn 1·33 / 1·37	Ga 1·22 / —	Ge 1·22 / 1·39	As 1·25 / —
Rb 2·43 / 2·51	Sr 2·15 / 2·15	Y 1·81 / 1·81	Zr 1·56 / 1·60	Nb 1·43 / 1·47	Mo 1·36 / 1·40	Ma — / —	Ru 1·33 / 1·33	Rh 1·34 / 1·34	Pd 1·37 / 1·37	Ag 1·44 / 1·44	Cd 1·49 / 1·52	In 1·62 / 1·57	Sn 1·40 / 1·58	Sb 1·45 / 1·61
Cs 2·62 / 2·70	Ba 2·17 / 2·24	La 1·86 / 1·86	Ce 1·82 / 1·82	Pr 1·81 / 1·82	Nd 1·80 / 1·82	Er 1·86 / 1·86								
			Hf 1·58 / 1·58	Ta 1·43 / 1·47	W 1·36 / 1·41	Re — / —	Os 1·35 / 1·35	Ir 1·35 / 1·35	Pt 1·38 / 1·38	Au 1·44 / 1·44	Hg 1·50 / 1·55	Tl 1·70 / 1·70	Pb 1·75 / 1·75	Bi 1·55 / 1·82
	Ra — / —	Ac — / —	Th 1·80 / 1·80	Pa — / —	U 1·38 / —									

the A sub-groups follow closely the relation

$$\frac{r}{n} = \frac{a}{Z^x}.$$

Here n is the principal quantum number of the outermost shell of electrons in the ion of the element, a a constant for any one group but having different values for different groups, Z the atomic number and x a constant approximately equal to $\frac{1}{3}$.

Within any one period the radii of the first two or three elements also appear to show regularities. Thus Hume-Rothery found that the radii of the elements at the beginning of a period vary as $1/Z^p$, where p has the value 1 for the first period, 2 for the second, 3 for the third and 5 for the fourth. The significance of these empirical relationships is, however, not known, and no success has attended any attempt to give them a theoretical foundation. The interpretation originally placed on them by Hume-Rothery has been criticized by Goldschmidt (1931a).

The lanthanide contraction.

A further important feature which appears from Fig. 21, p. 102, is the decrease in radius which occurs in the rare earth elements following lanthanum. As a result of this so-called *lanthanide contraction* the radii of the transition and B sub-group elements of the third long period are substantially the same as those of the elements of the second long period. This is to be contrasted with the increase in radius between the first and second long periods. To take a single example, while the radii increase from 1·28 to 1·44 A. in passing from copper to silver, the radii of silver and gold are almost exactly the same: the increase in radius to be expected between silver and gold is just compensated by the lanthanide contraction. This contraction is also responsible for the very close chemical resemblances between certain corresponding members of the second and third long periods, as, for example, between zirconium and hafnium or between niobium and tantalum. The lanthanide contraction has been discussed at length by Goldschmidt, Barth and Lunde (1925).

CHAPTER V

ALLOY SYSTEMS

INTRODUCTION

The development of X-ray methods of structure analysis has provided metallurgists with their most powerful tool for the investigation of the metallic state, and the extension of our knowledge and understanding of the properties of inter-metallic systems which has resulted in one of the greatest achievements of crystal chemistry. Prior to the application of X-ray methods, the investigation of the properties of alloy systems was confined principally to observations of their behaviour in the liquid state, and the behaviour of the metal as a solid could be determined only by inference from these observations. Transitions in the solid state and the effect of mechanical or heat treatment could naturally not be observed in this way, and for information on these properties the microscope and other purely physical methods had to be invoked. Even so, these methods were all more or less indirect, and it is only since the application of X-ray analysis that it has been possible to investigate directly in the solid state, under the precise conditions which are of technical interest and without damage to the specimen, the exact positions of all the atoms in the structure, and so to refer to their ultimate cause the physical and chemical properties of the alloy.

It is not surprising that the application of such a powerful method of investigation has not only led, on the experimental side, to a vast extension in our knowledge of the properties of metallic systems, but has also demanded, on the theoretical side, a considerable modification in our interpretation of many of these properties and a profound re-orientation of many of the accepted principles of chemistry when applied in this field. The development of metallurgy has in the past been largely hampered by attempts to make metal systems conform to the laws of chemical combination established by observations on bodies in which forces of an entirely different character are operative. Alloys differ profoundly in many of their properties from other chemical compounds. They can generally be formed by no more elaborate synthesis than the simple melting together of their constituents in the appropriate proportions. In marked contrast to other chemical compounds they still preserve, at least qualitatively, the general character of the elements of which they are composed. In spite of these differences, however, it has been common practice to regard many intermetallic systems as chemical compounds and to attempt to assign to them formulae based on ideas of valency derived from ionic and homopolar compounds. Somewhat inconsistently, however, the essentially identical forces operating in the structure of a metallic element have never been regarded as chemical in nature at all. The extent to which it is justifiable to speak of chemical combination in alloy systems will be discussed more fully later, but we may say at once that if we are so to interpret these systems it must be in terms of a wider and far less rigid picture of chemical combination than that of classical chemistry. Hume-Rothery (1926) early pointed out that any attempt to express metallic combination by formulae based on the normal valencies was meaningless, and the study of alloy systems emphasizes that the laws of chemical combination are of far less fundamental significance than has often been supposed and that only in ionic and homopolar compounds are they generally obeyed, and then only as a trivial consequence of geometrical or electrical demands. In metal systems compounds of variable composition are often found, and it is no longer necessary for the constituents to be present in simple stoichiometric proportions.

It is not within the scope of this book to discuss the purely physical applications of X-ray methods to alloys in such problems as qualitative and quantitative analysis, the determination of purity and grain size and the detection of strain, although all these applications are of the greatest technical importance. The reader who wishes for further information on these matters is referred to the general reviews of Evans (1935) and of Norton (1937) and to the publications of the Department of Scientific and Industrial Research (1931, 1934).

The classification of alloys.

The number of systems to which X-ray methods have been applied is now sufficiently large for many of the general principles of metal chemistry to have emerged. As always, we shall here make no attempt to review the whole field, but merely illustrate these general principles by appropriately chosen particular examples. A general classification of binary alloys, which alone we shall consider, can be based on our classification of the metallic elements into the true metals and those of the B sub-groups. Accordingly we shall divide these alloys into the three groups:

(1) Alloys of two true metals;

(2) Alloys of a true metal with a B sub-group metal;

(3) Alloys of two B sub-group metals.

To these may be added a fourth group:

(4) The interstitial structures,

which are most conveniently considered with the alloy systems.

In general terms we may say that in passing through the first three of these groups the properties become progressively less metallic and the intermetallic systems show increasingly marked resemblances to true chemical compounds.

The classification here adopted serves to emphasize the point which will become increasingly clear as various typical systems are discussed that any distinction between elementary metals and alloy systems is purely artificial. The true and the B sub-group metals are essentially special cases of the first and third groups of alloys respectively, and the general structural properties, whether of the element or of the alloy, are those characteristic primarily of the group as a whole.

ALLOYS OF TWO TRUE METALS

The copper-gold system.

A typical example of an alloy of this class, and one which has, perhaps, been more completely investigated than any other, is the system copper-gold. These two metals are chemically closely related, have a similar electronic configuration and have both a cubic close-packed crystal structure. The atomic radii are not very different being 1·28 and 1·44 A. respectively.

The crystal structure of a specimen of gold to which a small amount of copper has been added is found to be exactly the same as that of the parent metal, the copper and gold atoms being distributed at random over the points of a face-centred cubic lattice. The statistical replacement of gold atoms by the smaller atoms of copper results in a slight reduction in the cell size but otherwise no alteration in the structure takes place. As more and more copper is added, more gold atoms in the lattice are replaced by copper, but the substitution remains purely statistical and the sites occupied are still those of the face-centred cubic cell, the appropriate proportion of copper and gold atoms being randomly distributed among them. This progressive substitution of gold by copper takes place throughout the whole range from pure gold to pure copper, and results in a range of complete solid solution between the two elements. The change in cell size with composition is in accordance with *Vegard's law*, which states that in solid solutions the cell dimensions vary linearly with the concentration of solute. Precision measurements (Vegard and Kloster, 1934) have, however, revealed that over the whole range the linear relationship is true only as a first approximation.

The range of complete solid solution described in the last paragraph is observed only if the alloy is investigated at a high temperature, or, more conveniently, if a quenched specimen is employed. When, however, the alloy is carefully annealed an entirely different state of affairs results. Once again we may consider the addition of progressively more and more copper to initially pure gold. At first, a random replacement of the gold by the copper atoms takes place as before, but when a sufficient quantity of copper has been added it is found that the distribution is no longer statistical but that instead the two kinds of atoms tend to occupy definite geometrical positions relative to one another. This segregation is complete when the composition corresponds to equal

atomic proportions of the two elements and the structure is then that illustrated in Fig. 22. Several unit cells are here shown and a moment's consideration will reveal that the sites occupied are still those of a cubic close-packed structure, but that, on account of the ordered instead of random distribution of the atoms, the lattice is actually no longer face-

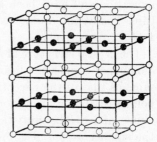

Fig. 22. The structure of the
ordered phase CuAu.

centred. The segregation of the atoms into layers and the difference in atomic radius between copper and gold result in a small departure from cubic symmetry, and the unit cell is actually tetragonal but pseudo-cubic with axial ratio $c:a = 0.932$ (Johansson and Linde, 1925).

The addition of more copper, followed by careful annealing, results initially in the random replacement of some of the gold atoms of the tetragonal structure, but with increasing concentration of copper this replacement tends to take place

in a regular way such that at an atomic composition of 75 per cent copper the structure of Fig. 23 is formed. Here it will be noticed that once again the pattern of sites is that of a cubic close-packed arrangement, but on account of the regular way in which the atoms are distributed the lattice is actually

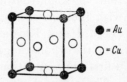

● = Au
○ = Cu

Fig. 23. The structure of the
ordered phase Cu_3Au.

primitive and not face-centred. This structure is truly cubic and it is clear that it corresponds to a composition Cu_3Au. The addition of still further copper results in the gradual replacement of the remaining gold atoms until finally the structure of pure copper results.

Structures such as those described above for CuAu and Cu_3Au in the ordered state, in which the pattern of sites is that of the parent random solid solution but in which the two kinds of atoms are distributed over these sites in some regular way, are termed *superlattices*. We defer until later any discussion of whether or not these structures are to be regarded as definite chemical compounds, but here we may remark that physically they often show pronounced differences from the corresponding disordered structure. Thus, before the application of X-ray structure analysis to the problem, Kurnakow, Zemczuzny and Zasedatelev (1916) found that the electrical resistance of quenched copper-gold alloys showed a smooth variation with composition whereas with the annealed alloys two sharp minima were observed corresponding to the compositions CuAu and Cu_3Au. The more recent work of Borelius, Johansson and Linde (1928) has shown that the resistance of the superlattice at these compositions is less than half that of the corresponding disordered alloy. Similarly, changes occur in many other properties. Thus Sachs and Weerts (1931) found that the elastic constants of the alloy Cu_3Au were profoundly dependent on the heat treatment which it had received, while Dehlinger and Graf (1930) have shown that the tetragonal superlattice of CuAu is nearly as soft as pure copper whereas the disordered phase is hard and brittle. In all such cases it is clear that the composition alone is quite inadequate to characterize the alloy.

The iron-aluminium system.

Another system which illustrates the transition from the random arrangement of the solid solution to the ordered structure of the superlattice is that of iron and aluminium. Strictly speaking this system should be considered under our second group of alloys since we have classed aluminium as a *B* sub-group metal. We have already emphasized, however, that the position of aluminium is somewhat anomalous in that it also behaves in many respects as a true metal, and it is therefore not out of place to consider this system here.

Compared with the copper-gold system, that of iron-aluminium is somewhat more complex in that the two constituents have different crystal structures, for iron is cubic body-centred at ordinary temperatures and aluminium cubic close-packed. Although the physical properties of the iron-aluminium alloys have not been investigated as completely as those of the copper-gold system, the purely structural features of the order-disorder transformation have been observed in great detail in the range 0–50 atomic per cent of aluminium by Bradley and Jay (1932 a, b). Their work may be described in terms of the diagram of Fig. 24. This diagram illustrates eight unit cells of the body-centred structure of iron in which different sites, although of course structurally precisely equivalent, are distinguished by different symbols. If small quantities of aluminium are added to the iron the aluminium atoms replace those of iron quite at random, and in the

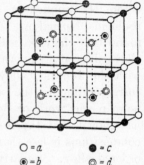

$O = a$ $● = c$
$◉ = b$ $◎ = d$

Fig. 24. The structures of certain phases in the iron-aluminium system.

quenched alloy this obtains throughout the range 0–25 atomic per cent of aluminium. At the composition corresponding to the formulae Fe_3Al the probability of finding any one of the sites a, b, c or d occupied by an aluminium atom is, therefore, $\frac{1}{4}$. This condition is represented in Fig. 25, where the probability, expressed as a percentage, of finding any given site occupied by an aluminium atom is shown as a function of the composition and heat treatment. The purely statistical arrangement of the quenched alloy from 0 to 25 atomic per cent of aluminium is represented by the straight line (1)–(2) which shows that all four sites a, b, c and d are equally favoured. In this arrangement the unit cell is still, of course, one-eighth of the volume shown in Fig. 24, and the lattice remains body-centred.

In the range 25–50 atomic per cent of aluminium the arrangement of atoms is entirely different. The aluminium atoms are no longer distributed at random over all the sites but now occupy only the positions b and d. There is a zero probability of finding an aluminium atom in the sites a and c, which are always occupied by iron atoms, and a correspondingly greater probability of finding an aluminium atom at b or d. At the composition Fe_3Al there is a probability of $\frac{1}{2}$ of finding an aluminium atom in these positions, just one-half of these sites, on the average, being occupied by aluminium and one-half by iron atoms. As the concentration of alu-

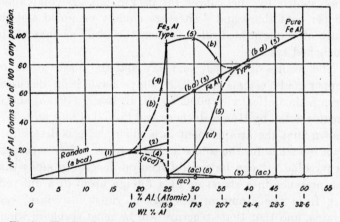

Fig. 25. The distribution of atoms over the sites a, b, c and d of Fig. 24 in the iron-aluminium system.

minium increases, so also does this probability, until at the composition FeAl every b and d site is occupied by aluminium, every a and c site by iron. This is represented in Fig. 25 by the line (3). The unit cell is still one-eighth of the volume shown in Fig. 24, but the lattice is no longer body-centred since the sites are not now structurally equivalent. At the composition FeAl the structure is, in fact, that of caesium chloride.

When the annealed alloy is investigated a different state of affairs is observed. At small concentrations of aluminium the distribution of these atoms is still statistical, but beyond about 18 atomic per cent the aluminium atoms show a marked tendency to favour the b positions and to forsake the positions a, c and d. This is represented by the two curves (4) in Fig. 25, p. 113, from which it will be seen that at the composition Fe_3Al almost every b site is occupied by aluminium while all the other positions contain iron atoms. With this arrangement Fig. 24, p. 112, now represents only one unit cell. Beyond 25 atomic per cent of aluminium the b sites remain fully occupied and the new aluminium atoms enter the d positions, and from about 30 per cent of aluminium onwards the concentration in these sites grows also at the expense of the b positions in the way shown by the curves (5) in Fig. 25. Beyond about 38 per cent the b and d sites are equally occupied and the state of the annealed alloy is then the same as that of the quenched system.

The results of Bradley and Jay and the observations on copper-gold systems described above have been discussed from a theoretical viewpoint by W. L. Bragg (1933b) and in greater detail by Hume-Rothery and Powell (1935), who have shown that the arrangement in a superlattice is determined by a tendency for the solute atoms to be as widely separated as possible. It can be readily seen on general grounds that the presence in a structure of a foreign atom of a different size from the atoms of the solvent must introduce local strains, and that that structure will be most stable in which these strains are as uniformly distributed as possible. This is, indeed, experimentally demonstrated by the fact that when the alloy is carefully annealed to give it every opportunity of reaching equilibrium it is the ordered arrangement which results: in the disordered structure two or more solute atoms must here and there be immediate neighbours.

The actual stability of the superlattice compared with the disordered structure is determined both by the number of solute atoms and by the size of these atoms relative to those of the solvent. If the number of dissolved atoms is small there is, even in the disordered state, a very small probability of finding two of these atoms close together and there is therefore little gain in stability in the ordered structure.

Similarly, if the two kinds of atoms are of very nearly the same size the strain produced by the introduction of the solute atoms is small and the superlattice is not appreciably more stable than the random solid solution. This point is illustrated by the system silver-gold. In this case the two elements have the same cubic close-packed structure and are, moreover, almost identical in size owing to the lanthanide contraction. In consequence this system forms a complete range of disordered solid solution without superlattices, not only in the quenched condition, as with the analogous copper-gold system, but also when carefully annealed. Conversely, the stability of a superlattice is large when there is a considerable disparity in the sizes of the atoms concerned, but it is clear that this stability is never very great since nothing more than the energy of thermal agitation is required to bring about the transition to the disordered state.

Other systems.

Many other binary alloys of two true metals have been investigated by X-ray methods, but few in such detail as the two already described. Here it is impossible even to enumerate all the systems studied, but while they necessarily differ in detail they all show general resemblances in many of their properties. Thus a wide range of solid solution, specially at high temperatures, is a characteristic feature of all such systems, and if the radii of the two atoms are not very different and the individual structures identical a single solid solution may cover the whole range of composition, as in the system silver-gold. If the radii are neither very nearly equal nor very dissimilar superlattices are generally formed. When the individual structures of the two metals differ, as with iron and aluminium, complications necessarily arise, and then the range of solid solution is restricted and a series of two or more separate phases results.

A list of systems studied, with references, is given by Wyckoff (1931, 1935).

THE ORDER-DISORDER TRANSFORMATION

The transition between the ordered and disordered states described above, which was first observed by Johansson and Linde (1925) in the copper-gold system, has since been the subject of many experiments and of much theoretical work. As early as 1919 Tammann (1919) had been led to suggest, as a result of corrosion experiments, that the atoms of a binary solid solution might sometimes be arranged in a regular way, but it was not until the application of X-ray methods of structure analysis that this hypothesis could be directly confirmed. It then soon became clear that the states of order and of disorder were but two extremes of a complete series of intermediate states, any of which the alloy could be made to assume by the appropriate heat treatment, and in which the distribution of atoms was neither the completely regular structure of the superlattice nor yet the entirely disordered arrangement of the solid solution. Thus Borelius, Johansson and Linde (1928), whose work on the resistance of copper-gold alloys we have already mentioned, found that the marked increase in resistance which occurs when the superlattice of composition Cu_3Au or $CuAu$ breaks down with increasing temperature into the random arrangement of the solid solution, was not a discontinuous change but a gradual increase extending over a temperature range of the order of $100°$ C. Moreover, on lowering the temperature of the solid solution conditions could be reversed and the superlattice regenerated, but in this case a pronounced hysteresis was observed and a given resistance was reproduced only at a considerably lower temperature. These observations at once led to a picture of the transition as a thermodynamic equilibrium between the two extreme states in which the intrinsically more stable superlattice could be destroyed by the energy of thermal agitation.

A similar viewpoint was adopted by Gorsky (1928, 1934) and by Dehlinger and Graf (1930) who investigated the transition in the alloy $CuAu$ by measuring the axial ratio of the tetragonal unit cell as a function of the heat treatment which the system had received. When the alloy was quenched after having been maintained for some time at a temperature T it was found that the axial ratio depended on the exact value of this temperature. When T was appreciably higher than 392° C., the quenched alloy was found to have the completely disordered cubic structure with axial ratio unity. When T was lower than 320° C. the tetragonal superlattice with an axial ratio of 0·932 was obtained. If, however, the temperature from which the system was quenched lay between these limits a tetragonal structure was obtained, but one in which the axial ratio had appreciably larger values revealing a tendency towards the cubic arrangement of the disordered structure. The axial ratios observed by Dehlinger and Graf are shown in Table 18.

TABLE 18

AXIAL RATIOS OF THE PARTIALLY ORDERED
TETRAGONAL PHASE AuCu

Quenched from	$c:a$
320° C.	0·932
380° C.	0·939
392° C.	0·947

Since these pioneer investigations, the order-disorder transformation has been observed in many other systems, not only by purely physical methods but also more conveniently by X-ray analysis. With the superlattice certain X-ray reflections occur which are forbidden in the corresponding disordered structure. These reflections therefore provide a convenient means of detecting the superlattice, while their intensity affords a measure of the degree of order prevailing.

The order-disorder transformation has been considered theoretically from a thermodynamical standpoint by many authors (Dehlinger and Graf, 1930; Dehlinger, 1931 *a*, 1932 *a, b*, 1933, 1934, 1937; Wagner and Schottky, 1930; Borelius, 1934 *a, b*, 1935 *b*; W. L. Bragg and Williams, 1934, 1935; Williams, 1935; Bethe, 1935; Peierls, 1936). Space does not permit us to give here a full account of all this work. Nor, indeed, is such a treatment called for, since many of the papers are purely physical in their approach while others are so formal as to be of limited practical application. We shall therefore confine ourselves to a brief discussion of the work of Bragg and his school.

The Bragg-Williams theory.

Let us consider a binary alloy in a state of thermal equilibrium in which the atoms seek to assume the ordered structure of lowest potential energy while thermal agitation seeks to promote a state of disorder. It is then clear that the actual degree of order which obtains will be determined both by the temperature and by some parameter of the system representing the difference in energy between the ordered and disordered states. We may express this parameter in terms of a quantity V, the energy required to transfer one atom from an ordered to a disordered position. The degree of order of the system may be represented by a quantity S, which is unity for the ordered arrangement of the super-lattice and zero for the state of complete disorder. The exact definition of S is irrelevant for our purpose, but the quantity may be roughly regarded as measuring the probability of finding a given atom in the site which it would occupy in the perfect superlattice.

At very low temperatures the equilibrium state is that of complete order, but at higher temperatures the degree of order is determined in terms of the quantity V by the Boltzmann theorem. If V is constant this at once leads to a relation between S and T of the form shown by the full line in Fig. 26. As the temperature increases more atoms are shuffled into 'wrong' sites till at very high temperatures the curve approaches $S = 0$ and the arrangement becomes quite random. It is clear, however, that V cannot be regarded as constant, for, with increasing disorder, the distinction between 'right' and 'wrong' sites becomes less and less significant and disappears completely when S is zero. V must therefore vary from a maximum value V_0 when $S = 1$ to zero

when $S = 0$. Bragg and Williams assume that this variation
is linear, so that $V = S.V_0$, and it is then found that the relation between the degree of order and temperature is of the
general form shown by the dotted curve in Fig. 26. This
curve represents a very rapid collapse of the ordered state
and the complete disappearance of any trace of order at a
characteristic *critical temperature* T_c. At this temperature the
superlattice may be regarded as 'melting' into a solid
solution.

The existence of this critical temperature is one of the most
important features of the theory, for it is to be expected that
at this temperature many of the physical properties of the

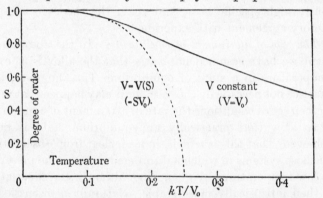

Fig. 26. The degree of order in an alloy AB as a function of temperature.

alloy will display sharp changes. In particular, anomalies in
the specific heat will be expected, for as the temperature of
the alloy is raised extra thermal energy must be supplied to
break down the ordered structure of the crystal. The specific
heat will, therefore, rise sharply near the critical temperature
and then, all order being destroyed, fall abruptly to its normal
value. Bethe (1935), who discusses the question of specific
heats in rather more detail, shows that, although the order
as defined by Bragg and Williams disappears at the temperature T_c, there is still a measure of 'local order' which
persists above this temperature and contributes to the energy
of the structure. Above T_c, therefore, the specific heat is still
somewhat larger than its normal value. In this form, the

theory gives a very satisfactory explanation of the specific heat measurements of Sykes (1935) on the alloy CuZn.

The relation between S and T of the form shown in Fig. 26 holds only for binary alloys in which the two components are present in equal atomic proportions. For other systems the detailed form of the curve is different. Thus in the case of the alloy Cu_3Au, for which also specific heat measurements are available, the degree of order does not decrease smoothly to zero at the critical temperature but instead suffers a discontinuous change from some finite value. Here the energy change associated with the transformation must be regarded as a latent heat of transformation rather than as an anomalously high specific heat, and again the theory is in satisfactory agreement with experiment.

The rate of attainment of equilibrium. In the above treatment we have assumed implicitly that the alloy is at every temperature in a state of equilibrium. This, however, is in practice not necessarily the case, for it may happen that under a given set of conditions the rate of attainment of equilibrium is so slow that practically an equilibrium state is never achieved. That this is true is, indeed, clear from observations on those systems in which a disordered state can be preserved at low temperatures by quenching, although the superlattice is then intrinsically more stable. Naturally a discussion of the rate of attainment of equilibrium is of the greatest importance in considering the effect of heat treatment.

The rate at which disorder is established in any system at a given temperature is determined by that temperature and by the activation energy W associated with the order-disorder transition. This energy is a measure of the height of the potential barrier over which an atom has to pass in moving from an ordered to a disordered position, and is not to be confused with V, which is the difference in potential energy of the atom in its initial and final states. If V is large the ordered structure will at low temperatures be very much more stable than the disordered arrangement, but if W is very large the rate at which equilibrium is attained may nevertheless be very slow.

In terms of the energy W it is possible to define a time of relaxation τ in which the departure from equilibrium at any given temperature is reduced to $1/e$ of its initial amount. τ is given by

$$\tau = Ae^{W/kT},$$

where A is a constant of the order of 10^{-12} and k is the Boltzmann constant. The temperature at which the time of relaxation is one second may be designated T_1, and it is clear from the exponential form of the above expression that in the neighbourhood of T_1 the time of relaxation varies very rapidly with temperature. Thus when

$$T/T_1 = 1\cdot2, \qquad \tau = 0\cdot01 \text{ second},$$
$$T/T_1 = 0\cdot6, \qquad \tau = 3 \text{ years}.$$

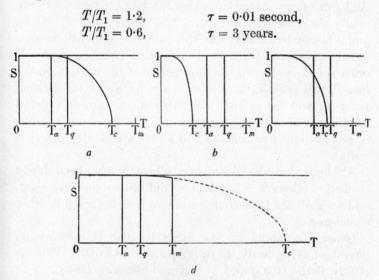

Fig. 27. Conditions determining the rate of attainment of equilibrium in the order-disorder transformation.

We may therefore define an *annealing temperature* T_a somewhat lower than T_1 below which equilibrium is in practice never attained, and a *quenching temperature* T_q somewhat higher than T_1 above which equilibrium is established practically instantaneously.

The actual behaviour of any system will be determined by the value of the critical temperature T_c relative to T_a and T_q. A number of possible cases are illustrated in Fig. 27. In case a,

T_c is so far above T_q that over practically the whole range in which the degree of order is changing equilibrium is established instantaneously. Even on quenching, the system will assume the condition of practically complete order corresponding to the temperature T_q. In case b the superlattice will remain ordered on heating well above T_c until T_a is reached, when order will rapidly disappear. On cooling, however, it will never be possible to reproduce an ordered condition since T_c is far below the temperature at which equilibrium can be established. Such a system can, therefore, never in practice exist as a superlattice at all, and this condition is typical, say, of the alloy AgAu or of any system in which the two atoms are of very nearly the same size. In case c, T_c is bracketed by T_a and T_q, and it is easy to see that here the quenched alloy will be completely disordered while in the annealed system a degree of order corresponding to the intersection of the curve with the line T_a will prevail. In case d, T_c lies far above the melting point T_m and the system will freeze direct into an ordered condition. This will be the case when V is large, as, for example, in any system in which the two atoms are of very different radius.

Although the order-disorder transformation has been chiefly studied in alloys it is not in fact confined to metal systems, and we shall see later that it has also been observed in other structures.

General accounts of the order-disorder transformation have been given by W. L. Bragg (1935), Nix (1937), Williams (1937), Bethe (1938) and by Nix and Shockley (1938).

ALLOYS OF A TRUE METAL AND A B SUB-GROUP ELEMENT

Compared with the alloys of two true metals, those of a true metal and an element of the B sub-groups show considerable complexity. The difference in the electronic and crystal structures of the two metals and particularly the transition to homopolar binding in the B sub-groups leads to much more restricted solid solution and a much greater tendency towards definite chemical combination or, at least, towards the formation of discrete geometrically ordered structures. A systematic classification is difficult and few general principles can be advanced. In so far as any classification is possible it is convenient for this purpose still further to subdivide the true metals and those of the *B* sub-groups. The former comprise:

(1) The transition metals, together with copper, silver and gold;

(2) The *A* group metals, i.e. the alkali and alkaline earth metals, and beryllium and magnesium;

which two classes may be symbolized by *T* and *A* respectively. The *B* sub-group metals may be less precisely divided into the classes:

(1) The more metallic of these elements: roughly those of the 2nd, 3rd and 4th groups;

(2) The less metallic: roughly those of the 4th, 5th and 6th groups.

If we symbolize these two classes by B_1 and B_2 respectively we may consider separately four types of system: T-B_1, T-B_2, A-B_1, A-B_2. The first type, for reasons which will appear later, may be termed *electron compounds*. Such systems display certain regularities and resemblances. Alloys of the other types have fewer common properties.

Systems of the type T-B_1: electron compounds.

The silver-cadmium system. The general properties of the electron compounds may be most conveniently described by first discussing fully the behaviour of one such system. The silver-cadmium system is one which has been investigated in detail with the results summarized in Figs. 28 and 29, p. 124. We shall consider the behaviour of this alloy only at room temperature.

Pure silver has the cubic close-packed structure α. This phase is capable of accommodating up to 42 atomic per cent of cadmium in solid solution by the purely random replacement of silver atoms. The sites occupied are still those of the cubic face-centred structure, no change in which occurs except a progressive and approximately linear variation of cell size with composition. At 42 per cent, however, the

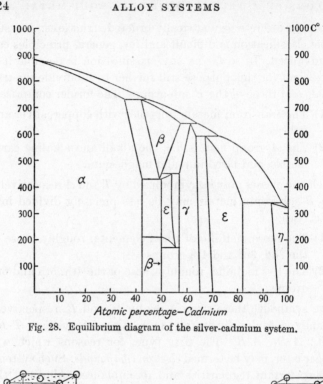

Fig. 28. Equilibrium diagram of the silver-cadmium system.

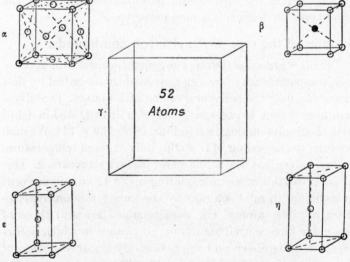

Fig. 29. The structures of the phases in the silver-cadmium system.

α-phase appears to be saturated and further cadmium can be taken up only by the formation of an entirely new phase. This new β-phase rapidly grows at the expense of the α-phase and becomes homogeneous at 50 per cent cadmium, when it has the simple caesium chloride structure shown in Fig. 29, corresponding to the composition AgCd. It must be emphasized, however, that it is the body-centred pattern rather than the actual caesium chloride structure which is characteristic of the β-phase, for by suitable heat treatment the phase can be obtained in the disordered form, while in some systems it occurs at a composition which does not admit of an ordered structure.

In the silver-cadmium system the β-phase is capable of taking up very little excess of either component in solid solution: it therefore appears only as a line on the equilibrium diagram. When the concentration of cadmium is increased beyond 50 per cent a new γ-phase develops and becomes homogeneous at a composition of about 57 per cent. This phase has an extremely complex cubic structure with a unit cell containing 52 atoms. It is also distinguished by a characteristic brittleness and hardness. In the particular system under consideration the γ-phase can accommodate in solid solution a considerable excess of either component, and on either side of the 'ideal' composition there is therefore a relatively wide range of a single homogeneous phase extending from 57 to 65 per cent of cadmium. Throughout this range there is a progressive change in the lattice dimensions but no alteration in the pattern of sites occupied.

Beyond 65 per cent of cadmium the γ-phase becomes saturated and a new ϵ-phase makes its appearance. This phase is simply a hexagonal close-packed arrangement in which silver and cadmium atoms must clearly be distributed at random, since all the sites of such a structure are geometrically precisely equivalent. In this case the phase can occur only in a disordered condition and no superlattice exists. The ϵ-phase grows at the expense of the γ-phase between 65 and 70 per cent of cadmium and becomes homogeneous at the latter composition. The range of homogeneity extends from

70 to 82 per cent of cadmium, when a new η-phase appears. This phase is the structure of elementary cadmium, which we have already described as being closely related to hexagonal close-packing and differing from it only in having a somewhat larger axial ratio. The η-phase is capable of taking up only a very small amount of silver in solid solution and the ϵ- and η-phases therefore co-exist throughout the range 82–96 per cent of cadmium. Only from 96 to 100 per cent of cadmium is the η-phase homogeneous.

The silver-cadmium system has been discussed at some length since its behaviour is typical of that of many other alloys containing a transition metal and an element from one of the earlier B sub-groups. While the initial and final phases are necessarily determined by the particular elements involved, the intermediate β-, γ- and ϵ-phases are of very general occurrence in a wide range of such systems. Although these three phases do not necessarily all appear in any given system, and although other phases are often found in addition, one or more of these characteristic phases have been observed in almost every T-B_1 system investigated. The widespread occurrence of these phases is shown by the data of Table 19 where the compositions of those so far observed are recorded. The significance of the composition will be discussed below, but the table serves to emphasize how widespread are the three phases. Thus in the systems Cu-Zn, Ag-Zn, Au-Zn, Mn-Zn, Ag-Cd, Au-Cd and Cu-Sn all three phases occur as in the system discussed above. In the Fe-Al system, on the other hand, only the β-phase FeAl appears, but we have already seen in our discussion of this system that there is also a characteristic and entirely different phase corresponding to the composition Fe_3Al. Recent work has shown moreover that on the aluminium-rich side of the composition FeAl there are several further phases of complex structure. In a few cases the simple β-phase is replaced by a more complex β'-phase in which the atoms are distributed at random in the appropriate proportions over the 20 sites per unit cell of the β-Mn structure. The factors determining the occasional appearance of this alternative arrangement are not known.

TABLE 19

β-, γ- AND ε-PHASES IN ELECTRON COMPOUNDS

Cu	Ag	Au	Mn	Fe	Co	Ni	Rh	Pd	Pt
CuBe									
CuBe$_3$									
	AgMg								
CuZn	AgZn	AuZn	MnZn$_3$		CoZn$_3$*				
Cu$_5$Zn$_8$	Ag$_5$Zn$_8$	Au$_5$Zn$_8$	Mn$_5$Zn$_{21}$	Fe$_5$Zn$_{21}$	Co$_5$Zn$_{21}$	Ni$_5$Zn$_{21}$	Rh$_5$Zn$_{21}$	Pd$_5$Zn$_{21}$	Pt$_5$Zn$_{21}$
CuZn$_3$	AgZn$_3$	AuZn$_3$	MnZn$_7$	FeZn$_7$					
CuCd?	AgCd	AuCd							
Cu$_5$Cd$_8$	Ag$_5$Cd$_8$	Au$_5$Cd$_8$				Ni$_5$Cd$_{21}$			
CuCd$_3$	AgCd$_3$	AuCd$_3$							
Cu$_5$Hg$_8$	Ag$_5$Hg$_8$								
		AuHg$_3$							
Cu$_3$Al	Ag$_3$Al*	Au$_3$Al*	MnAl?	FeAl	CoAl	NiAl			
Cu$_9$Al$_4$									
	Ag$_5$Al$_3$	Au$_5$Al$_3$							
Cu$_3$Ga									
Cu$_9$Ga$_4$									
Cu$_9$In$_4$									
Cu$_5$Si*									
Cu$_{31}$Si$_8$									
Cu$_3$Si									
Cu$_3$Ge									
Cu$_5$Sn									
Cu$_{31}$Sn$_8$									
Cu$_3$Sn	Ag$_3$Sn	Au$_3$Sn							

* β′-phase (β-Mn structure).

The composition of the phases. The attribution of chemical formulae to the several phases presents difficulties. Especially is this the case when a wide region of homogeneity exists embracing a number of possible simple compositions. In the silver-cadmium system the very restricted homogeneity range of the β-phase and the caesium chloride structure which it possesses at once justify the formula AgCd. The γ-phase, however, has a range of solid solution extending from 57 to 65 atomic per cent of cadmium, and this embraces such simple formulae as Ag_2Cd_3, Ag_3Cd_4, Ag_3Cd_5, etc. It is only the X-ray evidence, which demands a unit cell containing 52 atoms, that indicates that none of these is admissible and that the 'ideal' formula must be regarded as Ag_5Cd_8. With the ϵ-phase the position is still more difficult, for the purely statistical distribution of the atoms over the sites of the hexagonal close-packed structure can give no *a priori* reason for preferring any one of the several possible formulae included in the wide range of solid solution.

Even with the β- and γ-phases the position is not always as simple as in the case just discussed, and in fact it appears that the pattern of sites occupied, and not the actual distribution of the two kinds of atom, is the only significant feature of the structure, for a given phase may appear in different systems at widely different compositions. Thus in the copper-tin system the β-phase appears at a composition of about 17 atomic per cent of tin, corresponding approximately to the formula Cu_5Sn. Such a composition is clearly not consistent with the caesium chloride structure, but it is found that the phase is actually a body-centred cubic arrangement with the atoms distributed at random in these proportions.

A similar state of affairs arises with the γ-phases, which again occur at widely different compositions in different systems. In some cases an ideal formula may be determined by structure analysis, as with γ-brass. The original analysis of the γ-structure (Bradley and Thewlis, 1928) revealed that the 52 sites of the unit cell were divided into four groups of equivalent positions containing 8, 8, 12 and 24 atoms respectively, and that two of these groups consisted of $8 + 12$ copper atoms and the remaining two of $8 + 24$ zinc atoms. In this case there is an ordered distribution of atoms in the structure and the ideal composition is Cu_5Zn_8. Solid solution can, of course, occur within certain limits on either side of this composition by the random replacement of some atoms by atoms of the other kind. In the chemically closely analogous copper-cadmium system (Bradley and Gregory, 1931) the structure of the γ-phase is entirely different. The sites occupied remain, as always, the same but now $8 + 8$ positions contain 16 copper atoms, while the remaining $12 + 24$ positions are occupied by 32 cadmium and 4 copper atoms distributed quite at random. The copper-cadmium system also differs from that of copper-zinc in showing, in addition to the β-, γ- and ϵ-phases, others of considerable complexity (Owen and Pickup, 1933). Such an example illustrates that in alloy systems the chemical properties of the elements concerned play little part in determining the structures which obtain, and that chemical analogy does not necessarily lead to the formation of analogous phases.

Hume-Rothery's rule.

The first satisfactory explanation of the widespread occurrence of the β-, γ- and ϵ-phases in systems chemically dissimilar and at widely differing compositions was advanced by Hume-Rothery (1926), who pointed out that the appearance of a given phase is conditioned, not by the chemical properties of the elements concerned or by any arguments based on valency conceptions, but solely by the relative number of valency electrons and atoms in the crystal lattice. This generalization, usually known as Hume-Rothery's rule, is illustrated by the data of Tables 20, 21 and 22, p. 130, from which it will be seen that the β-, γ- and ϵ-phases are characterized by electron : atom ratios of $3:2$, $21:13$ and $7:4$ respectively. In each case this ratio alone determines the structure, and the relative number of atoms and the particular atoms by which the electrons are contributed appear to be of little importance. For this reason Bernal (1929) has proposed the description 'electron compounds' for such systems.

In systems containing manganese or any of the elements of

group 8 Hume-Rothery's rule is satisfied only if these elements are assumed to make no electron contribution to the structure. Goldschmidt (1931 a) has pointed out that in such systems an element of very high and one of very low ionization potential are in combination, and has suggested that under these conditions only the loosely bound electrons are given up, those of the group 8 metal being retained. This suggestion finds some support in the very large volume contraction (Westgren and Almin, 1929; Ekman, 1931) which accompanies the formation

TABLE 20

ELECTRON: ATOM RATIOS FOR SOME β-PHASES

Phase	Electrons	Atoms	Ratio
CuZn, AgCd, etc.	$1+2$	2	$3:2$
CoZn$_3$, etc.	$0+2\times3$	4	$6:4=3:2$
Cu$_3$Al, etc.	$3+3$	4	$6:4=3:2$
FeAl, etc.	$0+3$	2	$3:2$
Cu$_5$Sn, etc.	$5+4$	6	$9:6=3:2$

TABLE 21

ELECTRON: ATOM RATIOS FOR SOME γ-PHASES

Phase	Electrons	Atoms	Ratio
Cu$_5$Zn$_8$, etc.	$5+2\times8$	13	$21:13$
Fe$_5$Zn$_{21}$, etc.	$0+2\times21$	26	$42:26=21:13$
Cu$_9$Al$_4$, etc.	$9+3\times4$	13	$21:13$
Cu$_{31}$Sn$_8$, etc.	$31+4\times8$	39	$63:39=21:13$

TABLE 22

ELECTRON: ATOM RATIOS FOR SOME ϵ-PHASES

Phase	Electrons	Atoms	Ratio
CuZn$_3$, etc.	$1+2\times3$	4	$7:4$
Ag$_5$Al$_3$, etc.	$5+3\times3$	8	$14:8=7:4$
Cu$_3$Sn, etc.	$3+4$	4	$7:4$

of any of these alloys from the parent elements, in which all the valency electrons are free. In the cases of platinum and palladium magnetic measurements also indicate that no electron contribution is made by these metals (Dehlinger, 1932c).

All the phases shown in Table 19, p. 127, will be found to obey Hume-Rothery's rule. In cases where the composition of any phase has been determined on structural grounds it has, with few exceptions, been found to be consistent with the rule. In the majority of cases, however, the formula quoted is that chosen to give the appropriate electron : atom ratio. In the copper-tin system, for example, the γ-phase has a purely statistical distribution of atoms so that structurally no particular composition can be preferred. The range of homogeneity is in this case very narrow, but once the possibility of a formula as complex as $Cu_{31}Sn_8$ is admitted, several of no greater complexity could doubtless be found; this particular formula is chosen because it gives the appropriate electron : atom ratio of 21 : 13. In such cases, however, it is significant that the composition satisfying Hume-Rothery's rule is found always to lie within the range of homogeneity of the phase, while purely physical measurements reveal characteristic properties at this composition.

The β'-phase occurs at the same electron : atom ratio as the β-phase.

Exceptions to Hume-Rothery's rule. A few exceptions to Hume-Rothery's rule have been observed although most of these do not fall strictly within the $T\text{-}B_1$ group of alloys, to which alone we have regarded the rule as applicable. Thus the system silver-lithium has a γ-phase of composition Ag_3Li_{10} although clearly any alloy of these elements must have an electron : atom ratio of 1 : 1. This system, however, contains no B sub-group element. Similarly many phases such as LiAg, LiAl, NaTl, NaBi, CaTl and CdHg, all of which have the caesium chloride structure but an electron : atom ratio different from 3 : 2, are frequently quoted as exceptions to the rule, but here again they are all systems falling outside the classification here adopted.

The theoretical basis of Hume-Rothery's rule.

The Hume-Rothery rule was originally advanced as a purely empirical generalization without theoretical foundation, but the recent developments of metal theory have thrown much light on its physical significance and have led to an interpretation of many of the properties of electron compounds. We have seen in Chap. III that the energy of an electron in a metal cannot assume any value, but only values lying in a series of discrete 'zones' separated, in general, by regions of forbidden energy. Energy values lying near the middle of the permitted zones are approximately those of free electrons but this is not true of energy values close to the zone boundaries. For such electrons the energies just below the forbidden values are abnormally depressed and those just above these values abnormally raised. It follows that in general a system in which those Brillouin zones occupied are just filled, without overlap into higher zones, will be one of special stability, and that an alloy system in which such overlap occurs will seek if possible to alter the zonal configuration by a phase change.

In terms of these ideas Jones (1934a) has explained the characteristic electron:atom ratio 21:13 of the γ-phase. In this structure the Brillouin zones corresponding to the 52 atoms of the unit cell can accommodate 90 electrons without overlap. Further electrons could be received only in states of considerably higher energy. The actual number of electrons per unit cell being 84, the zone is very nearly completely filled. Similar arguments applied to the ϵ-phase give a characteristic electron:atom ratio very close to the observed value of 7:4 (Jones, 1934b; Dehlinger, 1935a).

The theory has also been applied to investigate the range of solid solution possible within a given phase. Thus if we consider the α-phase of the copper-zinc system in which zinc is taken up without change of the copper structure, it is clear that every zinc atom so accommodated involves an increase of one in the number of valency electrons in the phase. A limit to the extent of solid solution may therefore be expected to occur at an electron : atom ratio at which overlap into a higher zone impends, and this ratio will be characteristic of the α-phase and independent of the solute. With metals of higher valency as solute the range of solid solution will be correspondingly restricted and will in fact be approximately inversely proportional to the valency. The data of Table 23 show that this generalization is very roughly true. The range of solid solution of the various metals in copper decreases rapidly with increasing valency even where the relative sizes are favourable, but the electron : atom ratio in the saturated phase is approximately constant.

TABLE 23

SOLUBILITY OF METALS OF DIFFERENT VALENCIES IN COPPER

System	Atomic composition of saturated α-phase (%)	Electron : atom ratio of saturated phase
Cu-Zn	38·4	1·38
Cu-Al	20·4	1·41
Cu-Ga	20·3	1·41
Cu-Si	14·0	1·42
Cu-Ge	12·0	1·36
Cu-Sn	9·3	1·27

Elementary accounts of the application of the Jones theory to metal systems have been given by W. L. Bragg (1935), Evans (1936) and Mott (1937). More detailed and rigid treatments, embracing also its application to many of the physical properties of these systems, are available in the reviews of Slater (1934 a, 1937) and in the works of Mott and Jones (1936) and of A. H. Wilson (1936).

General accounts of electron compounds have been given by Westgren and Phragmén (1928), Westgren and Ekman (1930), Westgren (1931, 1932 a, b), Ekman (1931), Dehlinger (1931 b, 1935 b) and Hume-Rothery (1936). Lists of systems studied, with references, are given by Wyckoff (1931, 1935).

Systems of the type T-B_2.

The electron compounds described above occur primarily in systems containing a transition metal and an element from the

B sub-groups 2, 3 or 4. When the *B* sub-group metal belongs to the 5th or 6th group, or when any *B* sub-group metal is combined with an *A* group metal (including beryllium and magnesium), the heterodesmic character of the system becomes more pronounced and an increasing tendency towards the formation of definite chemical compounds is apparent. With the increasingly homopolar character of the *B* sub-group metal the range of solid solution becomes more restricted, and definite structures of varying degrees of complexity, entirely different from those of the constituents, are formed. While these structures are often semi-metallic in appearance and are relatively good conductors of electricity, the fact that this conductivity is a minimum at the stoichiometric composition, and the large diamagnetic susceptibility of these crystals, reveal the influence of chemical binding.

We shall not here attempt to describe all the structures which these various systems show, for many of them are characteristic only of the system considered and illustrate no general principles. The essential feature of all these systems which we wish to emphasize is the occurrence of a series of discrete structures, each approximating in nature to a definite chemical compound and capable of taking up in solid solution only limited excess of either constituent, and yet showing in many respects more or less typically metallic properties. Nevertheless, there are a few characteristic structures common to many of these systems which illustrate their properties and which we shall briefly discuss.

The nickel arsenide structure. The commonest structure among systems of this type is the nickel arsenide arrangement which appears when the two constituents are present in equal atomic proportions. Several hexagonal cells of the structure are illustrated in Fig. 30. The characteristic feature of this structure is the particular type of co-ordination which obtains. Each atom is surrounded by six neighbours of the opposite kind but the disposition of these neighbours is different for the two types of atom. The arsenic neighbours of a nickel atom are arranged (as are the neighbours in sodium chloride) at the corners of a regular octahedron, but the six nickel atoms surrounding an arsenic atom are disposed quite differently at the corners of a trigonal prism. The low co-ordination reveals the departure from a purely metallic binding, but the structure nevertheless remains essentially metallic in many properties and can take up in solid solution considerable excess of the transition metal which, on account of its relatively small size, is readily accommodated in the lattice. Goldschmidt (1927*a*) was the first to point out that the nickel arsenide structure occurs only when a transition metal is combined with a large, readily polarized *B* sub-group element.

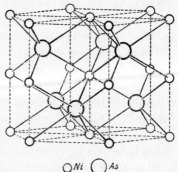

Fig. 30. The structure of nickel arsenide, NiAs. Several unit cells are shown.

Table 24 contains a list of most of the nickel arsenide structures.

TABLE 24

T-B_2 PHASES WITH THE NICKEL ARSENIDE STRUCTURE

	Cu	Au	Cr	Mn	Fe	Co	Ni	Pd	Pt
Sn	CuSn	AuSn			FeSn		NiSn		PtSn
Pb									PtPb
As				MnAs			NiAs		
Sb			CrSb	MnSb	FeSb	CoSb	NiSb	PdSb	PtSb
Bi							NiBi		PtBi
S					FeS	CoS			
Se			CrSe		FeSe	CoSe	NiSe		
Te			CrTe	MnTe	FeTe	CoTe	NiTe	PdTe	PtTe

The pyrites structure. A second structure type of common occurrence in this group is that of pyrites and the closely related marcasite, corresponding to the composition AB_2, where A is the transition metal and B the sub-group element. Here the homopolar nature of the binding has been established by Fourier analysis but nevertheless the metallic appearance and moderately high electrical conductivity indicate the persistence of some measure of metallic binding.

The molybdenum sulphide structure. The geometrical arrangement of the pyrites structure implies a high degree of polarization of the B sub-group metal, and in consequence, as Goldschmidt (1931 a) has pointed out, this structure can only occur when the transition metal is sufficiently small to exert the necessary polarizing influence. When the atom of the transition metal is large a layer lattice of the cadmium iodide or molybdenum sulphide type results. We defer a description of the former structure until we come to consider ionic crystals in detail, but the latter may be briefly considered here. The

hexagonal unit cell of molybdenum sulphide is illustrated in Fig. 31, and it will be seen that the structure is formed by the superposition of a series of sheets. Each sheet is itself built up of a layer of molybdenum atoms enclosed between two layers of sulphur atoms. The co-ordination round the molybdenum resembles that round the arsenic atoms in the nickel arsenide structure and is characteristic of a homopolar binding. The separate sheets of the structure may therefore be regarded as discrete mole-

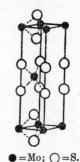

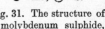
● =Mo; ○ =S.

Fig. 31. The structure of molybdenum sulphide, MoS_2.

cules. Between the sheets the binding is predominantly metallic.

Layer structures of the cadmium iodide and molybdenum sulphide types represent a transition between the purely ionic binding and a more nearly molecular structure, such as that of pyrites, which results from the drastic polarization of the ionic bond. A number of compounds having pyrites or layer structures are shown in Table 25 where the influence of the radius of the metal atom is made clear. Metals with small atoms, the polarizing power of which is therefore large, always give rise to the pyrites structure, but elements of larger radius, such as palladium and platinum, have some structures of each type.

TABLE 25

THE TRANSITION FROM LAYER LATTICES TO
THE PYRITES STRUCTURE

Metal	Radius	S	Se	Te	As	Sb	Structure type
Zr	1·60	ZrS_2	$ZrSe_2$				⎫
Sn	1·58	SnS_2					⎬ CdI_2
Ti	1·46	TiS_2	$TiSe_2$	$TiTe_2$			⎭
W	1·41	WS_2	WSe_2	WTe_2			⎫ MoS_2
Mo	1·40	MoS_2	$MoSe_2$	$MoTe_2$			⎬
Pt	1·38	PtS_2	$PtSe_2$	$PtTe_2$			⎫ CdI_2
Pd	1·37			$PdTe_2$			⎬
Pt	1·38				$PtAs_2$	$PtSb_2$	⎫
Pd	1·37				$PdAs_2$	$PdSb_2$	⎪
Mn	1·37	MnS_2		$MnTe_2$			⎪
Os	1·35	OsS_2	$OsSe_2$	$OsTe_2$			⎬ Pyrites
Ru	1·33	RuS_2	$RuSe_2$	$RuTe_2$			⎪
Fe	1·26	FeS_2					⎪
Co	1·25	CoS_2	$CoSe_2$				⎪
Ni	1·24	NiS_2	$NiSe_2$				⎭

Systems of the type A-B_1.

In systems containing a *B* sub-group element and a true metal from one of the *A* groups the less pronounced polarizing power of the latter, as compared with the transition metals, results in structures which are ionic rather than molecular in character. In these systems, again, many structures of considerable complexity are found, but, as before, there are also several characteristic arrangements of common occurrence.

The caesium chloride structure. When the sub-group metal is drawn from one of the earlier groups the caesium chloride structure (Fig. 2, p. 20) is common at the composition AB. This is, of course, the structure of the β-phase in the silver-cadmium system and in other electron compounds, but for reasons already given it seems desirable not to regard the structure as a β-phase in this case. It is among such systems that most of the normally quoted exceptions to Hume-Rothery's rule are found.

The sodium thallide structure. A closely related structure which is found in some of these systems instead of the caesium chloride arrangement is that of NaTl. The structure is illustrated in Fig. 32, where it will be seen that the pattern of sites is still that of a cubic body-centred lattice. The distribution of atoms, however, is such that each atom has four neighbours of each kind, and it therefore follows that the structure can only occur with atoms of approximately the same size. This equality of size, however, is often achieved by a considerable reduction in the radius of a metal in the structure compared

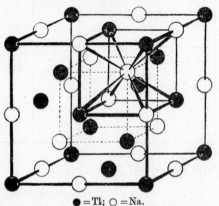

● = Tl; ○ = Na.

Fig. 32. The structure of sodium thallide, NaTl.

with its value in the elementary state. Thus Zintl and Dullenkopf (1932) found that in NaTl the radius of sodium is reduced from its normal value of 1·86 A. (in 8-fold co-ordination) by 13 per cent to 1·62 A. Zintl and Brauer (1933) have since shown that this contraction is a characteristic feature of all the NaTl structures and also of the alloys in this class having the caesium chloride arrangement. In this respect they differ markedly from the β-phase of the electron compounds, and this seems a further reason for not associating them with this phase.

A list of systems having the caesium chloride and sodium thallide structures is given in Table 26.

TABLE 26

A-B_1 PHASES WITH CAESIUM CHLORIDE AND
SODIUM THALLIDE STRUCTURES

	Li	Na	Mg	Ca	Sr
Zn	LiZn (S)				
Cd	LiCd (S)				
Hg	LiHg (C)				
Al	LiAl (C)				
Ga	LiGa (S)				
In	LiIn (S)	NaIn (S)			
Tl	LiTl (C)	NaTl (S)	MgTl (C)	CaTl (C)	SrTl (C)

(C) Caesium chloride structure.
(S) Sodium thallide structure.

Other structures. At other compositions most systems of this
class have complex structures which are not of common occurrence or general interest. One system, however, which has
been discussed in detail by Dehlinger (1935 c) and which serves
to emphasize the typically heterodesmic character of these
alloys, may be briefly mentioned here.

The magnesium-aluminium system at a composition of
approximately Mg_3Al_2 is found to have a structure in which the
atoms are distributed over the sites of the α-manganese
structure. This is a complex arrangement of 58 atoms in the
unit cell divided into three sets of 24, 24 and 10. The true
composition of the phase must therefore be $Mg_{17}Al_{12}$. A detailed
consideration of the interatomic distances reveals that these
differ from the values to be expected on the basis of the normal
radii. Thus the aluminium atoms are all found to be grouped in
pairs with a separation considerably smaller than twice the
aluminium radius. We may regard these atoms as bound into
diatomic molecules by homopolar bonds for which, however,
two further electrons per pair of atoms are required. These
electrons may be derived by the ionization of magnesium

atoms, in which case we shall have in each unit cell 12 negatively charged molecules, $[Al_2]^{2-}$, 24 positively charged magnesium ions and 10 neutral magnesium atoms:

$$[Al_2]^{2-}_{12} Mg^+_{24} Mg_{10}.$$

In confirmation of this picture it is found that the distance between the aluminium and the 24 magnesium atoms of the first kind is substantially smaller than that between the aluminium and the remaining 10 magnesium atoms. In this structure homopolar, ionic and metallic forces are involved, and, since residual forces are necessarily also operative, it is a structure displaying simultaneously all four types of interatomic binding. Dehlinger has suggested that in elementary manganese itself the binding may be similarly heterodesmic.

Systems of the type A-B_2.

When the B sub-group element with which the A group metal is combined belongs to one of the later groups (roughly the 4th, 5th or 6th) the ionic character of the binding is even more marked and the simple sodium chloride and fluorite structures characteristic of purely ionic compounds are common. Table 27 shows a number of compounds of this type having the sodium chloride and fluorite structures. The

TABLE 27

A-B_2 PHASES WITH SODIUM CHLORIDE AND FLUORITE STRUCTURES

	Sodium chloride						Fluorite			
	Mg	Ca	Ba	Sr	(Mn)	(Pb)	Li	Na	Mg	(Cu)
Ge									Mg_2Ge	
Sn									Mg_2Sn	
Pb									Mg_2Pb	
S	MgS	CaS	BaS	SrS		PbS				
Se	MgSe	CaSe	BaSe	SrSe	MnSe	PbSe	Li_2Se	Na_2Se		Cu_2Se
Te		CaTe	BaTe	SrTe		PbTe	Li_2Te	Na_2Te		

latter structure will be described in detail when ionic crystals are discussed.

The tendency of metals to form negative ions has been discussed in the light both of structural and of chemical evidence by Zintl and Kaiser (1933) who have concluded that such ionization is limited to the *B* sub-group elements of the 4th, 5th, 6th and 7th groups.

ALLOYS OF TWO *B* SUB-GROUP ELEMENTS

In systems containing two *B* sub-group metals the heterodesmic character of these elements leads to a still more pronounced tendency towards the formation of definite chemical compounds. When the metals both belong to the earlier groups the generally metallic character of the systems persists, but any considerable extent of solid solution obtains only between metals of the same group and even then only when the radii are very nearly equal. Thus cadmium and mercury form a much wider range of solid solution than cadmium and zinc, while cadmium and tin are practically immiscible. When both metals belong to the later *B* sub-groups the sodium chloride structure is common, as in the compounds SnSb, SnTe, PbSe, PbTe.

The zincblende and wurtzite structures. By far the commonest structures in this class, however, are those of zincblende (Fig. 4, p. 29) and wurtzite. These two structures, which are closely related, have in common a regular tetrahedral co-ordination of each atom by four neighbours of the other kind. The zincblende structure has already been briefly discussed as one in which purely homopolar forces are in operation, and it is clear that for such a 4-fold co-ordinated structure to be entirely bound by homopolar bonds an aggregate of two electrons per bond or four electrons per atom must be available. It was first pointed out by Grimm and Sommerfeld (1926), in a generalization usually termed the *Grimm-Sommerfeld rule*, that it is not necessary that these electrons should be contributed equally by the two atoms and that, therefore, the zincblende or wurtzite structure is to be expected in any compound XY for which the constituent X stands in the periodic table as many places before the group of tetravalent elements as the constituent Y stands after that group. The data of Table 28 show how common are these structures in systems of the type now under consideration. The wurtzite structure is described fully in Chap. VI, p. 158.

TABLE 28

B-B PHASES WITH ZINCBLENDE AND WURTZITE STRUCTURES

Zincblende structure

	Be	Zn	Cd	Hg	Al	Ga	In
S	BeS	ZnS	CdS	HgS			
Se	BeSe	ZnSe	CdSe	HgSe			
Te	BeTe	ZnTe	CdTe	HgTe			
As					AlAs	GaAs	
Sb					AlSb	GaSb	InSb

Wurtzite structure

	Mg	Zn	Cd
S		ZnS	CdS
Se			CdSe
Te	MgTe		

The stibnite structure. Although so far observed in only two minerals, the structure of stibnite, Sb_2S_3, and bismuthinite, Bi_2S_3, is of some theoretical interest. In this structure chains or bands of closely linked antimony and sulphur atoms extend indefinitely through the crystal. Within each chain the binding is homopolar in character, but between the neighbouring chains very much weaker forces operate giving rise to a corresponding anisotropy of physical properties. The semimetallic nature of the two minerals indicates that these weaker forces must be at least partially metallic in origin and justifies the inclusion of the structure in the metal section of our classification. The chief interest of the stibnite arrangement lies in the fact that it is the first structure we have described, other than that of selenium, in which discrete molecules infinitely extended in one dimension occur. The structures of zincblende, molybdenum sulphide, stibnite and, say, carbon tetrachloride (to be described later) may therefore be regarded as forming a series in which homopolar molecules exist having indefinite extent in three, two, one and no dimensions respectively.

This closes our description of the three principal classes into which we have divided the alloy systems. As a summary a condensed survey of the chief structural characteristics of these classes is given in Table 29. The remaining class of alloys to be considered is that embracing the interstitial structures, but before passing on to discuss these systems we give in the next section an account of certain structural features of metal systems which are common to all the classes of alloy so far described.

TABLE 29

THE CLASSIFICATION OF BINARY INTERMETALLIC SYSTEMS

Some common structure types

		True metals	*B* sub-group metals	
			B_1 Groups 2, 3, 4	B_2 Groups 4, 5, 6
True metals	Transition metals and Cu, Ag, Au	Wide range of solid solution. Superlattices	Electron compounds	NiAs, FeS$_2$, MoS$_2$ and CdI$_2$ structures
True metals	*A*-group metals	Wide range of solid solution. Superlattices	CsCl and NaTl structures	Ionic structures of NaCl and CaF$_2$ types
B sub-group metals	B_1 Groups 2, 3, 4	(See above)	Solid solution if chemically similar and of comparable size	Zincblende and wurtzite structures
B sub-group metals	B_2 Groups 4, 5, 6	(See above)	(See above)	NaCl structure

GENERAL FEATURES OF ALLOY SYSTEMS

The wide range of solid solution which obtains in many metal systems is perhaps the most characteristic feature of metal chemistry and the one which distinguishes metal structures most sharply from those of other chemical compounds. As we have seen, this solid solution is most common in systems containing true metals but it is not confined to such systems and is found wherever the metals involved are of similar electronic constitution. Once this condition is satisfied, the extent of solid solution is determined by purely geometrical considerations involving the relative sizes of the atoms concerned and the amount of distortion which the lattice can tolerate without change of structure. Hume-Rothery, Mabbott and Channel-Evans (1934a) have shown that the maximum difference in radius consistent with an extended range of solid solution is about 15 per cent of the atomic radius of the solvent. If the radii differ by more than this amount solid solution is very restricted, while within these limits the extent of solid solution is the greater the more nearly equal the radii. Occasional complications arise in the application of this generalization, as, for example, when a metal occurs in an alloy in a state of co-ordination very different from that which obtains in the elementary state, or when a metal changes its state of ionization on entering into solid solution. Nevertheless, the rule is of great utility in giving a general indication as to whether or not extended solid solution is likely to occur. At high temperatures solid solutions may be formed when the radii differ by somewhat more than 15 per cent and systems in which this is the case may be expected to show precipitation hardening on quenching from a high temperature.

Vegard's law. When extended solid solution is possible the cell dimensions of the homogeneous phase are found to vary very nearly linearly with composition in accordance with Vegard's law (Vegard and Dale, 1928). This generalization is, however, only approximately true, and, especially with chemical dissimilar metals, a contraction in the cell dimensions compared with the values to be expected from a linear relation is often observed. Nevertheless, over a narrow range the linear law is a sufficiently good approximation to enable phase boundaries to be determined with considerable accuracy by an extrapolation of the cell dimensions.

The relative valency effect. In systems of two chemically dissimilar metals the extent of solid solution is generally very restricted even when the size-factor is favourable, and the more electronegative the one metal and the more electropositive the other the greater is the tendency to form definite chemical compounds. In such systems, as Bernal (1929) has pointed out, mutual solubility is not a reciprocal property and a metal of lower valency will generally dissolve more of one of higher valency than *vice versa*. It is not difficult to see that in structures in which there is a tendency towards homopolar binding the electron deficiency resulting from the substitution of an element of low valency is much more likely to lead to a breakdown of the structure than the electron excess produced by the substitution of a metal of high valency. This effect is sometimes termed the 'relative valency effect' (Hume-Rothery, Mabbott and Channel-Evans, 1934b).

We have already seen (p. 132) that in electron compounds, where the structure is determined by the electron : atom ratio, the extent of solid solution, even when the size-factor is favourable, is governed by the maximum electron concentration at which the phase is stable and is therefore roughly inversely proportional to the valency of the solute atom.

The mutual solubility of metals has been discussed in detail, and from a more physical point of view than is here possible, by Bernal (1929, 1931a), who has tabulated many data on the subject.

INTERSTITIAL STRUCTURES

The interstitial structures comprise the compounds of the transition metals with the four light elements hydrogen, boron, carbon and nitrogen. In spite of the non-metallic nature of these latter elements these compounds are markedly metallic in their physical properties, being generally opaque conductors with a metallic lustre. They do, moreover, show the indeterminacy of composition and sequence of phases so characteristic of alloy systems and for this reason are most conveniently discussed under that heading. The interstitial structures differ strikingly from the compounds of the same light elements with the non-transition metals. These bodies behave as true chemical compounds with a definite composition and with physical properties entirely different from those of the constituent elements. Thus, while the phases Fe_4N, Mo_2C, Ni_2B and TiH are all metallic in properties, the carbides of the alkaline earth metals are transparent insulators. Technically the interstitial structures possess valuable properties, for they are generally distinguished by great infusibility and an extreme hardness often approaching if not exceeding that of diamond. Many of their physical properties have been tabulated by Becker (1933).

Structures of the 'normal' type.

The structural properties of the interstitial compounds have been investigated by Hägg (1929, 1930 a, b, 1931) who has shown that their characteristic properties are due to the small size of the non-metallic atom. Even when in combination with the transition metals these elements form simple interstitial structures only if the ratio of the radii of the atoms is less than about 0·59. If this condition is satisfied a structure of the so-called 'normal' type results, in which the parent metal atoms are in contact and the atoms of the non-metallic element are disposed in the interstices between them. The arrangement of the metal atoms is usually the same as in the pure element and therefore either cubic or hexagonal close-packed with a co-ordination number 12, or cubic body-centred with a co-ordination of 8. Occasionally the atoms are arranged on a simple hexagonal lattice and sometimes the idealized structure is slightly deformed.

The distribution of the non-metal atoms in the interstices of the metal lattice is found always to be such that these atoms are in contact with their metal neighbours. Subject to this condition, the non-metal atoms occupy the largest spaces in the structure in which this contact can be attained and so achieve the maximum possible co-ordination. Thus, if the metal has a cubic close-packed structure the non-metal atoms, if sufficiently large, occupy the 6-fold co-ordinated interstices at the centres of the sides of the unit cell. If all these sites are occupied the structure is that of sodium chloride and corresponds to the composition MX. If the non-metal atom is too small for this type of co-ordination it occupies instead the smaller 4-fold co-ordinated sites in the centres of the eight cubelets into which the unit cell can be divided. If all these sites are occupied the structure is that of fluorite and corresponds to the composition MX_2. If one-half of the sites are symmetrically filled the zincblende structure of composition MX results.

Classification. These observations provide a convenient basis for a classification of 'normal' interstitial structures, for, following Hägg, we may consider as of one type all those structures which are produced by the occupation of interstices of a given kind in a given type of metal lattice, regardless of the number of these interstices which are in actual fact so occupied. The classification is therefore expressed in terms of (1) the nature of the metal lattice, and (2) the co-ordination number of the non-metal atoms. The justification for such a classification lies in the observation that interstitial structures never occur in which more than one type of interstice is occupied, so that these structures never contain more atoms of the non-metal than are required completely to fill the equivalent positions of one kind. On the other hand a deficiency of non-metal atoms, with only some of the equivalent positions occupied, is possible.

Hägg's classification is summarized in Table 30, p. 148, where the radius ratio conditioning the appearance of each structure type is also given. In Table 31, p. 148, the structures of a number of interstitial compounds are shown. A study of these data reveals that structures based on a close-packed arrangement of metal atoms are far more common than those in which the metal is 8-fold co-ordinated. With structures of composition MX a cubic close-packing of metal atoms pre-

TABLE 30

CLASSIFICATION OF NORMAL INTERSTITIAL STRUCTURES

(After Hägg, 1931)

C.N.	Type of metal lattice	C.N. of non-metal	Type symbol	Condition for occurrence $R_X : R_M$
12	12a Cubic close-packed	6	12a, 6*	>0·41
		4	12a, 4†	>0·23
	12b Hexagonal close-packed	6	12b, 6	>0·41
		4	12b, 4‡	>0·23
8	8a Cubic body-centred	4	8a, 4	>0·29
	8b Simple hexagonal $c : a = 1$	6	8b, 6	>0·53

* Cf. NaCl.   † Cf. fluorite and zincblende.   ‡ Cf. wurtzite.

TABLE 31

THE STRUCTURES OF SOME INTERSTITIAL PHASES

(After Hägg, 1931)

System	$R_X : R_M$	M_4X	M_2X	MX	MX_2*
Zr-H	0·29	12a, 4	12b, 4	12a, 4	ThC$_2$
Ta-H	0·32	—	12b, 4	8a, 4	
Ti-H	0·32	—	12b, 4	12a, 4	12a, 4
Pd-H	0·34	—	12a, 4	—	
La Ce Pr }-C Nd	0·42–0·43	—	—	—	LaC$_2$
Th-C	0·43	—	—	—	ThC$_2$
Zr-N	0·45	—	—	12a, 6	
Sc-N	0·47	—	—	12a, 6	
U-C	0·48	—	—	—	LaC$_2$
Zr-C	0·48	—	—	12a, 6	
Nb-N	0·49	—	—	12a, 6	
Ti-N	0·49	—	—	12a, 6	
W-N	0·51	—	12a, 6	—	
Mo-N	0·52	—	12a, 6	8b, 6	
V-N	0·53	—	—	12a, 6	
Nb-C	0·53	—	—	12a, 6	
Ti-C	0·53	—	—	12a, 6	
Ta-C	0·53	—	12b, 6	12a, 6	
Mn-N	0·55	12a, 6	12b, 6	—	
W-C	0·55	—	12b, 6	8b, 6	
Cr-N	0·56	—	12b, 6	12a, 6	
Mo-C	0·56	—	12b, 6	—	
Fe-N	0·56	12a, 6	12b, 6	—	
V-C	0·58	—	12b, 6	12a, 6	

* LaC$_2$ and ThC$_2$ refer to the two types of X_2-structures (see p. 149).

dominates but with M_2X compounds hexagonal close-packing is of more frequent occurrence. The appearance of both these structures at different compositions in a single system, as in Ta-C or Cr-N, shows that the arrangement of the metal atoms is not necessarily that which obtains in the structure of the element. The occurrence of the structure type 12a, 6, of ideal composition MX, at the composition M_4X in the systems Mn-N and Fe-N reveals that interstitial structures may exist with only a fraction of the equivalent sites occupied by non-metal atoms.

X_2-structures.

Interstitial structures of the composition MX_2 appear to be found only in systems in which the radius ratio of non-metal to metal atom is particularly small. When this condition is satisfied, although structures of the types described above are sometimes found, a more common arrangement is one in which the non-metal atoms are grouped in pairs in the interstices of the metal lattice. These so-called X_2-structures are of two kinds, both of which may be most conveniently described in terms of a cubic close-packed lattice by the distortion of which they are formed. In the first, illustrated in Fig. 33a,

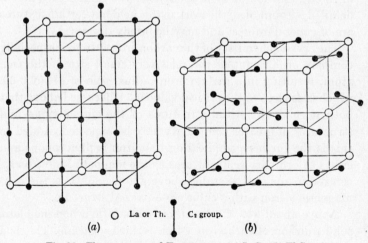

O   La or Th. | C₂ group.

(a)   (b)

Fig. 33. The two types of X_2-structure. (a) LaC$_2$, (b) ThC$_2$.

the X_2 groups are disposed in the 6-fold co-ordinated interstices of the metal lattice and are all arranged parallel to one
edge of the cube, which is thereby extended so that the cell
is in fact tetragonal with an axial ratio greater than unity.
This structure is found in LaC_2, CeC_2, PrC_2, NdC_2, UC_2 and
VC_2, in all of which the extent of the distortion is measured
by an axial ratio of $1\cdot15$–$1\cdot20$. The structure also occurs in
the dicarbides of the alkaline earth metals and is therefore not
exclusively confined to the compounds of transition metals.

In the second type of X_2-structure, shown in Fig. 33b, p. 149,
the X_2 groups occupy the same interstices but all lie parallel
to a cube face with their axes in two mutually perpendicular
directions. A tetragonal cell with an axial ratio less than unity
results. This structure is found in ThC_2 and ZrC_2, in both of
which compounds the axial ratio is $0\cdot90$, and also in ZrH_2.

The structure of steel.

The interstitial structures of by far the greatest technical
importance are those which occur in the carbon-iron system,
and the application of X-ray analysis to this system has
resulted in a great extension of our understanding of the
properties of carbon steels, and in a considerable simplification
in the description of their behaviour. We cannot give here a
detailed account of all the work in this field but certain features
are of general interest and may be briefly discussed.

The crystal chemistry of the carbon-iron system is especially
complex on account of the relatively small size of the iron
atom, resulting in a carbon : iron radius ratio of about $0\cdot60$,
which is so close to the critical value $0\cdot59$ discussed above that
both normal interstitial structures of the simple types and
structures of greater complexity may be expected. Added to
this is the further complication that iron is dimorphous and
exists at ordinary temperatures as the magnetic, cubic body-
centred α-iron, but is stable above about $880°$ C. as the non-
magnetic γ-iron with a cubic close-packed structure.

Above about $900°$ C. all carbon steels form a non-magnetic
solid solution of carbon in γ-iron termed *austenite*. This is a
simple interstitial solid solution of the type discussed above,

but the number of carbon atoms is clearly insufficient for them to be arranged in any regular way and they must be regarded as distributed at random in the interstices of the lattice. If cooled slowly this solid solution transforms at about 700° C. into *ferrite* and *cementite*. Ferrite is an interstitial solution of carbon in α-iron, but the amount of carbon which can be taken up in solution is limited to about 0·06 per cent. The excess of carbon is therefore thrown out of solution and appears in the definite compound cementite Fe_3C with a complex orthorhombic structure. The solid is no longer homogeneous and the characteristic appearance due to the separation of ferrite and cementite gives rise to the name *pearlite*. In this condition the steel is very soft.

When cooled more rapidly to low temperatures the transition from austenite to pearlite takes place much more slowly and can be suppressed altogether by the addition of other elements, so that non-magnetic austenite can be preserved in a stable state at ordinary temperatures. This, however, is not possible with pure carbon steel, for which the minimum rate of transformation obtains at about 200° C. When quenched to this temperature a period of the order of an hour is required for the change to pearlite to take place. At temperatures below 150° C. austenite transforms very much more rapidly but in an entirely different way and *martensite* is formed. This is found to be a supersaturated interstitial solid solution of carbon in α-iron, the unit cell of which, however, is deformed by the large carbon content and is tetragonal instead of cubic body-centred. The axial ratio depends upon the carbon content and has a maximum value of 1·07 corresponding to a composition of about 1·6 per cent carbon. It is the presence of martensite which gives quenched steel its characteristic hardness.

It is very important to realize that martensite is stable only below about 150° C. and that in the neighbourhood of this temperature its rate of formation from quenched austenite is far greater than that at which austenite is transformed to pearlite at somewhat higher temperatures. This point is made clear by the chart illustrated in Fig. 34, p. 152. Here the rate of transformation of austenite into pearlite and into martensite is shown as a function of temperature. At about 200° C. a period of the order of hours is required for the austenite→pearlite transition, but in the temperature range 0–100° C. the transformation austenite→martensite occurs almost instantaneously.

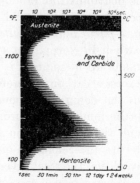

Above about 150° C. martensite is unstable and when tempered in the range 200–500° C. breaks down into ferrite and cementite. Although of the same composition as pearlite the solid thus formed is generally of a coarser micro-crystalline texture and is termed *sorbite*. The rate of transition from martensite to sorbite increases rapidly with temperature.

Fig. 34. Equilibrium diagram of the decomposition of austenite. The black area and the black lines represent the relative times for austenite to become unstable and to transform respectively. Above about 200° C. the transformation is to ferrite + cementite (pearlite), below this temperature to martensite.

The relation of martensite to austenite, on the one hand, and to the mixture of ferrite and cementite, on the other, may be readily understood if the decomposition of austenite is regarded as involving two separate processes: (1) the allotropic transformation from γ-iron to α-iron, and (2) the rejection of the carbon taken up in interstitial solid solution in the α-iron. If the first process takes place alone the carbon is retained in a supersaturated solid solution in α-iron and tetragonal martensite is formed. If the second process now follows carbon is precipitated from the martensite and taken up as cementite so that pearlite or sorbite results. This is exactly what occurs at low temperatures, when the rate of precipitation of carbon from the lattice is very slow compared with the rate of allotropic transformation of the iron. At higher temperatures, however, this is no longer the case, for then the precipitation of the carbon must be regarded as immediately following the allotropic transformation so that austenite is directly converted to ferrite and cementite: it is, therefore quite incorrect to consider martensite as a necessary intermediate product in the austenite → pearlite transformation. The tempering of martensite at temperatures of 200–500° C. is brought about by the rejection of the carbon from the supersaturated solution, and may be regarded as the second of the above processes previously inhibited by the original quenching.

We cannot here discuss further the structural properties of carbon steel, nor can we say anything about the many more complex alloy steels which have been investigated, but we have already said enough to emphasize the great power and convenience of the X-ray methods and to demonstrate the importance of a structural approach to metallurgical problems. Excellent and more detailed accounts of the structural properties of steel have been given by Desch (1934) and by van Horn (1935).

THE CHEMISTRY OF METAL SYSTEMS

The structural properties of the metal systems described above naturally challenge consideration from a purely chemical point of view, for occasionally the results of structure analysis cannot readily be reconciled with accepted chemical principles and demand a reorientation of the chemical picture of the metallic state. It has generally been the practice of the metallurgist to seek to represent the several phases in an alloy system by simple chemical formulae corresponding to idealized stoichiometric compositions, departures from which were possible by the solid solution in the ideal phase of excess of one or other of the components. Such formulae inevitably tend to convey the impression, implicitly if not explicitly, that these phases are to be regarded as definite chemical compounds, and it is necessary to consider carefully to what extent such a viewpoint is justifiable, and even whether there are valid grounds for attributing to the phases any formulae at all.

In our description of the metal structures we have, of course, included many which are heterodesmic and in which homopolar or ionic binding predominates. Such systems may often quite properly be regarded as chemical compounds, but it is not in such systems that the chief interest lies, and here we shall discuss only the systems of more pronouncedly metallic character, including the electron compounds. It was early pointed out by Hume-Rothery (1926) that if formulae are assigned to such phases they must not be expected to obey the ordinary chemical valencies of the metals concerned. In fact, the satisfaction of chemical valencies is the negation of metallic properties since in chemical combination the loosely bound electrons of the metal atoms are bound in the stable groups of the ionic and homopolar linkages. If free valency electrons are to be left over to form a truly metallic phase the valency relations must necessarily be different from those obtaining in definite chemical compounds. Chemical combination in the generally accepted sense is confined to homopolar and ionic structures, and alloy systems are sharply distinguished from such compounds by the indefiniteness of their composition, the readiness with which they are synthesized and their general qualitative resemblance to their component metals. If such systems are to be regarded as compounds it must be in terms of a wider conception of chemical combination. The extent to which such a wider conception is desirable is discussed below.

Even though metal systems must not be regarded as ordinary chemical compounds, it does not follow that it is unjustifiable to represent such systems by definite formulae. In homopolar and ionic structures stoichiometric proportions are normally necessitated by rigid electrostatic demands, but in a crystal structure simple proportions may be necessary to conform to purely geometrical requirements. If atoms of two different radii are to form a structure, a simple stable arrangement is possible only when the atoms are present in some simple proportions. It is this purely geometrical effect which justifies definite formulae for the phases of many true metal systems, but it must be clearly understood that such formulae are primarily geometrical in their origin and do not represent chemical combination in its generally accepted sense. In most cases the geometrical demands are not very exacting, and a greater or lesser degree of tolerance, together with a corresponding indefiniteness of composition, are permitted.

To meet the difficulties presented by metal systems Westgren and Phragmén (1925) have proposed the adoption of a wider definition of chemical combination in terms of crystal structure. These authors regard an ideal chemical compound as one in which structurally equivalent positions are occupied by chemically identical atoms, and an ideal solid solution as a structure in which all atoms are structurally equivalent. It is clear that such a definition of chemical combination embraces all the generally accepted compounds, but, as Hume-Rothery (1928) has emphasized, it is not without objection when applied to metal systems. Thus, to take only one example, the β-phase in the silver-cadmium system already discussed has, in its ordered state, the simple caesium chloride structure and must therefore be regarded as a definite compound. In the state of disorder, however, the two kinds of atom are distributed at random over the structurally equivalent sites of a body-centred cubic lattice and the phase then satisfies the definition of an ideal solid solution. It is difficult to view the distinction between solid solution and chemical compound as nothing more than the relatively trivial distinction between these two states, and when it is remembered that not only the two extremes but every intermediate condition of order can be realized, the difficulty is even greater.

The electron compounds present special difficulties of their own, for with them geometrical demands do not generally determine the structure and many phases occur only in the completely disordered state. In such cases, and especially when an extended range of solid solution occurs, it is possible to assign many formulae, a choice between which can be made only on structural grounds in terms of Hume-Rothery's rule. The β-phase in the system copper-aluminium has a considerable range of solid solution on either side of the composition Cu_3Al assigned to it, and clearly a phase of this composition cannot have the caesium chloride structure but must occur in the disordered state. From a structural point of view, therefore, any formula within the homogeneity range would be equally valid, and it is only the demands of the electron : atom ratio which determine the ideal composition of the phase. A similar difficulty arises with the β'-phase of the silver-aluminium system. This system has a vanishingly narrow homogeneity range coinciding with the composition Ag_3Al, and this composition has in fact long been attributed to the phase on purely chemical grounds. The structure, however, cannot give any confirmation of this or of any other formula, for the arrangement is that of β-manganese with 20 atoms in the unit cell divided into two equivalent groups of 12 and 8. It is clearly impossible to distribute two kinds of atoms regularly in such a structure in any other ratio than 3 : 2 and the phase Ag_3Al is therefore a completely disordered one. It is only from Hume-Rothery's rule that confirmation of the experimentally determined composition is obtained.

Exactly similar arguments apply to the γ-phases. Here the extent of the solid solution has often led to the assignation of incorrect formulae, especially since the composition satisfying Hume-Rothery's rule is relatively complex so that a composition differing but little from it can often be expressed by a simpler formula. Disordered structures are again common, and even when an ordered arrangement obtains the distribution of the atoms in closely related structures is not necessarily the same. We have already seen that in the phases Cu_5Zn_8 and Cu_5Cd_8 the disposition of the atoms is quite different although the sites occupied are the same in both cases.

These examples serve to show that in metal systems chemical analogy has no necessary counterpart in analogy of structure and that the positions occupied by particular atom types play a very incidental part in the structure. Only the pattern of sites is of importance, and this is determined primarily by the electron : atom ratio. In metal systems this is a much more significant quantity than the chemical composition.

This concludes our discussion of the crystal chemistry of the metallic state.

CHAPTER VI

HOMOPOLAR COMPOUNDS

INTRODUCTION

Of the four main classes into which crystal structures fall that which comprises the homopolar compounds contains by far the fewest members. As we have already seen, the molecular orbitals of the homopolar bond occupy a position intermediate between the atomic orbitals of an ionic structure and the macro-crystal orbitals of a metal. This fact and the exacting demands, both as regards valency and spatial configuration, of the homopolar bond result in the number of homodesmic homopolar compounds being very limited and in the structure types being both few and simple. These demands also compel homopolar compounds to conform more closely to the classical laws of chemistry, which strictly are applicable only to such compounds, and in consequence the indefiniteness of composition and random substitution so common in metallic and ionic structures are rarely observed. By far the most important homopolar compounds are the heterodesmic structures which embrace the whole of organic chemistry. In these, individual molecules exist bound within themselves by strong homopolar forces but held to their neighbours only by relatively feeble residual bonds. Such structures will be considered in due course in the chapter devoted to molecular compounds. Certain heterodesmic homopolar structures in which metallic forces are also operative have been discussed in Chaps. IV and V.

Simple structures.

Diamond and zincblende. These structures have already been described in our general discussion of the nature of the homopolar bond (p. 26) and we have seen that they provide the ideal example of a homodesmic homopolar structure. The general features of these structures do not need to be repeated here, but we may emphasize once again that the purely homopolar structure of diamond clearly indicates the essential identity of chemical forces with those determining the coherence of the crystal as a whole. In such a structure, if we wish to think of a 'molecule' it must be of a molecule of indefinite extent embracing the whole crystal. The same point is illustrated very convincingly by a comparison of the heat of evaporation of diamond with that required to sever the aliphatic single carbon-carbon bond, which reveals that the binding in the two cases is of very nearly the same strength. Similarly the characteristic carbon-carbon distance of $1 \cdot 54$ A. is very closely the same.

Wurtzite. Another structure of common occurrence in homopolar compounds of composition AX is that of wurtzite, the hexagonal cell of which is shown in Fig. 35. The difference between this structure and that of zincblende is of geometrical rather than of structural importance, for in both structures the co-ordination of each type of atom by its immediate neighbours is the same, and it is only when second nearest neighbours are considered that a distinction arises. Energetically the two arrangements must be very nearly equivalent

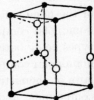

Fig. 35. The structure of wurtzite, ZnS.

since zinc sulphide is dimorphous and occurs with both structures.

The condition for the appearance of the zincblende and wurtzite structures has already been discussed in Chap. v, where we saw that the Grimm-Sommerfeld rule was merely an expression of the necessity for two valency electrons for each link formed. The structures are not, however, confined to the metallic or semi-metallic systems there described but occur also in many compounds containing the halogens or the non-metals oxygen, sulphur, nitrogen and phosphorus, as is shown by the data of Table 32. All the compounds will be seen to satisfy the Grimm-Sommerfeld rule in having an electron : atom ratio of 4 : 1.

The purely homopolar character of the binding in most of the compounds is illustrated in another way by a comparison of the interatomic distances within a group of structures for which the sum of the atomic numbers of the two components is constant. Data for a comparison of this kind are included in Table 32 where the structures are arranged in such groups. It will be seen that in any one group the interatomic distances remain very nearly constant, in marked contrast to the effect to be expected if such structures were ionic. In the

TABLE 32

COMPOUNDS WITH ZINCBLENDE AND WURTZITE STRUCTURES

Compound	Structure	Atomic numbers	Interatomic distance
BeO	W	4 + 8 = 12	1·64
C	Z	6 + 6 = 12	1·54
BeS	Z	4 + 16 = 20	2·10
AlN	W	13 + 7 = 20	1·87
SiC	Z	14 + 6 = 20	1·89
AlP	Z	13 + 15 = 28	2·36
Si	Z	14 + 14 = 28	2·35
BeSe	Z	4 + 34 = 38	2·20
ZnO	W	30 + 8 = 38	1·96
CuCl	Z	29 + 17 = 46	2·34
ZnS	ZW	30 + 16 = 46	2·35
GaP	Z	31 + 15 = 46	2·35
AsAl	Z	33 + 13 = 46	2·43
BeTe	Z	4 + 52 = 56	2·40
MgTe	W	12 + 52 = 64	2·76
AlSb	Z	13 + 51 = 64	2·64
SCd	ZW	16 + 48 = 64	2·52
CuBr	Z	29 + 35 = 64	2·46
ZnSe	Z	30 + 34 = 64	2·45
GaAs	Z	31 + 33 = 64	2·44
Ge	Z	32 + 32 = 64	2·44
CuI	Z	29 + 53 = 82	2·62
ZnTe	W	30 + 52 = 82	2·64
GaSb	Z	31 + 51 = 82	2·64
SeCd	W	34 + 48 = 82	2·62
AgI	ZW	47 + 53 = 100	2·80
CdTe	Z	48 + 52 = 100	2·80
InSb	Z	49 + 51 = 100	2·79
Sn	Z	50 + 50 = 100	2·80

Z = zincblende.   W = wurtzite.

latter case the influence of the increasing polarity of the bond in such a series as CuBr-ZnSe-GaAs would result in a pronounced decrease in the interatomic distance. This influence of increasing polarity is illustrated for a few typically ionic structures in Table 33 where a decrease in interatomic distance of about 10 per cent is seen to occur between a univalent and the corresponding divalent compound. Many of the zincblende-wurtzite structures are nevertheless not purely homopolar in nature and often display a tendency towards a partially ionic binding which is reflected in extreme cases in

TABLE 33

INTERATOMIC DISTANCES IN CERTAIN IONIC COMPOUNDS
WITH THE SODIUM CHLORIDE STRUCTURE

Sum of atomic numbers	Compounds		Interatomic distances		Δ per cent
20	NaF	MgO	2·31	2·10	10
28	NaCl	MgS	2·81	2·59	8
28	KF	CaO	2·67	2·40	11
36	KCl	CaS	3·14	2·84	10
46	NaBr	MgSe	2·98	2·72	10
46	RbF	SrO	2·82	2·57	10
54	KBr	CaSe	3·29	2·95	12
54	RbCl	SrS	3·29	3·00	10
64	CsF	BaO	3·01	2·75	9
72	KI	CaTe	3·52	3·17	11
72	RbBr	SrSe	3·43	3·11	10
72	CsCl	BaS	3·57	3·17	13
90	RbI	SrTe	3·66	3·32	10

small but significant changes in the interatomic distances. A detailed discussion of this gradual transition between the two types of binding is, however, best deferred until the simple ionic structures have been described in Chap. VII.

The zincblende and wurtzite structures are not found in AX compounds containing a transition metal even when the sum of the group numbers of the two elements is eight. Thus compounds such as scandium nitride and titanium carbide, although not ionic, have the sodium chloride structure.

Cuprite. Although not of very common occurrence, the very simple structure of cuprite, Cu_2O, the cubic unit cell of which is shown in Fig. 36, is of theoretical interest in that it illustrates the transition from the homopolar towards the metallic binding. The co-ordination is very low, each oxygen atom being surrounded by four copper neighbours at the corners of a regular tetrahedron and each copper atom by only two oxygen neighbours. The arrangement of the copper atoms alone is that of cubic close-packing and the structure can be regarded as an interstitial solution of oxygen in the metallic copper lattice. Such a picture

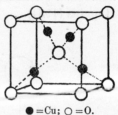

● =Cu; ○ =O.

Fig. 36. The structure of cuprite, Cu_2O.

is somewhat artificial in that the oxygen atoms are far too large to form a true interstitial structure of the type discussed in Chap. v, but nevertheless the looseness of the homopolar binding and the tendency towards a metallic linkage are illustrated by the perceptible electrical conductivity of cuprite and particularly by the marked internal photoelectric effect.

Other structures.

Many other homopolar structures, particularly among compounds of greater complexity such as A_2X_3, A_3X_4, etc., have been investigated, but few illustrate any general principles or call for discussion here. Certain sulphides, however, are of particular interest and may be considered briefly.

Platinum and palladium sulphides. These sulphides, PtS and PdS, are of interest in that they illustrate a plane co-ordination round the metal atom, the possibility of which we have seen to arise on theoretical grounds with elements of sufficiently high atomic number (see p. 69). In platinum sulphide (Bannister, 1932), the structure of which is shown in Fig. 37, p. 162, each sulphur atom is tetrahedrally co-ordinated by four platinum neighbours whereas the platinum atoms are surrounded by four sulphur neighbours arranged at the corners of a square. In palladium sulphide (Gaskell, 1937) the same type of co-ordination is found although the structure is more complex and the regularity of the co-ordination distorted.

References to many other sulphides which have been investigated are given by Bernal and Crowfoot (1934 *a*). Several homopolar structures are discussed critically by Pauling and Huggins (1934).

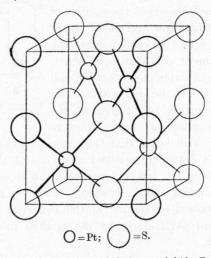

O = Pt;   = S.

Fig. 37. The structure of platinum sulphide, PtS.

ATOMIC RADII IN HOMOPOLAR STRUCTURES

The symmetrically co-ordinated structures of the zincblende-wurtzite type enable characteristic radii to be deduced for the atoms which they contain, and a list of such 'tetrahedral' radii has been drawn up by Pauling and Huggins (1934) and is reproduced in Table 34. These radii should, however, be employed with the greatest caution, for they are strictly applicable only in structures with tetrahedral co-ordination. In homopolar compounds with other types of co-ordination the radii may be significantly different, and it is, in fact, not possible to quote definite radii applicable to all homopolar structures. In organic crystals the unsymmetrical co-ordination within the molecule leads to distortion of the electronic structure of the atoms and to very great departures of interatomic distances from additivity. For this reason it is preferable in the case of homopolar compounds to consider characteristic bond lengths rather than characteristic atomic radii. Values for such bond lengths will be tabulated in the chapter devoted to molecular compounds.

TABLE 34

'TETRAHEDRAL' ATOMIC RADII

(After Pauling and Huggins, 1934)

	1	2	3	4	5	6	7
2		Be 1·07	B 0·89	C 0·77	N 0·70	O 0·66	F 0·64
3		Mg 1·40	Al 1·26	Si 1·17	P 1·10	S 1·04	Cl 0·99
4	Cu 1·35	Zn 1·31	Ga 1·26	Ge 1·22	As 1·18	Se 1·14	Br 1·11
5	Ag 1·53	Cd 1·48	In 1·44	Sn 1·40	Sb 1·36	Te 1·32	I 1·28
6	Au 1·50	Hg 1·48	Tl 1·47	Pb 1·46	Bi 1·46		

CHAPTER VII

IONIC COMPOUNDS: ISODESMIC STRUCTURES

INTRODUCTION

Ionic compounds comprise more of the structures so far investigated by X-ray methods than those of all other classes combined. In part this is due to the common occurrence of such bodies, which include almost all the compounds of inorganic chemistry and all the rock-forming minerals, and in part it is due to the practical convenience of dealing with substances which readily form crystals of convenient dimensions, are hard, stable, easy to handle and have relatively simple structures. The total number of organic bodies which has been synthesized doubtless exceeds the number of ionic compounds, but the structure investigation of such bodies is technically far more difficult, and it is only in recent years that it has been systematically prosecuted.

The wide extent of our knowledge of ionic compounds not only makes a systematic classification imperative, but also at the same time points the way to a rational basis for such a classification. The primary feature underlying the construction of ionic crystals is the purely geometrical disposition of a set of ions of characteristic radius and charge in a manner which is energetically stable, and a given structure type therefore includes all crystals in which the centres of positive and negative ions are similarly situated. Neither the radius nor the charge of the ions in different crystals of the same type need be the same, but there must be some relation between the radii for the given type to be the most stable, and some relation between the charges to maintain electrical neutrality.

In simple symmetrical structures the structure type is usually completely determined in terms of the co-ordination alone, but in more complex structures this is not always the case, and for such crystals it is necessary to extend the classification and to recognize the existence in the structure of bonds which, while all qualitatively the same and ionic in origin, differ quantitatively in the strength of their binding. A quantitative measure of the strength of an ionic bond arises from the picture of an ionic crystal as a stable system and one in which, therefore, the ions strive as far as possible to surround themselves by neighbours of opposite sign so that electrical charges are neutralized locally. The lines of force from a given ion thus tend to terminate on its immediate neighbours and the strength of the anion-cation link may be measured by the charge on the central ion divided by the number of these neighbours. In nearly all ionic crystals the structure is determined primarily by the arrangement of the anions around the smaller cations, so that if the charge on one of the cations is z and the number of neighbours is n, the strength of the bond is z/n. This quantity is usually called the *electrostatic valency* of the bond. If we now consider one of the anions, it is clear that for maximum stability it, too, must have its charge neutralized locally, so that the sum of the electrostatic valencies of the several bonds reaching it must equal its negative charge. In simple structures, where the cations are all of one kind, this principle is self-evident, but it finds its importance in more complex structures where several different cations occur combined with anions of the same or similar types. This point will be discussed more fully later, but for the moment we may use the conception of the electrostatic valency of a bond as the basis of our classification of ionic crystals.

THE CLASSIFICATION OF IONIC STRUCTURES

Consider a crystal containing anions X of charge z^-, and let the co-ordination of the several different cations A, B, ... round the anion be such that one of the cation-anion bonds, say A—X, is of strength greater than $\frac{1}{2}z$. Then it is clear that the single bond between X and A is stronger than all the remaining bonds linking X to the rest of the structure. In such a case the cation A and its several X neighbours form a discrete group in the structure, bound within itself by forces stronger than those by which it is linked to other cations. In such compounds, although all the bonds are qualitatively the same so that the crystal is homodesmic, it is convenient to recognize the pronounced quantitative difference between different bonds by describing the structure as *anisodesmic*.*

When, in a similar case, there is no bond reaching the anion X of strength as great as $\frac{1}{2}z$, it follows that the anion is not linked to any one cation as strongly as to all its other neighbours, and in this case no discrete groups in the structure appear. Such structures may be described as *isodesmic*, where the term is somewhat loosely used to imply that the bonds are not necessarily all of equal strength but that they are at least qualitatively comparable. Finally, a special case arises when the A—X bond strength is exactly equal to $\frac{1}{2}z$, and, on account of the special importance of this case in the silicates, such structures are best considered separately and described as *mesodesmic*.

Of the three classes of ionic crystals, the isodesmic and anisodesmic are still too large for adequate classification, and require further subdivision. Among isodesmic crystals we may recognize those of the *simple* type containing a single cation and those of the *multiple* type, such as spinel, $MgAl_2O_4$, in which two or more cations appear. Anisodesmic compounds are necessarily multiple, but here the important part played by water of crystallization makes it desirable to distinguish the *anhydrous* and *hydrous* structures.

The distinction between the three classes of ionic compounds just described may perhaps be illustrated at this point by a number of examples, although the basis of the classification will become clear as individual structures are considered. In sodium chloride the strength of each bond originating from a sodium ion is $\frac{1}{6}$, so that there are no bonds in the crystal as strong as $\frac{1}{2}$ and the structure is isodesmic. In all silicates the silicon ion Si^{4+} is found tetrahedrally co-ordinated by four oxygen ions O^{2-}, so that the strength of the Si—O bond is $\frac{4}{4} = 1$: this is exactly equal to the strength of

* Bernal has proposed describing such structures as heterodesmic ionic compounds. It seems to the author, however, that it is less confusing to confine the term 'heterodesmic' strictly to structures in which bonds occur essentially different in *kind*, and to employ a new term when they differ only in *degree*.

all the other bonds reaching the oxygen ions and the structure is therefore mesodesmic. All carbonates, nitrates, sulphates and many other common salts to be discussed later are anisodesmic. In nitrates, for example, the bonds within the NO_3 group, which consists of a N^{5+} ion symmetrically co-ordinated by three O^{2-} ions, are of strength $\frac{5}{3}$: since this is greater than one-half the total charge of the oxygen ion the group forms a discrete, tightly bound unit in the structure.

For reference the commonest anions and anion groups giving rise to the three types of ionic crystal are shown in Table 35.

TABLE 35

COMMON ANIONS IN THE THREE CLASSES OF IONIC CRYSTALS

Iso-desmic	Mesodesmic	Anisodesmic				
		Univalent		Divalent		Tri-valent
F^-	Borates	CN	NO_3	C_2	SiF_6	PO_3
Cl^-	Silicates	O_2	ClO_3	O_2	$TiCl_6$	AsO_3
Br^-	Germanates	CNO	BrO_3	CO_3	$SeCl_6$	SbO_3
I^-	AlF_6^{3-}	CNS	IO_3	SO_3	$ZrCl_6$	PO_4
OH^-	$Cr(CN)_6^{3-}$	CHC	ClO_4	SeO_3	$SnCl_6$	
O^{2-}		Cl_3	BrO_4	SO_4	$TeCl_6$	
S^{2-}		Br_3	IO_4	SeO_4	$PtCl_6$	
Se^{2-}		I_3	MnO_4	CrO_4	$PbCl_6$	
Te^{2-}		ClICl	ReO_4	MoO_4	S_2O_6	
N^{3-}		ClIBr	BF_4	WO_4	S_3O_6	
P^{3-}		ClO_2	PH_2O_2	$Ni(CN)_4$	S_2O_8	
C^{4-}		NO_2		$PdCl_4$	S_2O_5	
				$PtCl_4$		
				$S.SO_3$		

It will be seen from this table that, broadly speaking, ionic compounds include those bodies which would normally be classed as oxides, hydroxides and salts. The corresponding acids are also ionic in nature, but structurally the behaviour of the hydrogen ion H^+ is so different from that of any other cation that the distinction between acids and their corresponding salts must be clearly recognized. The anomalous behaviour of the hydrogen ion arises from its vanishingly small size, as a result of which it always appears in a structure in 2-fold co-ordination and always exerts a profound polarizing influence on the ions with which it is combined. The historical association of 'acids and their salts' finds no counterpart in the crystal structure, for no structure can withstand unaltered the substitution of a metallic cation by hydrogen. Often the substitution cannot be effected at all because the corresponding hydrogen structure is unstable, and in such cases the acid has no real existence: the hypothetical acids corresponding to the perfectly stable carbonates or to the various complex silicates are instances of this point. But in any case the properties of any anion are far more simply studied when in combination with large metallic cations than with the quite exceptional and super-polarizing hydrogen ion. For this reason we consider separately those compounds in which hydrogen occurs, and our final classification of ionic structures may therefore be summarized thus:

(1) Isodesmic structures $\begin{cases} \text{Simple} \\ \text{Multiple} \end{cases}$

(2) Mesodesmic structures

(3) Anisodesmic structures $\begin{cases} \text{Anhydrous} \\ \text{Hydrous} \end{cases}$

(4) Hydrogen compounds

Strictly speaking, we should include among ionic structures all organic acids, bases and salts, but to do so would confuse the classification by separating organic ions from the corresponding molecules. Moreover, the structures of these bodies are no longer determined by the packing of simple spherical ions or ion groups but by the packing of complex ions of irregular shape. A convenient dividing line between ionic and molecular structures is the point at which the shape and polarity of the ion becomes of more importance than its size or charge, and we shall therefore discuss in this chapter only those compounds containing ions or ion groups which are very roughly spherical in shape and not highly polar.

SIMPLE ISODESMIC STRUCTURES

These structures include many of the general type $A_m X_n$, of which those of composition AX and AX_2 are by far the most important. Here A may be any of the cations Li^+ to Cs^+, Be^{2+}

to Ba^{2+}, Al^{3+} to La^{3+}, NH_4^+, and occasionally Cu^+, Ag^+ and the ions of some of the transition metals. X may be any of the anions F^- to I^-, $(OH)^-$, O^{2-} to Te^{2-} and less frequently N^3, P^{3-} and C^{4-}. Not all the possible combinations of these ions, however, are ionic.

The earliest detailed and systematic study of ionic structures is due to Goldschmidt (1926 a, b) whose work on the morphotropy of simple ionic crystals may be regarded as laying the foundations of modern crystal chemistry. Much earlier, W. L. Bragg (1920) had recognized from the regularities of the interatomic distances in the alkali halides that in such salts the ions must be regarded as of characteristic and constant size. Goldschmidt, however, considerably extended the scope of these observations, enabling radii to be attributed to almost all common ions, and moreover clearly emphasized the distinction between 'commensurable' structures, in which forces of the same kind are in operation, and 'incommensurable' structures, in which different types of force operate, and in which, therefore, a comparison of radii is without significance.

Ionic radii.

The interatomic distances directly observed in crystals do not in general enable the individual radii to be deduced, for it is clear that the absolute determination of these radii requires an independent measurement of the radius of some one ion. The radii published by Goldschmidt are all based on those of the F^- and O^{2-} ions, for which Wasastjerna (1923) deduced from refractivity measurements values of 1·33 and 1·32 A. respectively.

In certain special cases a direct determination of absolute radii from structural observations alone is, however, possible by a method due to Landé (1920 a, b). The principle of this method may be illustrated by a comparison of the interatomic distances in the following compounds, all of which have the sodium chloride structure:

MgO	2·10 A.	MnO	2·24 A.
MgS	2·60 A.	MnS	2·59 A.
MgSe	2·73 A.	MnSe	2·73 A.

It will be seen from these data that while MgO and MnO have different interatomic distances the lattice dimensions of MgS and MnS, and again of MgSe and MnSe, are very nearly the same. This fact leads to the conclusion that here neighbouring anions are in contact and that the whole structure is to be regarded as a close-packed arrangement of these ions with the small cations disposed in the interstices. In this way we can deduce for the radius of the S^{2-} ion the value $2\cdot60\cdot\sqrt{2}/2 = 1\cdot84$ A., and for the Se^{2-} ion the value $2\cdot73\cdot\sqrt{2}/2 = 1\cdot93$ A. Radii found in this way, and others derived from them, are in very satisfactory agreement with those based on Wasastjerna's measurements.

Values for the radii of a number of ions, taken from the work of Goldschmidt and from more recent measurements, are summarized in Table 36, and shown graphically in Fig. 38, p. 172. For convenience the radii of the atoms of certain elements are included. These values are half the distance of closest approach in the structures of the elements. All the ionic radii are expressed in a form appropriate to 6-fold co-ordination and are immediately applicable in structures of this degree of co-ordination. The values proper to other co-ordinations will be considered later.

Certain general points which emerge from the data of Table 36 call for explicit mention:

(1) The very large difference between the radii of an element in its neutral and ionized states is apparent. Positive ions, having an electron deficiency, are smaller, and negative ions, with excess electrons in the extranuclear structure, are larger than the neutral atom:

$$S^{6+} \quad 0\cdot34 \text{ A.} \qquad S \quad 1\cdot04 \text{ A.} \qquad S^{2-} \quad 1\cdot74 \text{ A.}$$
$$Si^{4+} \quad 0\cdot39 \text{ A.} \qquad Si \quad 1\cdot13 \text{ A.} \qquad Si^{4-} \quad 1\cdot98 \text{ A.}$$

(2) Quite generally, the radius of a given element increases with increasing negative charge and decreases with increasing positive charge. The increase of radius with increasing negative charge, however, is partially compensated by the increased electrostatic attraction between neighbouring ions, while the decrease of radius with increasing positive charge is aggravated

The ionic radii are those for 6-fold co-ordination. The atomic radii are one-half the distance of closest approach in the element

	1	2	3	4	5	6	7	8	0
1							H⁻ 1·54 / H 0·46		He
2	Li 1·52 / Li⁺ 0·78	Be 1·12 / Be²⁺ 0·34	B 0·97	C 0·77 / C⁴⁺ < 0·2	N 0·71 / N⁵⁺ 0·1-0·2	O²⁻ 1·32 / O 0·60	F⁻ 1·33		Ne 1·60
3	Na 1·86 / Na⁺ 0·98	Mg 1·60 / Mg²⁺ 0·78	Al 1·43 / Al³⁺ 0·57	Si⁴⁻ 1·98 / Si 1·17 / Si⁴⁺ 0·39	P 1·30 / P⁵⁺ 0·3-0·4	S²⁻ 1·74 / S 1·04 / S⁶⁺ 0·34	Cl⁻ 1·81 / Cl 1·07		A 1·91
4	K 2·31 / K⁺ 1·33 / (NH₄⁺ 1·43)	Ca 1·96 / Ca²⁺ 1·06	Sc 1·51 / Sc³⁺ 0·83	Ti 1·46 / Ti³⁺ 0·69 / Ti⁴⁺ 0·64	V 1·30 / V³⁺ 0·65 / V⁴⁺ 0·61 / V⁵⁺ ca. 0·4	Cr 1·25 / Cr³⁺ 0·64 / Cr⁶⁺ 0·3-0·4	Mn 1·18 / Mn²⁺ 0·91 / Mn³⁺ 0·70 / Mn⁴⁺ 0·52	Fe 1·24 / Fe²⁺ 0·83 / Fe³⁺ 0·67; Co 1·25 / Co²⁺ 0·82; Ni 1·24 / Ni²⁺ 0·78	
4	Cu 1·28 / Cu⁺ 0·96	Zn 1·33 / Zn²⁺ 0·83	Ga 1·22 / Ga³⁺ 0·62	Ge 1·22 / Ge⁴⁺ 0·44	As 1·25 / As³⁺ 0·69 / As⁵⁺ ca. 0·4	Se²⁻ 1·91 / Se 1·16 / Se⁶⁺ 0·3-0·4	Br⁻ 1·96 / Br 1·19		Kr 2·01
5	Rb 2·43 / Rb⁺ 1·49	Sr 2·15 / Sr²⁺ 1·27	Y 1·81 / Y³⁺ 1·06	Zr 1·56 / Zr⁴⁺ 0·87	Nb 1·43 / Nb⁴⁺ 0·69 / Nb⁵⁺ 0·69	Mo 1·36 / Mo⁴⁺ 0·68	Ma	Ru 1·33 / Ru⁴⁺ 0·65; Rh 1·34 / Rh³⁺ 0·68; Pd 1·37	
5	Ag 1·44 / Ag⁺ 1·13	Cd 1·49 / Cd²⁺ 1·03	In 1·62 / In³⁺ 0·92	Sn⁴⁻ 2·15 / Sn 1·40 / Sn⁴⁺ 0·74	Sb 1·45 / Sb⁵⁺ 0·90	Te²⁻ 2·11 / Te 1·43 / Te⁴⁺ 0·89	I⁻ 2·20 / I 1·36 / I⁵⁺ 0·94		Xe 2·20
6	Cs 2·62 / Cs⁺ 1·65	Ba 2·17 / Ba²⁺ 1·43	La 1·86 / La³⁺ 1·22	Ce 1·82 / Ce³⁺ 1·18 / Ce⁴⁺ 1·02	Pr 1·81 / Pr³⁺ 1·16 / Pr⁴⁺ 1·00	Nd 1·80 / Nd³⁺ 1·15	Il		
6	Sm³⁺ 1·13	Eu³⁺ 1·13	Gd³⁺ 1·11	Tb³⁺ 1·09 / Tb⁴⁺ 0·89	Dy³⁺ 1·07	Ho³⁺ 1·05	Er 1·86 / Er³⁺ 1·04		
6	Tm³⁺ 1·04	Yb³⁺ 1·00	Lu³⁺ 0·99	Hf 1·58 / Hf⁴⁺ 0·84	Ta 1·43 / Ta⁵⁺ 0·68	W 1·36 / W⁴⁺ 0·68	Re	Os 1·35 / Os⁴⁺ 0·67; Ir 1·35 / Ir⁴⁺ 0·66; Pt 1·38	
6	Au 1·44 / Au⁺ 1·37	Hg 1·50 / Hg²⁺ 1·12	Tl 1·70 / Tl⁺ 1·49 / Tl³⁺ 1·05	Pb⁴⁻ 2·15 / Pb 1·75 / Pb²⁺ 1·32 / Pb⁴⁺ 0·84	Bi 1·55	Po	85		Rn
7	87	Ra	Ac	Th 1·80 / Th⁴⁺ 1·10	Pa	U 1·38 / U⁴⁺ 1·05			

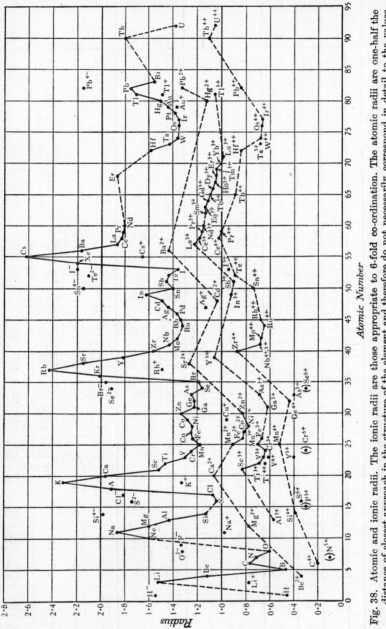

Fig. 38. Atomic and ionic radii. The ionic radii are those appropriate to 6-fold co-ordination. The atomic radii are one-half the distance of closest approach in the structure of the element and therefore do not necessarily correspond in detail to the values

by the same cause. Highly charged positive ions are therefore very small, but highly charged negative ions are less conspicuously large.

(3) In a series of positive ions with the same extranuclear structure the radius decreases rapidly with increasing positive charge:

Na^+ 0·98, Mg^{2+} 0·78, Al^{3+} 0·57, Si^{4+} 0·39, S^{6+} 0·34 A.

On the other hand, in a series of negative ions having the same extranuclear structure the influence of the increase in nuclear charge is roughly compensated by the decrease in the force of attraction between the ions in the structure, so that no very pronounced change in radius takes place:

$$O^{2-} \quad 1·32 \text{ A.} \qquad F^- \quad 1·33 \text{ A.}$$
$$Si^{4-} \quad 1·98 \text{ A.} \qquad S^{2-} \quad 1·74 \text{ A.} \qquad Cl^- \quad 1·81 \text{ A.}$$

(4) The effect of the lanthanide contraction, already described in our discussion of the radii of the elements (p. 105), is seen also in the radii of the ions. Thus the radii of the trivalent rare earth ions decrease in passing through the series from 1·18 A. for Ce^{3+} to 0·99 A. for Lu^{3+}, so that elements immediately following these metals have radii no larger than those of members of the same group in the period preceding the rare earths. Since similarities in crystal structure depend primarily on similarities in ionic size, the lanthanide contraction is largely responsible for the remarkable chemical resemblances between such pairs of elements as zirconium and hafnium or niobium and tantalum. The influence of the lanthanide contraction in ionic structures has been discussed at length by Goldschmidt, Barth and Lunde (1925).

The influence of polarization on ionic radii. The picture of an ion as a rigid sphere of constant radius is one which is true only as a first approximation, and, just as with the atomic radii of the elements discussed in Chap. IV, the exact value of the radius of an ion depends on the co-ordination in which it occurs. Polarization may be crudely regarded as the deformation of an ion by the presence of its neighbours, and it can readily be seen in a general way that this deformation may be expected to be particularly marked in structures of low or irregular co-ordination. This is in fact found to be the case, so that in the three common structures of AX compounds, namely the zincblende, sodium chloride and caesium chloride arrangements, a small but significant increase in the effective radius of any given ion takes place with increasing co-ordination number. If the radii corresponding to the sodium chloride structure are taken as standard, those in the 8-fold co-ordinated caesium chloride structure are systematically about 3 per cent larger and in the 4-fold co-ordinated zincblende structure about 5 per cent smaller. Just as with metal systems, it is desirable that all radii should be expressed in a form appropriate to some particular co-ordination and that of the sodium chloride structure is conventionally chosen as standard. For other co-ordinations the radii must be appropriately corrected.

In ionic structures there is, however, a second factor which may also have an important influence on interatomic distances, for in different ionic crystals a given ion may occur co-ordinated by neighbours of different charge. Thus the fluorine ion occurs in potassium fluoride, KF, and in calcium fluoride, CaF_2, bound respectively to a singly and a doubly charged cation: in the latter compound the polarization is greater and the radius of the fluorine ion correspondingly some 3 per cent less. The influence of polarization on the radii of ions has been discussed in detail by Goldschmidt (1926 b).

Univalent radii. The changes in ionic radii in polar crystals due to polarization have led to attempts to draw up standard radii and to formulate rules by which these radii may be corrected for any co-ordination and valency so as to be applicable to all such structures. Pauling (1927, 1928a) and Zachariasen (1931a) have introduced for this purpose the conception of a 'univalent radius', which may be defined as the radius which any ion would have in a 6-fold co-ordinated crystal if it was univalent but preserved its electronic structure. In univalent compounds with the sodium chloride structure these radii are, therefore, those actually observed, but in other cases they are hypothetical values which must be appropriately corrected. Formulae are given for making this correction so that the interionic distances can be deduced in any structure. An account of this work has been given by Hassel (1935) but we shall not discuss it in detail here. In simple structures the interatomic distances deduced rarely differ by more than 1 or 2 per cent from those based on Goldschmidt's radii, while in more complex structures of low and irregular co-ordination, where different neighbours may be at slightly different distances, only approximate values for the radii are in any case of much significance.

The geometrical basis of morphotropy.

The detailed and accurate information on ionic sizes collected by Goldschmidt provided the data for important advances in the understanding of ionic structures. As early as 1922 Magnus (1922) had suggested that ionic crystals might be regarded as formed by a packing of rigid ions of characteristic size, and had sought to explain the appearance of different structures in a series of chemically closely related compounds in terms of purely geometrical principles based on the relative sizes of the ions concerned. The absence of reliable data on atomic radii, however, precluded any experimental confirmation of this viewpoint, and it was not until the publication of Goldschmidt's radii that its essential validity was established.

Let us consider a structure in which a small cation is surrounded by a number of anions. It is clear that the maximum possible co-ordination is determined by the relative sizes of the two ions and will obtain when the anions are simultaneously in contact with each other and with the central cation. If the radius of the anions increases beyond the value corresponding to this condition these ions are forced apart from each other and can no longer all be in contact with the cation. Such a separation of positive and negative charge requires the expenditure of work against the Coulomb forces of attraction, so that the potential energy of the system is increased and its stability reduced. For a given type of co-ordination there is therefore a critical value of the radius ratio beyond which the structure becomes unstable and may be expected to change to one of different co-ordination.

It is very simple to deduce geometrically the critical values corresponding to the various possible types of co-ordination. We may consider first the 8-fold co-ordination of the caesium chloride structure. Here each ion is surrounded by eight neighbours at the corners of a cube. If we consider eight ions of unit radius thus disposed on a cube of such size that they are in contact, the side of the cube must be two units. The radius of the ion which can be accommodated in the 'hole' in the centre of the cube is then readily seen to be $\sqrt{3} - 1 = 0.732$. We may therefore expect the caesium chloride structure to be stable as long as $R_A : R_X > 0.732$. If this condition is not satisfied a structure of lower co-ordination will result.

TABLE 37

RADIUS RATIO CONDITIONS FOR VARIOUS
TYPES OF CO-ORDINATION

Co-ordination round A	Disposition of X ions	Radius ratio condition $R_A : R_X$
8	Corners of a cube	1 – 0.732
6	Corners of a regular octahedron	} 0.732–0.414
4	Corners of a square	
4	Corners of a regular tetrahedron	0.414–0.225
3	Corners of an equilateral triangle	0.225–0.155
2	Linear	0.155–0

In the sodium chloride structure, in which the six neighbours of any ion are situated at the corners of a regular octahedron, the corresponding critical radius ratio is $\sqrt{2} - 1 = 0.414$, and it is clear that the ratio will have the same value for an arrangement of four X ions co-ordinating the ion A at the corners of a square. For the zincblende structure, in which the four neighbours of any ion are arranged at the corners of a regular tetrahedron, the critical ratio is $\sqrt{6}/2 - 1 = 0.225$, while for 3-fold co-ordination, with three X ions grouped round the ion A at the corners of an equilateral triangle, it is $2\sqrt{3}/3 - 1 = 0.155$. These values of the radius ratio corresponding to different types of co-ordination are summarized in Table 37.

Naturally it is not to be expected that the critical values deduced in this simple way will be very exact, for no account has been taken of the deformation of the ions by polarization, while the contribution of the van der Waals forces to the total energy of the system has of course been ignored. Nevertheless, the radius ratio does give a very valuable indication of the structure to be expected, and the data of Table 38 show the extent to which AX compounds conform to these principles. A consideration of the data in this table reveals that although there is a general correspondence between co-ordination and radius ratio there are nevertheless many cases in which the ratios lie outside the permitted range. Especially is this true of the transition between caesium chloride and sodium chloride structures.

TABLE 38

THE STRUCTURES AND RADIUS RATIOS OF
SOME IONIC AX COMPOUNDS

Caesium chloride structure	Sodium chloride structure			Zincblende or wurtzite structure
Theoretical range $R_A : R_X$ 1–0·732	0·732–0·414			0·414–0·225
CsCl 0·91	KF 1·00	KCl 0·73	CaSe 0·56	MgTe 0·37
CsBr 0·84	SrO 0·96	SrS 0·73	NaCl 0·54	BeO 0·26
CsI 0·75	BaO 1/0·94	RbI 0·68	NaBr 0·50	BeS 0·20
	RbF 0·89	KBr 0·68	CaTe 0·50	BeSe 0·18
	RbCl 0·82	BaTe 0·68	MgS 0·49	BeTe 0·17
	BaS 0·82	SrSe 0·66	NaI 0·44	
	CaO 0·80	CaS 0·61	LiCl 0·43	
	CsF 1/0·80	KI 0·60	MgSe 0·41	
	RbBr 0·76	ScTe 0·60	LiBr 0·40	
	BaSe 0·75	MgO 0·59	LiI 0·35	
	NaF 0·74	LiF 0·59		

The influence of the radius ratio in determining the structure of simple ionic crystals has been discussed from a more rigid point of view by Born and Mayer (1932), who have calculated the Coulomb contribution to the total energy of the several AX structures as a function of the radius ratio. Their results are shown in Fig. 39, p. 178, and it will be seen that although the various structures become inherently unstable at the critical values predicted, the difference in energy between a stable and an unstable structure is often very small. This is particularly the case with the caesium chloride and sodium chloride structures, and it is therefore easy to understand that with these structures the radius ratio plays a less important part, and that small contributions from the polarization or van der Waals energy may determine which structure obtains. It is principally in structures of lower co-ordination that considerations of radius ratio are of value.

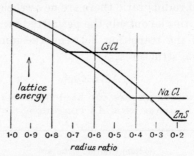

Fig. 39. The Coulomb lattice energy of AX structures as a function of the radius ratio.

Polarization in ionic structures.

We have regarded polarization in a crystal as the distortion of the electronic configuration of the ions which occurs especially in structures of low co-ordination. This polarization is normally manifested only as a small reduction in the interatomic distances and necessarily in a corresponding reduction of the dipole moment of the polar link, but, if sufficiently drastic, may result in the more profound change of a complete electron transfer from anion to cation and the formation of a non-polar bond. The homopolar bond may therefore be regarded as arising by the extreme polarization of a link originally ionic in nature. While such a picture is naturally somewhat artificial in the case of such obviously homopolar compounds as, say, zincblende, its value arises when we are considering the many structures which occupy an intermediate position between the two extremes and share in part the properties characteristic of both the homopolar and the ionic linkages. The entirely continuous nature of the transition between these two extremes will become apparent as we consider particular structures, and in fact, as Fajans (1928a) and Lennard-Jones (1931a) have emphasized, it is probable that rigorously homopolar binding can exist only between atoms of a single element, as in diamond or the chlorine molecule, and that in all other homopolar structures some dissymmetry in the distribution of charge confers on the bond a small dipole moment and some of the corresponding properties of an ionic binding.

The polarizability of ions. The extent to which polarization may be expected in any structure is determined not only by the co-ordination but also by the polarizability and polarizing power of the ions concerned. The polarizability of an ion is determined roughly by the size and looseness of the binding of its electronic structure, so that marked polarization is primarily confined to anions and is especially pronounced when these anions are large. Intimately associated with the polarizability of an ion in a crystal is its polarizability in the field of an electromagnetic wave, so that the molecular refraction of an ion can be regarded as a measure of its polarizability. We have already given data (p. 25) for the refractivities of a number of ions and these emphasize how rapidly polarization increases with ionic size and how relatively insignificant is the polarizability of the cations.

The polarizabilities of a number of ions of common occurrence in ionic crystals have been discussed from a rather more rigid point of view by Born and Heisenberg (1924), who express this property quantitatively as the dipole moment induced in an ion by unit electric field. Values for this quantity, based on spectroscopic and other optical data, are shown in Table 39, p. 180, and it will be seen again from these figures that the polarizability of anions is in general far greater than that of cations, so that, except in structures containing very large cations, the polarizability of the latter can usually be ignored.

The polarizing power of ions. The polarizing power of an ion is determined primarily by its electric field and is therefore greatest for small ions of high charge. Goldschmidt (1926a) has proposed using the quantity ze/r^2, where ze is the charge and r the radius of an ion, as a measure of its polarizing power, and on the basis of this expression gives the values for this quantity shown in Table 40. Although these values are useful as giving a general indication of the relative polarizing powers of different ions, it is now clear that polarizing power depends not only on the charge and radius of an ion but also on its electronic structure, so that two ions of the same size and charge may differ considerably in their polarization properties. This point is considered more fully below.

TABLE 39

POLARIZABILITIES OF SOME IONS

(After Born and Heisenberg, 1924)

Values in arbitrary units

	1	2	3	4	5	6	7
2	Li^+ 0·075	Be^{2+} 0·028	B^{3+} 0·014			O^{2-} 3·1	F^- 0·99
3	Na^+ 0·21	Mg^{2+} 0·12	Al^{3+} 0·065	Si^{4+} 0·043		S^{2-} 7·25	Cl^- 3·05
4	K^+ 0·85	Ca^{2+} 0·57	Sc^{3+} 0·38	Ti^{4+} 0·27		Se^{2-} 6·4	Br^- 4·17
5	Rb^+ 1·81	Sr^{2+} 1·42	Y^{3+} 1·04			Te^{2-} 9·6	I^- 6·28
6	Cs^+ 2·79	Ba^{2+} 2·08	La^{3+} 1·56	Ce^{4+} 1·20			

The variation of polarizability and polarizing power with ionic size and charge is summarized in Table 41.

The physical properties of polarized structures. Although almost all ionic structures are probably partially polarized without any marked influence on their physical properties, those in which extensive polarization occurs often show to a greater or lesser extent properties characteristic of homopolar binding. The increase in the lattice energy due to the polarization results in a decrease in the solubility, so that strongly polarized compounds, such as the silver halides, resemble homopolar structures and are nearly insoluble. Similarly,

TABLE 40

Polarizing powers of some ions expressed as ze/r^2

(After Goldschmidt 1926a)

Values in arbitrary units

	1	2	3	4	5	6	7
1							H^- 0·62
2	Li^+ 1·64	Be^{2+} 17·30				O^{2-} 1·15	F^- 0·57
3	Na^+ 1·04	Mg^{2+} 3·29	Al^{3+} 9·23	Si^{4+} 26·30		S^{6+} 51·90 S^{2-} 0·66	Cl^- 0·30
4	K^+ 0·57	Ca^{2+} 1·78 Zn^{2+} 2·90	Sc^{3+} 4·35 Ga^{3+} 7·80	Ti^{4+} 9·76 Ge^{4+} 20·66		Se^{2-} 0·55	Br^- 0·26
5	Rb^+ 0·45 Ag^+ 0·78	Sr^{2+} 1·24 Cd^{2+} 1·88	Y^{3+} 2·67 In^{3+} 3·54	Zr^{4+} 5·28 Sn^{4+} 7·30	Nb^{5+} 10·50	Te^{2-} 0·45	I^- 0·21
6	Cs^+ 0·37	Ba^{2+} 0·98 Hg^{2+} 1·59	La^{3+} 2·01 Tl^{3+} 2·72	Ce^{4+} 3·84 Pb^{4+} 5·67			
7				Th^{4+} 3·31			

TABLE 41

The variation of polarizability and polarizing power among common ions

(After Grimm, 1927)

Decreasing polarizability
Increasing polarizing power
Decreasing radius

O^{2-}	F^-	Ne	Na^+	Mg^{2+}	Al^{3+}
S^{2-}	Cl^-	A	K^+	Ca^{2+}	Sc^{3+}
Se^{2-}	Br^-	Kr	Rb^+	Sr^{2+}	Y^{3+}
Te^{2-}	I^-	X	Cs^+	Ba^{2+}	La^{3+}

Decreasing polarizability
Increasing polarizing power
Decreasing radius

with the halides of any of the alkali metals the solubility decreases with increasing polarization. The change in lattice energy due to polarization also results in irregularities in the melting points of ionic crystals (Fajans, 1925).

The deformation of the electronic orbits due to strong polarization gives rise to characteristic optical properties. Thus Meisenheimer (1921) has emphasized that the colour of many salts (e.g. silver iodide), the ions of which are individually uncoloured, indicates some departure from truly ionic linkage. Similarly, strongly polarized salts often resemble homopolar compounds in their photoelectric conductivity (Gudden and Pohl, 1923).

AX STRUCTURES

The three common structures of AX compounds, namely those of caesium chloride, sodium chloride and zincblende* corresponding to $8:8$, $6:6$ and $4:4$ co-ordination respectively, have already been described, and in the last section we have considered the factors determining the appearance of one or other of these arrangements. The purely geometrical considerations there outlined are, however, as already explained, subject to qualification in structures in which extensive polarization takes place, and we now proceed to consider a number of AX structures in which polarization is more or less marked and in which a transition towards homopolar binding occurs.

The influence of polarization in AX structures.

The alkali halides. Among the alkali halides polarization increases with a given cation from the fluoride to the iodide and with a given anion from the caesium to the lithium salt. In all these salts, however, the ionic character of the binding predominates and the properties are essentially those of typically ionic crystals, so that only detailed measurements of lattice energy, interatomic distances or molecular refraction reveal the presence of polarization.

The molecular refraction of the alkali halides has been

* Zincblende itself is, of course, homopolar but the zincblende structure is found in a few purely ionic compounds.

discussed by Spangenberg (1923), Fajans and Joos (1924) and by Fajans (1925), who have compared the molecular refractivities in the solid state with those of the free ions in dilute solution, where no polarization can occur. We may illustrate their results by considering the several sodium halides. Data for these salts are summarized below:

	NaF	NaCl	NaBr	NaI
(1) Mol. ref. of cation in solution	0·50	0·50	0·50	0·50
(2) Mol. ref. of anions in solution	2·50	9·00	12·67	19·24
(3) Sum of (1) and (2)	3·00	9·50	13·17	19·74
(4) Mol. ref. of solid	3·02	8·52	11·56	17·07
(5) Difference between (3) and (4)	− 0·02	0·98	1·61	2·67

It will be seen from these figures that in all the salts except sodium fluoride discrepancies occur between the refractivities of the ions in the solid and in the free state due to polarization, and that the extent of this polarization increases rapidly with increasing size of anion. Although these salts would normally be regarded as ionic in character, all except NaF show a partial transition towards homopolar binding. A purely homopolar binding for structures of such high co-ordination is excluded since the number of available electrons is insufficient to form the necessary bonds.

The influence of valency. In structures containing ions of valency higher than unity polarization is naturally more marked and the occurrence of homopolar structures more common, so that in practice ionic structures among *AX* compounds are confined to those containing univalent or divalent metals. This point is illustrated by the series of compounds NaF, MgO, AlN and SiC. Of these, the first two have the sodium chloride structure and are undoubtedly ionic, although NaF is soluble and MgO insoluble in water. In AlN, however, and still more in SiC, the strong polarizing power of the cation makes an ionic bond unstable and both of these substances are typically homopolar compounds, the former with the wurtzite and the latter with the zincblende structure. The change in the type of binding is also brought out by a comparison of the interatomic distances in the four compounds. These distances are:

NaF	MgO	AlN	SiC
2·31 A.	2·10 A.	1·87 A.	1·89 A.

It will be seen from these figures that while there is a decrease in $A-X$ distance of about 10 per cent in passing from NaF to MgO, due to the increased strength of the ionic binding, there is no corresponding change between AlN and SiC, indicating that here the binding cannot be ionic in nature. The physical properties of AlN and SiC, and particularly the very great hardness, also indicate a homopolar bond.

The influence of the electronic structure. We have already mentioned that the polarizing power of a cation is not determined solely by its charge and radius but also depends upon the electronic configuration, and it appears that cations which do not have an inert gas extranuclear structure have a particularly great polarizing power. Among common substances silver and cuprous salts illustrate this point. The radius of Ag^+ is 1·13 A., a value intermediate between that of Na^+ and K^+, so that the silver halides might be expected to simulate the alkali halides in their properties. Actually, however, only AgF, AgCl and AgBr have the sodium chloride structure and AgI has that of zincblende. Even in the first three salts the binding is not purely ionic, for only AgF is soluble in water, and the interatomic distances show increasingly great departures from those calculated on the basis of rigid ions, as the following figures reveal:

	AgF	AgCl	AgBr
$A-X$ calculated	2·46 A.	2·94 A.	3·09 A.
$A-X$ observed	2·46 A.	2·77 A.	2·88 A.

In AgI the binding is probably almost purely homopolar, for here the interatomic distance is actually less than in AgBr and very nearly the same as that in the closely related homopolar compounds CdTe and InSb. We have seen (p. 64) that the lattice energy of AgI is not to be reconciled with a polar binding and that spectroscopic observations have confirmed the presence of atoms in this structure. Nevertheless, the ionic conductivity in the solid state (Fajans, 1928*a*) indicates that the transition to homopolar binding is not entirely complete.

In cuprous salts the polarizing power of the cation is still more marked and all the halides have the zincblende structure. In CuI the radius ratio is sufficiently small for such a structure to arise with purely ionic binding, but the properties of this compound, and the fact that the same structure is found for CuF, CuCl and CuBr, indicate that all these halides are actually homopolar. The same conclusion is supported by lattice energy arguments and also by the close agreement between the interatomic distances in the cuprous halides and the closely related homopolar structures having the same total number of electrons:

CuF 1·83 A.	CuCl 2·34 A.	CuBr 2·46 A.	CuI 2·62 A.
ZnO 1·96 A.	ZnS 2·35 A.	ZnSe 2·45 A.	ZnTe 2·64 A.
	GaP 2·35 A.	GaAs 2·44 A.	GaSb 2·64 A.

Polarization in simple ionic structures and the transitions from the ionic to the homopolar bond have been discussed at length by Fajans (1923, 1925, 1928*a, b*), Hund (1925), Goldschmidt (1926*a, b*, 1928*a*), Grimm (1928), and van Arkel and de Boer (1931).

The occurrence of ionic *AX* compounds.

The ions of most frequent occurrence in simple ionic compounds of the type *AX* are shown in Table 42, p. 186. This list calls for certain qualifications. Not all the possible compounds of these ions are ionic. Thus Ag^+ and Tl^+ form ionic compounds only in combination with anions of low polarizability. Similarly the sulphides of only the alkali and alkaline earth metals are ionic. On the other hand, many metals form ionic structures with F^- and O^{2-} but not with any other anions. Certain carbides, nitrides and phosphides of the more electropositive metals appear to be ionic, so that C^{4-}, N^{3-} and P^{3-} are also included in the list of anions (von Stackelberg, 1934). The alkali hydrides have been investigated by Zintl and Harder (1931): they all have the sodium chloride structure and give a radius for H^- of about 1·54 A.

Certain complex ions are included in Table 42. On account of the vanishingly small size of the H^+ ion, NH_4^+ behaves as a spherical ion of radius 1·46 A. The other complex ions, although not intrinsically of spherical symmetry, sometimes acquire this symmetry by free rotation at temperatures near the melting point. Of the ions quoted the effect is common only with CN^-.

TABLE 42

MONATOMIC IONS FOUND IN AX COMPOUNDS

Cations
Li^+, Na^+, K^+, Rb^+, Cs^+, Ag^+, Tl^+, (NH_4^+)
Be^{2+}, Mg^{2+}, Ca^{2+}, Sr^{2+}, Ba^{2+}, Ti^{2+}, Pb^{2+}, Mn^{2+}, Fe^{2+}, Co^{2+}, Ni^{2+}
Ti^{3+}, Zr^{3+}, V^{3+}, Nb^{3+}, Ta^{3+}, Cr^{3+}
Ti^{4+}, Zr^{4+}, V^{4+}, Nb^{4+}, Ta^{4+}
Anions
H^-, F^-, Cl^-, Br^-, I^-, (OH^-), (CN^-), (NO_3^-)
O^{2-}, S^{2-}, Se^{2-}, (CO_3^{2-}), (SO_4^{2-})
N^{3-}, P^{3-}
C^{4-}

AX_2 STRUCTURES

The different structures of common occurrence among AX_2 compounds are far more numerous and show a far greater diversity of type than those found in AX compounds. In the more symmetrical of these structures the co-ordination round the ion A is necessarily twice that round X, so that as before the structures may be classified primarily in terms of the co-ordination.

Common structure types.

Fluorite. The highest possible co-ordination is that which obtains in the structure of fluorite, CaF_2, illustrated in Fig. 40. Here the calcium ions are arranged on a cubic face-centred lattice while the fluorine ions are at the centres of the eight cubelets into which the unit cell may be divided. Each calcium ion is therefore co-ordinated by eight fluorine neighbours at the corners of a cube, while the calcium neighbours of a fluorine ion number four and are at the corners of a regular tetrahedron. This is the only structure in which $8:4$ co-ordination is found.

Rutile. A $6:3$ co-ordination occurs in several AX_2 structures of which the commonest is that of rutile, TiO_2. The tetragonal unit cell of this structure is illustrated in Fig. 41. Here each titanium ion is surrounded by six oxygen neighbours at the

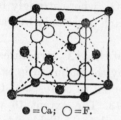

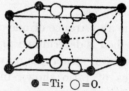

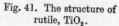

● = Ca; ○ = F.

Fig. 40. The structure of fluorite, CaF₂.

● = Ti; ○ = O.

Fig. 41. The structure of rutile, TiO₂.

corners of a slightly distorted regular octahedron, while the three titanium ions co-ordinating any oxygen atom lie in a plane at the corners of a nearly equilateral triangle. A similar type of co-ordination is found in the other forms of TiO_2, namely anatase and brookite, although the actual structures are considerably more complex.

Cristobalite. A co-ordination of $4:2$ is found in all the structures of silica in its various forms and may be illustrated by that of cristobalite, the structure stable above 1470° C. This structure is illustrated in Fig. 42, and is most simply described as an arrangement of silicon ions occupying the positions of the carbon atoms in diamond, with an oxygen ion midway between every such pair of silicon ions. Every silicon ion is therefore surrounded by four oxygen neighbours at the corners of a regular tetrahedron, while

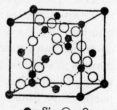

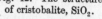

● = Si; ○ = O.

Fig. 42. The structure of cristobalite, SiO₂.

every oxygen ion is co-ordinated by only two neighbours arranged diametrically opposite to one another. The co-ordination in the other silica structures is similar and will be considered in more detail below. The co-ordination in the cuprite structure already described is also $4:2$, but this structure does not seem to occur in ionic crystals.

It is clear that no homodesmic AX_2 structure can exist with a co-ordination $2:1$, for with such a co-ordination each X ion is linked only to one A ion and no further ionic bonds are available for the coherence of the structure as a whole. The co-ordination is, however, found in many heterodesmic molecular structures, such as that of CO_2, where strongly bound X-A-X molecules occur linked to each other only by van der Waals forces.

The appearance of one or other of the AX_2 structures just described is determined primarily by the radius ratio, so that the several structures may be expected to correspond to the ranges of ratio shown in Table 43. The extent to which this is in fact true is shown by the data of Table 44, from which it will be seen that the general correspondence between co-ordination and radius ratio is close. Naturally the radius ratio cannot determine which of several structures of the same co-ordination shall appear, but the polymorphism of TiO_2 shows that energetically the distinction between such structures is trifling.

The influence of polarization in AX_2 structures.

As in AX compounds, the influence of polarization in AX_2 structures becomes more marked with decreasing co-ordination number. We have already seen that structures with $2:1$ co-ordination cannot be ionic, but it is also probable that in many $4:2$ co-ordinated compounds the binding is partially or wholly homopolar. The several structures of silica provide a particularly illuminating illustration of this point. The ratio of the radii of the Si^{4+} and O^{2-} ions is $0{\cdot}39:1{\cdot}32 = 0{\cdot}29$, and is therefore within the range corresponding to $4:2$ co-ordination. Cristobalite may therefore be quite properly regarded as a purely ionic structure. On the other hand, in all the other forms of silica, as α- and β-quartz and as tridymite, a significant difference arises. In these structures the co-ordination is still 4 : 2, so that the silicon atom always appears linked to four oxygen atoms, but these oxygen atoms are no longer found to lie on the line joining two silicon atoms; instead, they are dis-

TABLE 43

RADIUS RATIO CONDITIONS FOR VARIOUS
STRUCTURES IN AX_2 COMPOUNDS

Structure and co-ordination		Radius ratio condition $R_A : R_X$
Fluorite	8 : 4	> 0·732
Rutile	6 : 3	0·732–0·414
Cristobalite, etc.	4 : 2	0·414–0·225

TABLE 44

THE STRUCTURES AND RADIUS RATIOS OF SOME
IONIC AX_2 COMPOUNDS

Fluorite structure		Rutile structure		Quartz structure
Theoretical range $R_A : R_X > 0.732$		0·732–0·414		0·414–0·225
BaF₂ 1·05	ZrF₂ 0·67	TeO₂ 0·67	MoO₂ 0·52	GeO₂ 0·36
PbF₂ 0·99	HfF₂ 0·67	MnF₂ 0·66	WO₂ 0·52	SiO₂ 0·29
SrF₂ 0·95		PbO₂ 0·64	OsO₂ 0·51	BeF₂* 0·26
HgF₂ 0·84		FeF₂ 0·62	IrO₂ 0·50	
ThO₂ 0·83		CoF₂ 0·62	RuO₂ 0·49	
CaF₂ 0·80		ZnF₂ 0·62	TiO₂ 0·48	
UO₂ 0·79		NiF₂ 0·59	VO₂ 0·46	
CeO₂ 0·77		MgF₂ 0·58	MnO₂ 0·39	
PrO₂ 0·76		SnO₂ 0·56	GeO₂ 0·36	
CdF₂ 0·74		NbO₂ 0·52		

* BeF₂ has the β-cristobalite structure. The co-ordination is 4 : 2 as in quartz.

placed to one side so that the angle between the two bonds is less than 180°. Such a condition is clearly energetically impossible for a purely ionic binding, and in the characteristic disposition of the oxygen links we see a tendency towards the spatially directed bonds of a homopolar type. It is possible that in cristobalite the oxygen bonds are similarly inclined and that the apparent higher symmetry arises from the rotation of the oxygen atom.

Layer lattices. In AX_2 compounds, in which the polarization, although appreciable, is insufficient to bring about the transition from the rutile or other 6:3 co-ordinated structure to a purely molecular crystal, characteristic *layer lattice* structures

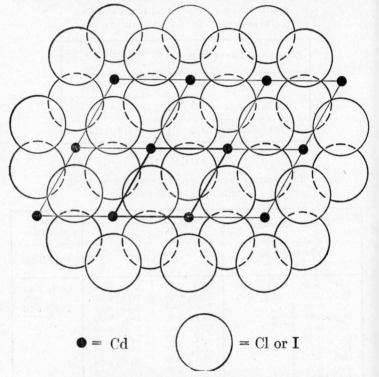

● = Cd   ◯ = Cl or I

Fig. 43. A single layer of the structures of cadmium chloride, $CdCl_2$, and
cadmium iodide, CdI_2.

are often formed. The layer lattices of most common occurrence are those of the closely related cadmium chloride and cadmium iodide types. These two structures are formed by the superposition of a series of composite layers, each of which consists of a sheet of cations enclosed between two sheets of strongly polarized anions. The arrangement of one such layer is shown in Fig. 43, and it will be seen that the characteristic feature of the structure is the asymmetry of the co-ordination, for while the cations are symmetrically surrounded by six anions at the corners of an octahedron, the three cation neighbours of any anion all lie to one side of it. The strong polarization resulting from this arrangement is reflected in a pronounced decrease in the $A–X$ distances compared with the values to be expected from normal ionic radii, and in CdI_2 the Cd–I distance is reduced in this way from 3·23 to 2·98 A. Nevertheless, the binding within the layers is purely ionic in character. That between the layers, however, clearly cannot be attributed to electrostatic attraction, since here ions of the same kind are in contact, and the bonds can only be residual in nature. The layer lattices are, therefore, all heterodesmic, and are, strictly speaking, molecular structures in which the single layers constitute discrete molecules infinitely extended in two dimensions.

The hexagonal unit cell of cadmium iodide is illustrated in Fig. 44, and a somewhat more extended portion of the structure in Fig. 45, p. 192, which shows clearly the co-ordination and arrangement of the layers. The cadmium chloride structure differs from that of cadmium iodide only in the geometrical disposition of successive layers, but although the distinction between the two arrangements is therefore primarily geometrical, the cadmium iodide structure appears to correspond to a somewhat greater degree of polarization than that of cadmium chloride.

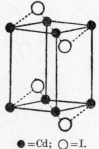

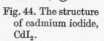
● = Cd; ○ = I.

Fig. 44. The structure of cadmium iodide, CdI_2.

The transition with increasing polarization from the symmetrically co-ordinated fluorite and rutile structures to layer lattices of the cadmium chloride and cadmium iodide types is clearly shown by the data summarized in Table 45, p. 193, and it will be seen that in each case the appearance of the layer lattice is associated with the presence of a large and readily polarizable anion.

In addition to the cadmium chloride and cadmium iodide structures other layer lattices are also found among AX_2

compounds, but they are mostly of rare occurrence and illustrate no further principles and so will not be described here.
That of HgI_2, however, is interesting for in it the radius ratio
is so small that only 4-fold co-ordination round the cation
obtains. Layer lattices of such low co-ordination are, however,

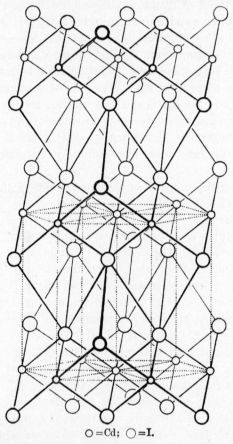

O = Cd;   ◯ = I.

Fig. 45. The structure of cadmium iodide, CdI_2, showing several unit cells.

rare, and more frequently increasing polarization results
directly in the formation of a molecular structure. Quite
generally layer lattices are of common occurrence among
chlorides, bromides, iodides and hydroxides of divalent metals
and among certain disulphides and diselenides.

TABLE 45

TRANSITION FROM SYMMETRICAL TO LAYER STRUCTURES IN AX_2 COMPOUNDS

Symmetrical structures		Layer lattices	
Fluorite	Rutile	$CdCl_2$	CdI_2
Increasing polarization→			
CaF_2			CaI_2
	MgF_2	$MgCl_2$	$MgBr_2$
	ZnF_2	$ZnCl_2$	
CdF_2		$CdCl_2$, $CdBr_2$*	CdI_2
	MnF_2		MnI_2
	FeF_2	$FeCl_2$	$FeBr_2$, FeI_2
	CoF_2	$CoCl_2$	$CoBr_2$, CoI_2
	NiF_2	$NiCl_2$, $NiBr_2$*, NiI_2	
	SnO_2		SnS_2
	TiO_2		TiS_2
ZrO_2			ZrS_2

* See p. 212.

Physical properties of layer lattices. In their physical properties layer lattices reveal the asymmetry of their structure, and the relatively weak binding between the layers results in most of these structures having a very pronounced cleavage. Similarly the coefficient of thermal expansion is very much greater normal to the layers than in their plane.

The influence of radius ratio and polarization in determining the structures of AX_2 compounds is summarized in Table 46.

TABLE 46

TRANSITION FROM SYMMETRICAL TO MOLECULAR STRUCTURES IN AX_2 COMPOUNDS

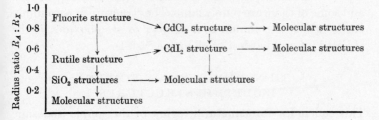

A_mX_n STRUCTURES

Among compounds of this type few homodesmic ionic crystals are found, and the structures are generally of far greater diversity and complexity than those of AX and AX_2 compounds. With increasing valency of cation the influence of polarization becomes more important and layer or molecular lattices are increasingly common. Thus among AX_3 compounds only the fluorides have symmetrical structures, while most of the other halides and the hydroxides have typical layer lattices differing from each other in detail but all displaying the general features already described as characteristic of such structures.

The structure of yttrium fluoride, YF_3, is, however, of particular interest on account of its relationship to that of fluorite, and it can in fact be regarded as a fluorite structure with yttrium replacing calcium and with extra fluorine ions at the centre of the unit cell and at the middles of its edges. So close is the relationship between these two structures that mixed crystals containing up to 40 atomic per cent of YF_3 can be formed between them.

Probably no AX_n compounds with $n > 3$ have symmetrical ionic structures, and purely molecular arrangements are the general rule in such cases. In SiF_4, however, the binding may be partially ionic.

Symmetrical A_2X structures are quite common among oxides and sulphides of univalent metals, many of which have the anti-fluorite structure, i.e. a fluorite structure in which the positions of the anions and cations are interchanged. Several A_2X_3 compounds have been investigated (Zachariasen, 1928a) and some of these are purely ionic. The structure of corundum, Al_2O_3, which is common to a number of sesquioxides, is the closest knit and hardest of all ionic crystals.

THE CHEMISTRY OF SIMPLE
ISODESMIC STRUCTURES

This concludes our structural review of the simple isodesmic ionic compounds, but before passing on to discuss more complex structures it is of interest to consider these compounds once again from a more conventional chemical point of view in order to emphasize the extent to which their chemical properties are determined by the crystal structure, and to make clear the advantages and shortcomings of the crystallographic as compared with the chemical classification.

Structurally fluorides and oxides may be considered together, since the ions F^- and O^{2-} have almost exactly the same radius, and in consequence we find that most fluorides of a metal of valency z have as counterparts isomorphous oxides of a metal of similar radius and valency $2z$. Thus the pairs of compounds NaF, CaO; KF, SrO; MgF_2, SnO_2; CaF_2, ThO_2 all have the same structures. The low polarizability of the F^- ion, and to a lesser extent also of the O^{2-} ion, makes layer and molecular lattices rare among oxides and fluorides, so that the structures of these compounds are determined primarily by purely geometrical considerations.

Among simple structures, oxides and fluorides are of comparable importance, but in complex structures, including almost all inorganic salts, oxygen is by far the most important anion, and, as we shall find later, the structures of all these bodies are determined principally by the co-ordination of the various cations by oxygen. The oxygen co-ordinations of most cations which occur in ionic structures are listed in Table 47, p. 196. Not all these cations, of course, are capable of forming ionic oxides, and in fact the capacity to do so is limited practically to those of oxygen co-ordination six or more. With increasing charge of cation and decreasing co-ordination the tendency towards homopolar or molecular binding becomes more marked, and when the charge exceeds the co-ordination number isodesmic structures are necessarily excluded. Thus the oxides P_2O_5, SO_3 and Cl_2O_7 are all molecular, as must also be all tetra-, penta- and hexa-fluorides.

With halides other than fluorides on the one hand, and the sulphides and selenides on the other, the possibility of ionic compounds is very limited. The increased size of the anion causes a lower co-ordination to prevail for a given cation, while at the same time the greater polarizability still further promotes the transition towards a homopolar or molecular binding. As a result of these considerations symmetrical ionic halides, excluding fluorides, are practically confined to those of the metals Li, Na, K, Rb, Cs, Tl, NH_4, Sr and Ba, although unsymmetrical layer structures are found with the halides of many metals from the third group and transition series. Ionic sulphides and selenides are still less numerous, due to the greater polarizing power of the more highly charged cation, and are practically limited to the compounds of the first two A groups.

TABLE 47

THE OXYGEN CO-ORDINATIONS OF COMMON CATIONS

C.N.	Cations
3	B^{3+}, C^{4+}, N^{5+}
4	Be^{2+}, B^{3+}, Al^{3+}, Si^{4+}, P^{5+}, S^{6+}, Cl^{7+}, V^{5+}, Cr^{6+}, Mn^{7+}, Zn^{2+}, Ga^{3+}, Ge^{4+}, As^{5+}, Se^{6+}
6	Li^+, Mg^{2+}, Al^{3+}, Sc^{3+}, Ti^{4+}, Cr^{3+}, Mn^{2+}, Fe^{2+}, Fe^{3+}, Co^{2+}, Ni^{2+}, Cu^{2+}, Zn^{2+}, Ga^{3+}, Nb^{5+}, Ta^{5+}, Sn^{4+}
6–8	Na^+, Ca^{2+}, Sr^{2+}, Y^{3+}, Zr^{4+}, Cd^{2+}, Ba^{2+}, Ce^{4+}, Sm^{3+}—Lu^{3+}, Hf^{4+}, Th^{4+}, U^{4+}
8–12	Na^+, K^+, Ca^{2+}, Rb^+, Sr^{2+}, Cs^+, Ba^{2+}, La^{3+}, Ce^{3+}—Sm^{3+}, Pb^{2+}

The hydroxides are of special importance and will be discussed more fully later, but here we may say that it appears that the OH^- ion can occur only in a strongly polarized form. Thus although many hydroxides such as $Mg(OH)_2$ and $Ca(OH)_2$ have layer lattices of the cadmium iodide type, others such as KOH, of which the structure might be expected to be simple, are found to be extremely complex. No symmetrical hydroxide structure has yet been found.

CRYSTAL STRUCTURE AND MORPHOLOGY

The X-ray investigation of crystal structures provides the material for a classification of crystals which, as we have seen, is both more precise and more detailed than that based on external form alone. Nevertheless, many of the classical conceptions, such as that of isomorphism and the formation of mixed crystals, which originally had a purely morphological foundation, are still of the utmost importance, and it is therefore of interest to review some of these conceptions in the light of the more recent work on structure analysis, and to interpret their significance in terms of the more detailed features of the structures involved. It is convenient to make such a review at this stage in order that the results of our discussion may be available when we pass on to consider more complex structures.

Isomorphism.

Substances are said to be isomorphous when a close but inexactly defined crystallographic relationship exists between them. As originally advanced by Mitscherlich the conception of isomorphism was supposed to apply only to substances which were also chemically closely related, and a close chemical analogy was in fact assumed to be imperative for analogy of crystal form. It soon became clear, however, that this condition was not, in fact, necessary, and various supplementary tests for detecting isomorphism were proposed. The ability of two substances to form mixed crystals and orientated overgrowths, or to precipitate each other from supersaturated solution, were applied as criteria, but such tests proved no more discriminating than the simple condition of crystallographic resemblance, and still revealed as isomorphous chemically unrelated bodies. Thus the silicates $CaAl_2Si_2O_8$ and $NaAlSi_3O_8$ form a continuous series of mixed crystals, and, again, sodium nitrate is isomorphous with calcite, $CaCO_3$, by which it is precipitated from supersaturated solution and on which it will form orientated overgrowths.

In terms of the internal structure of a crystal a somewhat more precise definition of isomorphism can be given, and we may follow Goldschmidt (1926a) in regarding as isomorphous substances with analogous crystal structures. Such a definition is purely physical in nature and does not demand any resemblance of chemical properties. It does, however, clearly demand a formal analogy of chemical composition in that it must be possible to represent all the structures by formulae of the same general type. Even so, a wide latitude is admissible since the possibility of replacing a single atom or ion by a radical or complex group must be entertained.

On the basis of this structural definition two substances will be isomorphous if they have analogous formulae and are composed of atoms or ions of comparable relative sizes and polarizabilities, these being the factors which determine the appearance of any given structure type. Such a definition covers isomorphism in its widest sense, and associates as isomorphous substances which are chemically entirely unrelated and which show no tendency to form mixed crystals or orientated overgrowths. Thus, in this wide sense NaCl and PbS, both with the sodium chloride structure, are isomorphous.

Mixed crystals. In a narrower sense the term 'isomorphism' is applied by some authors only to structures which form a complete or partial series of mixed crystals with one another, and for this to be the case, as Goldschmidt (1926a) early showed, not only the relative but also the absolute sizes of the several atoms or ions must correspond within close limits. This is the most important structural contribution to the study of mixed crystals and isomorphism, for it emphasizes once again the geometrical basis of morphotropy and at the same time explains why certain compounds can form extended solid solution while others, chemically more closely related and morphologically similar or even identical, do not form mixed crystals at all.

The extent to which mixed crystal formation between two substances is possible is determined by the closeness of the correspondence of atomic radii, and Goldschmidt has shown that provided corresponding radii differ by not more than about 15 per cent of the smaller, a wide range of solid solution may be expected at room temperature. At higher temperatures a somewhat greater tolerance is permitted, but, speaking generally, if the difference in radii exceeds this limit only restricted mixed crystal formation is to be expected. We may illustrate this general principle by a number of examples drawn from substances with the sodium chloride structure.

Among the alkali halides, KCl and KBr are completely miscible in all proportions giving rise to a structure in which the two halogens are distributed at random. Extensive solid solution is to be expected in this case since the radii of the anions, 1·81 and 1·96 A., differ by only about 8·5 per cent of the smaller. In KCl and KI the difference in radius is considerably greater, about 21 per cent of that of the chlorine ion, and here only partial solid solution occurs. Solid solution between KCl and NaCl is extremely limited due to the large relative difference between the sizes of the potassium and the sodium ions. On the other hand, NaCl forms a wide range of solid solution with the chemically less closely related AgCl on account of the closer correspondence between the radii of the two cations.

The system AgBr-AgI is of particular interest, for here mixed crystals can be formed although the two compounds have different structures. The silver : halogen radius ratios for the two salts are 0·58 and 0·51 respectively, and both these values are considerably above the critical limit of 0·41 corresponding to the transition between the zincblende and sodium chloride structures. Actually, however, only AgBr has the latter arrangement and, on account of the very strong polarizing power of the silver ion, the AgI structure is that of zincblende. Nevertheless, this structure can be little more stable than the sodium chloride arrangement, as is indicated by the fact that AgBr can take up in solid solution as much as 70 per cent of AgI. On the other hand, AgBr shows little inclination to appear with the zincblende structure and only very limited solution of AgBr in AgI is possible (Barth and Lunde, 1926). This example emphasizes that the formation of mixed crystals is not a safe criterion for isomorphism, and that substances may form mixed crystals although not structurally isomorphous even in the widest sense of that term. The solid solution between CaF_2 and YF_3, already described, is a further example of the same point.

The purely geometrical basis of isomorphism is a general principle of which many further examples, particularly among more complex structures, will emerge later.

*Anti-isomorphism.** This term is used to describe the relationship between substances of the same geometrical structure but in which the positions of corresponding atoms or ions are interchanged. Thus ThO_2 and Li_2O are anti-isomorphous, for, while both have the fluorite structure, the anions in the one compound must clearly occupy the positions of the cations in the other. For obvious reasons such structures do not form mixed crystals. Among symmetrical structures of the AX type AgI and NH_4F may be regarded as anti-isomorphous. Both the compounds have the wurtzite structure, in which, of course, geometrically the two sets of atomic positions are equivalent. Nevertheless, physically the correspondence is between the cations of one structure and the anions of the other, for the known polarization properties of the ions involved leave no doubt that in AgI the anion and in NH_4F the cation is strongly polarized.

Polymeric isomorphism. A further type of structural relationship closely akin to isomorphism is one in which the correspondence between the compounds considered is revealed in a comparison not between the single unit cells of the structures but between equivalent groups of several unit cells. The isomorphism of rutile, TiO_2, and $FeNb_2O_6$ is of this type. The structure of $FeNb_2O_6$ is identical with that of rutile if the distinction between the iron and niobium ions is ignored. When this difference is taken into account, however, the true unit cell is three times as large and corresponds to three cells of rutile superposed. For isomorphism of this type Goldschmidt (1926a) has proposed the name 'polymeric isomorphism', and he has shown that in such cases orientated overgrowths, but only rarely mixed crystals, are formed.

Model structures. This term has been applied by Goldschmidt (1926b) to describe the relationship between isomorphous structures in which ions occur closely equivalent in size and polarization properties but differing in charge. Thus CaS is a model of $NaCl$ in that both have the same structure and the radii of the Na^+ and Ca^{2+} and of the Cl^- and S^{2-} ions are not very different. Similarly, $ZrSe_2$ and CdI_2, both with the cad-

* The cacophanous term 'antisomorphism' is employed by many authors.

mium iodide structure, ThO_2 and CaF_2, with the fluorite structure, and TiO_2 and MgF_2, with the rutile arrangement, are model structures, while many others among more complex compounds will appear later. The particular importance of the model structures lies in the fact that their study enables the purely physical properties associated with the strength of binding to be distinguished from the structural properties associated with the geometrical arrangement of the ions. Thus, with increasing ionic charge a series of model structures shows increasing hardness, melting point and molecular refractivity and decreasing solubility and general chemical reactivity. Model structures of the silicates are particularly valuable, since the strong electrostatic binding in these compounds, and the resulting insolubility and inactivity, render a direct chemical study difficult.

Polymorphism.

Polymorphous substances are those for which the geometrical conditions determining the structure lie close to the critical values corresponding to a transition from one structure type to another, and in which, therefore, the structure is so sensitive to external conditions that a variation in these conditions is sufficient to occasion a change to a structure of another type. Goldschmidt (1926 a) has shown that generally it is the influence of temperature on polarization which is the principal factor in bringing about this change, and if, for example, the substitution of one cation by another of greater polarizing power produces a definite morphotropic transition, we may in general expect that at a sufficiently high temperature a polymorphic transition of the first substance will take place, since an increase in temperature usually results in an increase in polarizing power. We shall later find numerous examples of such polymorphic transitions especially among the more complex ionic structures.

The structural basis of the various morphological relationships is summarized in Table 48, p. 202. They have been discussed at much greater length than is here possible by Goldschmidt (1926 a), Wolff (1928), and Grimm and Wolff (1933).

TABLE 48

THE STRUCTURAL BASIS OF SOME MORPHOLOGICAL RELATIONSHIPS

(After Grimm and Wolff, 1933)

	Chemical formulae	Crystal structures	Types of binding	Interatomic distances	Mixed crystal formation	Examples
Morphotropy	Analogous→ similar→ different	Analogous→ similar→ different	Same	Same→ different	Similar members miscible, others not	M_2SO_4, where M=Li, Na, K, Rb, Cs, Tl, NH_4
Isomorphism in wide sense	Analogous	Same	Same	Different	Not miscible	NaF and RbI, NaCl and PbS
Isomorphism in narrow sense	Analogous	Same	Same	Similar	Miscible over wide range	KCl and KBr
Anti-isomorphism	Analogous but with cations and anions interchanged	Same	Same	Similar or different	Not miscible	ThO_2 and Li_2O, CaF_2 and $K_2[PtCl_6]$
Polymeric isomorphism	One formula a multiple of the other	Several cells of one structure equivalent to one of the other	Same	Similar or different	Occasionally miscible	TiO_2 and $FeNb_2O_6$
Model structures	Analogous but charges in one case multiples of those in the other	Same	Same	Similar	Not miscible	NaCl and CaS, MgF_2 and TiO_2
Polymorphism	Identical	Different	Same or	Same or	Not miscible	C, S, TiO_2, $CaCO_3$, etc.

MULTIPLE ISODESMIC STRUCTURES

Multiple isodesmic structures are those in which a single cation is combined with two or more anions or in which a single anion is combined with two or more cations. In practice, however, the only compounds of this type of which a sufficient number has been investigated for any general principles to have emerged are those in which oxygen appears combined with two cations. We shall therefore confine our discussion of these compounds to those of which the general formula may be written $A_m B_n O_x$.

The characteristic feature of all the structures of such oxides is an oxygen co-ordination round the two types of cation, so that, while the metal ions are necessarily bound only to oxygen, a given oxygen ion may be linked to cations of both kinds. For such structures to fall within our definition of isodesmic no cation-oxygen bond may be of electrostatic strength as great as unity, so that the co-ordination round any cation must always exceed its valency. This co-ordination is determined by the cation : oxygen radius ratio, and corresponding to each valency there is therefore a minimum cation radius which must be exceeded for an isodesmic structure to be formed. These minimum radii, based on a radius of 1·32 A. for the O^{2-} ion, are:

Valency of cation	1 and 2	3	4 and 5	6 and 7
Minimum admissible radius in A.	0·20	0·29	0·54	0·96

A comparison of these figures with the ionic radii given in Table 36, p. 171, shows that almost all metal ions satisfy the condition for an isodesmic structure, but that the majority of non-metallic cations, such as C^{4+}, Si^{4+}, N^{5+}, S^{6+}, etc., do not do so. We are therefore primarily concerned in this class with the complex oxides of two metallic elements. Among such oxides two structures are of particularly common occurrence, namely those of perovskite and spinel.

The perovskite structure.

The structure of perovskite corresponds to the composition ABO_3 and has the cubic or pseudo-cubic unit cell shown in Fig. 46. A ions are situated at the corners of the cell and a B ion at its centre, while the faces are centred by oxygen. Each A ion is 12-fold and each B ion 6-fold co-ordinated by oxygen neighbours, and each oxygen ion is linked to four A and to two B cations. As is to be expected, the larger cation always occupies the position A of higher co-ordination. In such a structure it is clear that a simple relationship must exist between the ionic radii, and it is easy to see that ideally the condition

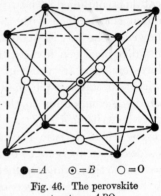

$\bullet = A$ $\odot = B$ $\bigcirc = O$

Fig. 46. The perovskite structure, ABO_3.

$$R_A + R_O = \sqrt{2}(R_B + R_O)$$

should be satisfied. Goldschmidt (1927 a) has shown, however, that a certain tolerance is permissible, and that the structure appears whenever the condition

$$R_A + R_O = t \cdot \sqrt{2}(R_B + R_O)$$

holds, where t is a 'factor of tolerance' which may lie between the limits 0·8 and 1·0. If t is outside these limits other structures obtain.

We have deliberately refrained from making any statement concerning the valencies of the cations in the perovskite structure, since it appears that this is a matter of only secondary importance and any pair of ions, provided they have radii appropriate to the co-ordination and an aggregate valency of 6 to confer electrical neutrality on the structure as a whole, can appear. Thus all the compounds shown in Table 49 have the perovskite structure, and it will be seen that these include pairs of cations of valencies 1 and 5, 2 and 4, and 3 and 3.

The appearance of KIO_3 and $RbIO_3$ among the compounds with the perovskite structure is of particular interest because these bodies would normally be regarded as salts rather than as mixed oxides. The perovskite structure arises here, however, on account of the exceptional size of the I^{5+} ion, which is considerably larger than the minimum radius permissible for a pentavalent ion in an isodesmic crystal. The chlorates, on the other hand, due to the much smaller size of the Cl^{5+} ion, form entirely different anisodesmic structures. In $LiIO_3$ the perovskite arrangement does not obtain because the lithium ion is too small for such a high co-ordination by oxygen. A typical isodesmic structure is nevertheless still found in which both lithium and iodine ions are co-ordinated by six oxygen neighbours and in which there is no trace of any discrete iodate radical (Zachariasen and Barta, 1931).

TABLE 49
SOME OXIDES WITH THE PEROVSKITE STRUCTURE

$NaNbO_3$	$CaTiO_3$	$YAlO_3$	$(KMgF_3)$
$KNbO_3$	$SrTiO_3$	$LaAlO_3$	$(KNiF_3)$
KIO_3	$CaZrO_3$	$LaGaO_3$	$(KZnF_3)$
$RbIO_3$	$CuSnO_3$		

The appearance of the perovskite structure with any pair of cations of the appropriate total charge illustrates a very important feature of ionic structures of which numerous other examples will arise later, for it appears that in many such structures, provided the condition of electrical neutrality is satisfied, the individual charges and the exact distribution of the cations are matters of secondary importance admitting of considerable latitude: it is even possible for some of these cations to be entirely absent from the structure provided that the appropriate adjustment of charge is somehow achieved. A very remarkable example of this phenomenon is afforded by the sodium-tungsten bronze of ideal composition $NaWO_3$. This body has the perovskite structure but shows very variable composition and colour. Hägg (1935a) has found that in the sodium-poor varieties the structure remains essentially unaltered, but that some of the sites normally occupied by sodium are vacant. To preserve neutrality one tungsten ion is converted from W^{5+} to W^{6+} for every site so unoccupied, and this change in ionization gives rise to the characteristic alteration in colour and explains its association with the sodium content. Such a structure is also of interest crystallographically since it is clear that no single unit cell can satisfy the cubic symmetry of the crystal as a whole. Only by a random distribution of the vacant sites is this symmetry statistically preserved, and in this respect the structure resembles some of the alloy systems already discussed.

The spinels.

The spinel structure is shown in plan in Fig. 47, and corresponds to the composition AB_2O_4. There are 32 oxygen ions in the cubic unit cell, and each A ion is tetrahedrally co-ordinated by four and each B ion octahedrally co-ordinated by six oxygen neighbours. Each oxygen ion is bound to one A and to three B ions. The structure is common to very many mixed oxides of the type shown in Table 50, in which normally A is a divalent and B a trivalent metal. As with the perovskite structure, however, it appears that the total cation charge is the most significant factor and that other cation combinations which yield a neutral structure are admissible. Thus $Ti^{4+}Mg_2^{2+}O_4$, $Ti^{4+}Mn_2^{2+}O_4$ and $Mo^{6+}Ag_2^{+}O_4$ all have the spinel structure.

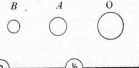

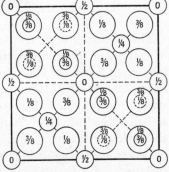

Fig. 47. The spinel structure, AB_2O_4. The plan shows the contents of only the lower half of the unit cell.

It was first pointed out by Barth and Posnjak (1931) that in the case of the mineral spinel itself, of composition $MgAl_2O_4$, the previously accepted arrangement just described was not in conformity with the general principles determining the structure of ionic compounds. Thus, in particular, although the Al^{3+} ion is considerably smaller than that of Mg^{2+} it appears in the structure in positions of higher co-ordination. Alternatively, the radius of the Mg^{2+} ion must here have a very much smaller value than in other ionic crystals. A re-interpretation of the X-ray data (Barth and Posnjak, 1932) then revealed that the spinels are not all of one kind, but that there are in fact two different structure types. In those of the

TABLE 50
SOME COMPOUNDS WITH THE SPINEL STRUCTURE

'Normal' type	Structure type unknown			
$MnAl_2O_4$	$BeLi_2F_4$	$MgCr_2O_4$	$MnFe_2O_4$	$CoCo_2S_4$
$FeAl_2O_4$	SLi_2O_4	$MnCr_2O_4$	$FeFe_2O_4$	$CuCo_2S_4$
$CoAl_2O_4$	$MoLi_2O_4$	$FeCr_2O_4$	$CoFe_2O_4$	$GeNi_2O_4$
$NiAl_2O_4$	$SnMg_2O_4$	$CoCr_2O_4$	$NiFe_2O_4$	$NiNi_2S_4$
$ZnAl_2O_4$	$MgAl_2O_4$	$NiCr_2O_4$	$CuFe_2O_4$	$ZnGa_2O_4$
	$CuAl_2O_4$	$ZnCr_2O_4$	$ZnFe_2O_4$	WAg_2O_4
Equipoint	$(LiAl_5O_8)$	$CdCr_2O_4$	$CdFe_2O_4$	$ZnSn_2O_4$
structure	$ZnK_2(CN)_4$	$MnCr_2S_4$	$MgCo_2O_4$	
	$CdK_2(CN)_4$	$ZnCr_2S_4$	$TiCo_2O_4$	
$MgTiMgO_4$	$HgK_2(CN)_4$	$CdCr_2S_4$	$CoCo_2O_4$	
$FeMgFeO_4$	$ZnTi_2O_4$	$TiMn_2O_4$	$CuCo_2O_4$	
$FeTiFeO_4$	FeV_2O_4		$ZnCo_2O_4$	
$ZnSnZnO_4$			$SnCo_2O_4$	
$GaMgGaO_4$				
$InMgInO_4$				

'normal' type the structure is that already described, but in others there prevails a somewhat different arrangement which may be best illustrated in terms of a specific example such as $MgGa_2O_4$. In this body the pattern of sites in the structure and the distribution of oxygen ions is exactly the same as in the normal spinels. The arrangement of the cations, however, is somewhat different, for it is found that one-half of the Ga^{3+} ions occupy the 4-fold co-ordinated positions in the structure while the rest of these ions, together with all the Mg^{2+} ions, are distributed at random over the positions of 6-fold co-ordination. Barth and Posnjak suggest writing the formulae of such spinels in the form $BABO_4$ to emphasize the structural departure from the normal type, and propose describing such structures as structures with 'variate atom equipoint'. Not all the spinel structures have been reinvestigated to determine to which type they belong, but where the information is available it is included in Table 50, p. 207. Even among the structures which are definitely of the normal type some unexpected compounds are included, and it is surprising to find in this group such members as $ZnAl_2O_4$, $NiAl_2O_4$, $FeAl_2O_4$, etc., in all of which the Al^{3+} ion is decidedly the smaller cation.

Yet another type of spinel has been described by Kordes (1935a) who finds that $LiAl_5O_8$ has a spinel structure and may be derived from $Mg_2Al_4O_8$ by replacing the two Mg ions by (Li + Al).

A second feature of the spinels which has long been known but has only recently received a structural explanation is their capacity to take up in solid solution indefinite quantities of the oxides Al_2O_3 and Fe_2O_3. The explanation of this phenomenon was provided by the investigation of the structures of γ-Al_2O_3 and γ-Fe_2O_3. As normally prepared, these oxides have the corundum structure already discussed, but by the careful oxidation of Fe_3O_4 (which is a spinel and may be written $Fe^{2+}Fe_2^{3+}O_4$) γ-Fe_2O_3, with an entirely different structure, is obtained. The unit cell of this new structure is of about the same size as that of Fe_3O_4, and the arrangement first proposed was one in which the iron ions occupied the same positions as in the spinel with the necessary four additional oxygen ions per unit cell accommodated in interstices in the lattice. It was difficult, however, to understand how such large ions as those of oxygen could be introduced into a structure already so tightly packed, and ultimately density measurements showed the impossibility of such an arrangement. It is now found (Verwey, 1935; Hägg, 1935b) that the actual structure must be regarded not as the spinel structure with an excess of oxygen but as a spinel structure with a cation deficiency, and the structure of these two oxides proves to be one in which 32 oxygen ions per unit cell are arranged exactly as in spinel, while the corresponding number of iron or aluminium ions, namely $21\frac{1}{3}$, are distributed at random over the 24 sites normally occupied by the cations. On the average there are therefore $2\frac{2}{3}$ vacant cation sites per unit cell.

In the light of this structure the ready solid solution of Al_2O_3 in the spinels is easily understood. Starting, say, with $MgAl_2O_4$ the aluminium content may be gradually increased by the substitution of Al^{3+} for Mg^{2+}. In other solid solutions which we shall discuss later, electrical neutrality is preserved in such a substitution by another simultaneous substitution elsewhere in the structure, but here it is achieved simply by the appearance of vacant sites in positions which would normally be occupied by cations. When the substitution has been completely effected just $2\frac{2}{3}$ such sites appear per unit cell and the γ-Al_2O_3 structure results (Hägg and Söderholm, 1935; Kordes, 1935a).

A number of other mixed oxides with multiple isodesmic structures have been analysed but they illustrate few general principles and will not be discussed here. They are tabulated, with references, by Bernal and Wooster (1932).

'DEFECT' STRUCTURES

The perovskite and spinel structures described above display a number of features which we have not so far encountered in other structures considered and which call for further discussion. The characteristic feature of both the perovskite and spinel compounds is the presence of a considerable amount of oxygen. On account of the large size of the oxygen anion compared with that of most cations, the volume of the unit cell is determined almost entirely by the anions alone, and to a first approximation both structures may be regarded as consisting of a rigid framework of oxygen anions in the interstices of which the much smaller cations are situated. In spinel the disposition of the oxygen ions alone is actually that of cubic close-packing; in perovskite the packing is somewhat less tight and each oxygen ion is surrounded by only eight others.

This picture of the essential nature of the structures under consideration enables us to understand some of their characteristic properties. Thus, if we regard the anion lattice as the dominating feature of the structure and consider the cations as serving only to establish electrical neutrality, it is easy to see that within limits any combination of cations may occur in the structure, provided only that their radii are appropriate to the co-ordination in which they appear and that the structure as a whole is electrically neutral. In such an arrangement, however, we can no longer regard the charges of all the ions as being neutralized locally by their immediate neighbours, and in the spinels with equipoint structure, for example, there must occasionally be regions of excess positive and excess negative charge where an unduly large number of trivalent and divalent ions respectively happen to be in close proximity. Nevertheless, even when the distribution of cations is primarily statistical it may be assumed that very large local concentrations of charge are avoided.

From the purely crystallographic point of view these structures are of importance in that they clearly demand a revision of what we may term the 'classical' conceptions of structure theory. In the equipoint spinel structures, for example, crystallographic symmetry is preserved in the lattice as a whole only in a statistical manner, and a single unit cell will not, in general, show the characteristic symmetry of the macroscopic structure. Moreover, we find in the lattice that structurally equivalent sites, namely those of 6-fold co-ordination, are occupied by two different kinds of ion. Similar difficulties arise in the sodium-tungsten bronzes and in γ-Al_2O_3.

In a comprehensive survey of such structures, Strock (1936) has proposed the term *defect structure* for all those which in any way show departures from classical structure theory, and has put forward a systematic scheme for their classification. The full details cannot be discussed here, but the classification is primarily into two types:

(1) Complete Lattices: structures in which two or more chemically different atoms occupy crystallographically equivalent sites.

(2) Incomplete Lattices: structures in which one or more sets of crystallographically equivalent sites are only partially occupied, leaving vacant spaces in the lattice.

A combination of the two types is also possible. The equipoint spinel structure is an example of the first type and that of γ-Al_2O_3 of the second. A solid solution of Al_2O_3 in spinel is a combination of the two.

The application of X-ray methods to more complex systems has revealed that such defect structures are by no means as uncommon as was at one time supposed, and that, in fact, in many types of compounds they are the rule rather than the exception. Numerous other examples will be considered as they arise, but even among the simple compounds already discussed a number of defect structures have been observed, and these may be conveniently considered at this point.

Defect structures with complete lattices.

Defect structures of this type are characteristic of all true mixed crystal systems, for it has long been recognized that in all such systems the distribution in the lattice of the atoms of the two or more components is purely statistical. Thus Vegard (1921) showed that in mixed crystals of KCl and KBr the cell size varies continuously with composition but that the sodium chloride structure is preserved at all concentrations with the Cl^- and Br^- ions distributed at random in the anion sites. We have already seen that the same random distribution also obtains in the mixed crystals of metal systems, and if such an arrangement is accepted in the structure of a mixed crystal there seems to be no valid reason why it should not also arise in that of a single chemical compound. In fact Hassel (1928) has proposed the term 'internal mixed crystal' for any structure showing such a random distribution of chemically dissimilar atoms over crystallographically equivalent sites.

Historically interesting because it was the first recorded example of a defect structure is that of $(NH_4)_3MoO_3F_3$. Here Pauling (1924) found that it was impossible to distinguish between the O^{2-} and F^- ions, which together occupy one set of crystallographically equivalent sites in the structure.

A more recent but particularly striking example of a complete defect structure is provided by $Li_2Fe_2O_4$ (Posnjak and Barth, 1931) and Li_2TiO_3 (Kordes, 1935b), both of which have the sodium chloride arrangement with a random distribution of the metal ions in the cation sites. These two compounds form a continuous series of mixed crystals not only between themselves but also with MgO, and the flexibility of this system is clearly due to the close similarity in the radii of the Li^+, Mg^{2+}, Fe^{3+} and Ti^{4+} ions. Li_2TiO_3 is also of interest chemically in that it is far more stable than the other alkali titanates, which, on account of the greater size of the alkali ion, have more complex structures.

Among layer lattices defect structures have been found in $CdBr_2$ (Bijvoet and Nieuwenkamp, 1933) and in $NiBr_2$ (Ketelaar, 1934a). Both these compounds have structures closely related to those of cadmium chloride and cadmium iodide, but differ from these structures in that the sequence of the layers is irregular and follows in part the arrangement of the one and in part that of the other structure. The crystal can thus be regarded as built up by the repeated intimate twinning together of portions of the cadmium chloride and cadmium iodide lattices.

Defect structures with incomplete lattices.

The discovery of defect structures with incomplete lattices has resolved difficulties presented by a number of substances which appeared to be irreconcilable with classical structure theory. We have already discussed the defect structures of γ-Al_2O_3 and of sodium-tungsten bronze as illustrations of this point and a further example is provided by that of the iron sulphide pyrrhotite. This mineral has the approximate composition FeS but always contains sulphur in considerable excess of the proportion indicated by this ideal formula. Attempts to deduce the structure by treating it as an interstitial solid solution of sulphur in FeS were, however, unsuccessful, and it now appears that it must instead be pictured as an FeS structure with a deficiency of iron. In this structure the large sulphur atoms build a rigid close-packed lattice but that of the iron is incomplete (Laves, 1930; Hägg and Sucksdorff, 1933).

Many of the metallic interstitial compounds already described (p. 145) must also be regarded as defect structures, for they usually display an indefiniteness of composition corresponding to a variable concentration of the non-metallic atoms. These atoms must, therefore, build a lattice in which some sites may be unoccupied.

A particularly striking defect structure with incomplete lattice is that of silver iodide (Strock, 1934, 1935). This compound is trimorphous, and in the β- and γ-forms has the zincblende and wurtzite structures respectively. Both these may be regarded as a close-packed iodine lattice with the silver atoms in the tetrahedral interstices. In α-AgI, stable above 146° C., a less tightly-packed cubic body-centred arrangement of iodine atoms obtains, with two molecules of AgI per unit cell. The silver atoms, however, now have no fixed positions and are able to wander freely in a fluid state throughout the structure, so that at the temperature of transition from the β- to the α-form the lattice of the silver atoms can be regarded as 'melting' into itself: the final breakdown of the iodine lattice takes place only when the true melting point of 555° C. is reached.

The structure of Ag_2HgI_4 (Ketelaar, 1934b) combines the characteristics of defect structure of both incomplete and complete types. Between 50 and 158° C. this compound has a structure closely related to zincblende. The four iodine atoms per unit cell replace the sulphur atoms, while the $(2Ag + Hg)$ atoms are statistically distributed over three of the four zinc positions. In this way a structure is obtained in which structurally equivalent sites are not only incompletely occupied but also accommodate atoms of two different kinds.

The chemical significance of defect structures.

Apart from their crystallographic interest defect structures are of importance in raising once again the question of the significance of chemical combination, already discussed in connection with the metal systems. In simple ionic structures, such as, say, that of sodium chloride, the conception of a definite compound is easy to understand, for in such a structure the classical laws of chemistry arise directly from geometrical and electrical demands. We can thus regard as a chemical compound any structure in which crystallographically equivalent positions are occupied by chemically identical atoms. This, in fact, as we have seen, is the definition of chemical combination proposed by Westgren and Phragmén. When applied to defect structures, however, such a definition presents immediate difficulties. Thus it would demand that among the spinels only those with the normal structure could be regarded as compounds, whereas chemically no difference can be detected between these and the equipoint structures and the distinction can be made only by X-ray means. Again, is such a body as $Li_2Fe_2O_4$ to be regarded as a compound, and if so, why not also the mixed crystals of composition $KCl + KBr$ in which the distribution of cations is exactly the same as in $Li_2Fe_2O_4$? If, however, such structures are regarded as compounds we must clearly so regard all solid solutions, for in a structure in which the anions are distributed statistically there can clearly be no especial significance in any particular composition. In $Li_2Fe_2O_4$ the relative number of Li^+ and Fe^{3+} ions is determined by the demands of electrical neutrality, but in mixed crystals of this compound with Li_2TiO_3 any relative proportion of Fe^{3+} and Ti^{4+} ions can be achieved. Nevertheless, there does not seem any valid reason why such mixed crystals should not be regarded as being just as definite chemical compounds as their two components. In the light of such arguments it seems clear that it is impossible to give an unimpeachable definition of chemical combination, and that, while in the great majority of structures there can be little doubt as to the correct description, there will always be some where ambiguity must arise. It is ultimately of little importance whether a given body is described as a chemical compound or not provided that its structure is known and the wider significance of that structure appreciated.

General discussions of defect structures have been given by Barth (1932), Hägg (1935c) and Strock (1936).

CHAPTER VIII

IONIC COMPOUNDS: MESODESMIC STRUCTURES

INTRODUCTION

We now come to our discussion of mesodesmic ionic structures, but before proceeding to a detailed account of these structures, and later of the anisodesmic compounds, it is convenient to preface our remarks by a discussion of a number of general features common to all the more complex ionic crystals.

Ionic structures as polyhedra of anions.

In all the compounds which we have so far considered the structures have been so simple that a description of the positions of the several ions has been sufficient to enable the essential features to be visualized and the co-ordination to be readily understood. In some of the more complex structures, however, this is not always the case, and some alternative form of presentation is often desirable.

We have seen that a characteristic feature of ionic structures as a whole is the regular co-ordination of cations by anions in a manner depending primarily on the radius ratio. It is this co-ordination, rather than that of anions by cations, which is significant since the anions are almost always the largest ions, and therefore only the co-ordination of them round the cations is determined by the ionic radii: that round the anions is governed by the number of cations available. A second practical reason for the importance primarily of the co-ordination round the cations lies in the fact that in the vast majority of the more complex ionic structures, namely the salts of oxy-acids, only one anion, that of oxygen, occurs, whereas two or more cations are necessarily present. Each cation is therefore co-ordinated only by oxygen although the latter ions are often irregularly linked to cations of several different kinds.

The characteristic oxygen co-ordination numbers of all the

cations of common occurrence in ionic structures have already been given in Table 47, p. 196. For any given co-ordination the distribution of the anion neighbours is necessarily as regular as possible, so that, corresponding to the several co-ordinations, the arrangement of oxygen ions round the cation is as shown in Table 51.

TABLE 51

ARRANGEMENT OF CO-ORDINATING ANIONS

C.N.	Arrangement
3	At corners of equilateral triangle
4	At corners of regular tetrahedron
6	At corners of regular octahedron
8	At corners of cube
12	At corners of cubo-octahedron

This picture of an ionic structure as one in which the anions co-ordinate the different cations at the corners of regular polyhedra makes it possible to describe such structures, not in terms of the positions of the individual ions, but solely in terms of the way in which the polyhedra are packed together. The point may be made clear by a number of examples.

In Fig. 48 the sodium chloride structure is shown in such a way as to emphasize the octahedra of Cl^- ions co-ordinating each Na^+ ion. A moment's consideration will reveal that the octahedra are so packed that every edge is common to two octahedra, and that in fact such a description is sufficient to specify the structure completely. A somewhat more complex case is illustrated by the rutile structure of which several unit cells are shown in Fig. 49. Here again the co-ordination round the cations is octahedral, but it will be seen that the mutual arrangement of these octahedra is quite different, and that only two opposite edges of each are shared with other octahedra. In the remaining forms of TiO_2, as anatase and brookite, octahedra of oxygen ions round the titanium are again found, and the difference between the structures lies only in the way in which these octahedra are linked together. In the spinels, AB_2O_4, two types of co-ordinating polyhedra occur, for the oxygen ions are arranged tetrahedrally about A and octa-hedrally about B. The whole structure is completely deter-

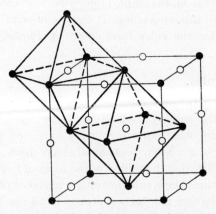

Fig. 48. The structure of sodium chloride, NaCl, showing the co-ordinating octahedra of anions round the cations.

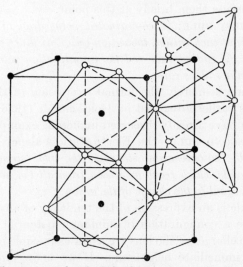

Fig. 49. The structure of rutile, TiO_2, showing the co-ordinating octahedra of anions round the cations.

mined by specifying the mutual disposition of these tetrahedra and octahedra.

In the simple structures of the type so far considered such

a description in terms of the arrangement of the anion polyhedra possesses few advantages, but we shall find that the
discussion of the more complex ionic structures is considerably
facilitated by this viewpoint. It does, moreover, provide the
foundation for the rules formulated by Pauling now to be
discussed.

Pauling's rules.

Certain general principles underlying the structures of all
ionic crystals, some of which we have already explicitly
discussed and others of which have appeared implicitly in
the structures we have considered, have been summarized
by Pauling (1929) and codified in the form of five rules. With
simple structures these rules are either trivial or platitudinous,
and have therefore not been expressly considered earlier, but
when applied to more complex structures they are often of
considerable value. It is convenient to formulate these rules
and to discuss them briefly at this point.

THE FIRST RULE: *A co-ordinated polyhedron of anions is
formed about each cation, the cation-anion distance being determined by the radius sum and the co-ordination number of the
cation by the radius ratio.*

This rule is merely the formal expression of the general
principles earlier advanced by Goldschmidt (1926 *a*, *b*, *c*), of
which we have already discussed numerous examples.

THE SECOND RULE—the Electrostatic Valency Principle:
*In a stable co-ordination structure the total strength of the
valency bonds which reach an anion from all the neighbouring
cations is equal to the charge of the anion.*

This rule is an expression of the tendency of any structure
to assume a configuration of minimum potential energy in
which the charges of the ions are as far as possible neutralized
by their immediate neighbours. If we know only the co-
ordinations round the cations in a structure this rule often
enables that round the anions to be determined. Thus in the
perovskite structure of $CaTiO_3$ each Ca^{2+} ion is 12-fold and
each Ti^{4+} ion 6-fold co-ordinated by O^{2-} ions. The electrostatic valency strengths of the Ca—O and Ti—O bonds are

therefore $\frac{2}{12} = \frac{1}{6}$ and $\frac{4}{6} = \frac{2}{3}$ respectively. If we now consider an oxygen ion, it is clear that its total valency of two is achieved if it in its turn is bound to two Ti^{4+} and to four Ca^{2+} ions.* This is the most valuable of Pauling's rules, and we shall have frequent occasion to make use of it later. As we have already explained in considering the spinels, it is not always rigidly obeyed in detail but large departures from the rule are not to be expected and have never been observed.

THE THIRD RULE: *The existence of edges, and particularly of faces, common to two anion polyhedra in a co-ordinated structure decreases its stability; this effect is large for cations with high valency and small co-ordination number, and is especially large when the radius ratio approaches the lower limit of stability of the polyhedron.*

This rule arises immediately from the fact that an edge or a face common to two anion polyhedra necessitates the close approach of two cations, and a corresponding increase in the potential energy of the system as compared with the state in which only corners are shared. It is readily seen that this effect will be the more marked the higher the cation charge and the lower the co-ordination. Thus SiO_4 tetrahedra usually share only corners while TiO_6 octahedra may have common edges and AlO_6 octahedra common faces.

THE FOURTH RULE: *In a crystal containing different cations those of high valency and small co-ordination number tend not to share polyhedron elements with each other.*

This rule follows at once from the same arguments as those on which the third rule is based.

THE FIFTH RULE—the Principle of Parsimony: *The number of essentially different kinds of constituent in a crystal tends to be small.*

This rule implies that as far as possible the environment of all chemically similar anions in a structure will be similar. Thus, even if the electrostatic valency rule admits several alternative types of co-ordination about the anions,

---

* Other combinations of Ca—O and Ti—O bonds are, of course, mathematically possible but structurally highly improbable.

only one of these types of co-ordination may be expected to obtain and to be common to all anions.

Many examples of the application of Pauling's rules, especially to more complex structures, are given below.

Mesodesmic structures.

We have defined mesodesmic structures as those in which the strongest binding has an electrostatic valency strength one-half the charge on the anion. In crystals in which this anion is oxygen, which alone we shall consider, the strength of this binding is therefore unity, and it follows that mesodesmic structures will arise whenever the oxygen co-ordination number of a cation is equal to its charge. A consideration of Table 47, p. 196, reveals that such structures are therefore practically confined, among compounds of common occurrence, to the borates, silicates and germanates. The tungstates and tellurates also satisfy the condition but have been little studied.

BORATES

The characteristic structural features of mesodesmic compounds arise from the fact that an anion bound by two mesodesmic links is completely saturated, and can be bound to no further cations. Thus, for example, in the borates each B^{3+} ion is surrounded by three O^{2-} ions at the corners of an equilateral triangle.* If two such BO_3 triangles share a common oxygen ion,

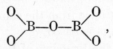

that ion is saturated and can be linked to no other cations. Further binding can take place only through the remaining four oxygen ions, and we can therefore regard the composite group B_2O_5 as a discrete unit in the crystal, and consider the structure as built by the packing together of these units and the co-ordinating polyhedra of the other cations. The case

---

* Occasionally the B^{3+} ion is tetrahedrally co-ordinated by four O^{2-} ions as in danburite, $CaB_2Si_2O_8$.

considered, however, is not the only manner in which two or
more BO_3 triangles can be linked together, and, in fact, as
we shall see below, such a linking can be achieved in an indefinite number of different ways. It is this possibility of
indefinitely extended composite groups which gives mesodesmic structures their peculiar complexity. In anisodesmic
crystals such a possibility does not arise, since any anion
already bound by a bond of strength greater than half its
charge cannot be linked to a second cation of the same type.

In Fig. 50 a number of different methods of linking BO_3
triangles in borate structures of various types are illustrated.

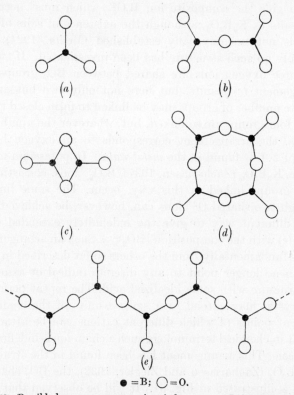

$\bullet = B; \ \bigcirc = O.$

Fig. 50. Possible boron-oxygen groupings in borates. (a) Independent triangles,
BO_3, e.g. orthoborates. (b) Triangles sharing one oxygen atom, B_2O_5. (c) and
(d) Triangles sharing two oxygen atoms to form closed rings, BO_2, e.g. metaborates. (e) Triangles sharing two oxygen atoms to form open chains, BO_2.

In (a) separate BO_3 groups occur, so that in a salt with such a structure the oxygen:boron ratio is necessarily $3:1$, corresponding to the *orthoborates*. The structure of hambergite, $Be_2BO_3(OH)$, is of this type (Zachariasen, 1931b). Here each Be^{2+} ion is surrounded by a tetrahedron of O^{2-} and OH^- ions, and the whole structure is formed by linking together these tetrahedra and the BO_3 triangles in such a way that only corners are shared. It is important to note that the OH groups cannot be directly linked to B since a single B—OH bond would satisfy the valency of the OH group.

In (b) two BO_3 groups are linked by sharing a single O^{2-} ion to give the composite ion $B_2O_5^{4-}$ which must occur in such salts as $K_4B_2O_5$, although the existence of salts of this type is not unequivocally established (Mellor, 1924), and certainly no such structure has been investigated. If two of the three oxygen ions are shared between BO_3 groups the arrangement (c) results, but here not only two but an indefinite number of groups may be linked to form closed rings. In (d) four groups are so linked, but, whatever the number of groups, the arrangement corresponds to an oxygen:boron ratio of $2:1$ as found in the *metaborates*. In potassium metaborate, $K_3B_3O_6$ (Zachariasen, 1937), $B_3O_6^{3-}$ ions, consisting of three groups linked in this way, occur. The same linking through two shared O^{2-} ions can, however, be achieved in a quite different way to give the indefinitely extended open chain (e) with the composition $(BO_2)_n^{n-}$. Such an arrangement differs fundamentally from the others so far described in that we can no longer point to any discrete radical or associate the structure with some idealized acid. The repeat period in the crystal may extend over several units of the chain, at different points of which different cations can be attached, so that in chemical terminology such a chain ion is indefinitely polybasic. This arrangement has been found in the structure of CaB_2O_4 (Zachariasen and Ziegler, 1932), the BO_2 chain of which is illustrated in Fig. 51. It will be observed that here the chain is somewhat crumpled, with an angle between the two oxygen valencies of less than $180°$, indicating a partial transition towards a homopolar binding within the chain.

When all three oxygen ions of the BO_3 groups are shared, no ion, of course, results, but instead the oxide B_2O_3. It is geometrically very difficult, however, to build a three-dimensional stable structure from triangles, and this no doubt accounts for the tendency for this oxide to occur only as a glass. It has, however, recently been prepared in crystalline form (N. W. Taylor and Cole, 1934) but the structure is still unknown.

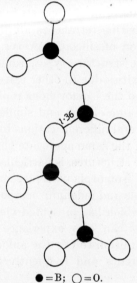

● = B; ○ = O.

Fig. 51. The boron-oxygen chain in CaB_2O_4.

SILICATES

From both a structural and a chemical point of view the silicates are of far greater importance than the borates, and, on account of their great petrological interest, have been more exhaustively studied by X-ray methods than any other class of ionic crystals. Here it is impossible to give anything approaching a complete account of all this work, for it would occupy an amount of space scarcely justified by its chemical importance. Nor is such an account necessary, since an exhaustive and readily accessible description of the silicate structures has recently been given by W. L. Bragg (1937).

Here, therefore, we shall confine our discussion of these structures to such features as illustrate general principles of crystal chemistry.

General features of silicate structures.

The fundamental characteristic of all silicate structures is the tetrahedral co-ordination of the Si^{4+} ion by oxygen, and these compounds may be classified in a manner formally analogous to that used for the borates in terms of the way in which the co-ordinating tetrahedra are linked together. The higher co-ordination of silicon, however, leads to a greater number of possible structure types, while at the same time additional complexities due to other causes arise.

In the first place the isomorphous replacement of cations by others of the same charge and similar size, or even the replacement of several different cations by others of different valencies but with the same aggregate charge, although possible in many ionic structures, is particularly common among the silicates. This isomorphous replacement confers on the structures a variable and indefinite composition, the chemical interpretation of which has presented many difficulties. The anions in silicates can also experience isomorphous substitution, for in addition to O^{2-} the anions OH^- and F^- are of common occurrence and frequently replace each other statistically.

A second feature of complex ionic structures, which is common only among the silicates, is the possibility of a stable mixed structure in which parts of the crystal are arranged according to one structure and the remainder according to another of similar type. When this occurs on a macroscopic scale parallel intergrowths of two crystal types are formed; when it occurs on the scale of a single unit cell new mixed structures result. Examples of such structures will be given below.

A third feature of silicate crystal chemistry is peculiar to silicates alone, and arises accidentally from the particular value of the radius of the aluminium ion. The Al:O radius ratio of 0·43 is so close to the critical value of 0·414 for transition from 6-fold to 4-fold co-ordination that this ion can occur in both conditions, sometimes in the same structure. When 4-fold co-ordinated the aluminium ion replaces silicon, and such replacement is purely random and may be of indefinite extent. For every aluminium ion so introduced a corresponding substitution of Ca^{2+} for Na^+, Al^{3+} for Mg^{2+} or Fe^{3+} for Fe^{2+} must simultaneously occur elsewhere in the structure to preserve neutrality. The appearance of aluminium in one structure in two entirely different rôles is a feature of the silicates which chemical analysis alone cannot reveal, and which has given rise to many difficulties in the interpretation of such systems.

The classification of silicates.

The classification of silicate structures is immediately analogous to that of the borates, and is most conveniently made in terms of the way in which the silicon tetrahedra are linked together. Such a classification, originally proposed by Machatschki (1928), must be regarded as one of the most valuable contributions to silicate chemistry, for it has introduced order in a field where previous classifications, based on hypothetical acids of which the silicates were supposed to be salts, led to considerable confusion; and it is interesting to find that this new classification supports in almost every detail that developed by the mineralogist from purely morphological and physical properties. We shall now proceed to discuss briefly a number of silicate structures in order to make clear the basis of the classification and to illustrate the characteristic features which these structures show.

Isolated SiO_4 groups: orthosilicates.

The simplest possible structural arrangement is that in which isolated SiO_4^{4-} groups, of the form shown in Fig. 52a, p. 226, are linked together only through the medium of other cations. Such groups are found in the *orthosilicates* and correspond to an oxygen:silicon ratio of 4:1 or greater.

Olivine. A typical structure of this kind is that of olivine, Mg_2SiO_4 (W. L. Bragg and Brown, 1926), a projection of the orthorhombic unit cell of which is illustrated in a slightly idealized form in Fig. 53. The main points of importance in the structure are: (1) The SiO_4 tetrahedra are isolated and occur pointing alternately up and down. (2) The tetrahedra are linked together only by O—Mg—O bonds. (3) The magnesium ions are of two kinds, only half of them lying at symmetry centres. The ions of both kinds, however, are similarly co-ordinated by six oxygen ions lying at the corners of a very

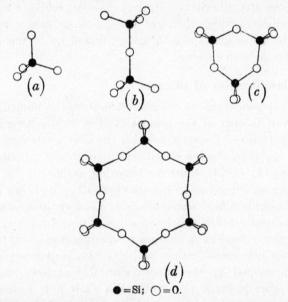

● = Si; ○ = O.

Fig. 52. Closed silicon-oxygen groupings in silicates. (a) Independent tetrahedra, SiO_4, e.g. orthosilicates. (b) Tetrahedra sharing one oxygen atom, Si_2O_7, e.g. thortveitite. (c) Tetrahedra sharing two oxygen atoms to form three-membered rings, Si_3O_9, e.g. benitoite. (d) Tetrahedra sharing two oxygen atoms to form six-membered rings, Si_6O_{18}, e.g. beryl.

nearly regular octahedron, so that the whole structure can be described as a packing together of tetrahedra and octahedra. (4) The disposition of the oxygen ions alone is approximately that of hexagonal close-packing. A close-packed arrangement of oxygen ions is a characteristic feature of many silicate structures and results from the large size of these ions compared with that of most others of common occurrence. (5) The electrostatic valency rule is satisfied.

The strength of each Mg—O bond is $\frac{2}{6} = \frac{1}{3}$, so that three such bonds are necessary, together with the Si—O bond of strength unity, to satisfy the oxygen valency. Each oxygen is in fact linked to three magnesium ions.

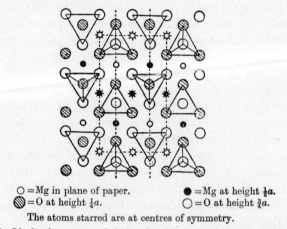

○ = Mg in plane of paper.   ● = Mg at height $\frac{1}{4}a$.
◉ = O at height $\frac{1}{4}a$.   ◯ = O at height $\frac{3}{4}a$.

The atoms starred are at centres of symmetry.

Fig. 53. Idealized structure of olivine, Mg_2SiO_4, projected on b-c plane.

Chondrodite. Closely related to olivine, and illustrative of the mixed structures already mentioned as occurring among silicates, are the minerals of the chondrodite series (W. H. Taylor and West, 1928, 1929). These may be represented by the general formula $Mg(F, OH)_2 . nMg_2SiO_4$, and members are known for all values of n from 1 to 4. The exact details of the structures will not be considered here, but briefly they may all be described as composed of alternate sheets of the olivine structure and of the layer lattice of $Mg(OH)_2$. The similarity in the arrangement of the oxygen ions in these two structures enables a 'fit' to be achieved.

Phenacite. The structure of phenacite, Be_2SiO_4 (W. L. Bragg and Zachariasen, 1930), is of interest in that in spite of its similarity in composition to olivine the atomic arrangement is entirely different, and a relatively complex rhombohedral structure obtains. This difference arises solely from the lower co-ordination of the beryllium ion due to its smaller radius. In phenacite both silicon and beryllium are tetrahedrally co-ordinated and the complexity of the resulting structure is merely an expression of the difficulty of linking together these tetrahedra in the manner demanded by the electrostatic valency rule.

Other orthosilicates. Many other orthosilicates with an oxygen:silicon ratio of 4:1 and isolated SiO_4 groups are known, but they are mostly among substances of primarily mineralogical interest. When the oxygen:silicon ratio exceeds 4:1 some oxygen atoms are necessarily not linked to silicon at all, and such atoms may occur either as isolated O^{2-} ions co-ordinated only by metallic cations, as in cyanite, Al_2SiO_5, or as hydroxyl ions OH^-, as in topaz, $(F, OH)_2Al_2SiO_4$. In either case these oxygen atoms must be ignored in deriving the oxygen:silicon ratio, for otherwise the value of this ratio characteristic of the isolated SiO_4 tetrahedra will be concealed. Thus the formula of euclase is often given as $HBeAlSiO_5$, but X-ray analysis has shown that it is actually a normal orthosilicate and therefore to be regarded as $(OH)BeAlSiO_4$.

Structures with Si_2O_7 groups.

When the SiO_4 groups in a silicate are not separate, but occur linked together through one or more shared oxygen ions, the number of possible arrangements is very large. The simplest of these is that shown in Fig. 52 *b*, p. 226, where two such groups share a single oxygen ion to form the composite group $Si_2O_7^{6-}$. Such an arrangement is found in thortveitite, $Sc_2Si_2O_7$ (Zachariasen, 1930*a*), and in a number of other minerals. A particularly interesting structure of this kind is that of hemimorphite. On the basis of chemical analysis this mineral is usually represented by the formula $H_2Zn_2SiO_5$. The structure analysis (Ito and West, 1932) reveals, however, that the mineral is not an orthosilicate and that the oxygen ions are of three kinds, those co-ordinating the silicon ions, those contained in hydroxyl groups and those in water molecules. The true arrangement is made clear by writing the formula $(OH)_2Zn_4Si_2O_7 . H_2O$ so that the characteristic oxygen:silicon ratio is revealed. In vesuvianite (Warren and Modell, 1931) a combination of independent SiO_4 tetrahedra and Si_2O_7

groups is found: $(OH)_4Ca_{10}Al_4(Mg, Fe)_2\{(Si_2O_7)_2.(SiO_4)_5\}$. On the basis of Pauling's fifth rule such a combination of two different types of co-ordination is not likely to be of common occurrence: in fact it is rare.

Ring structures.

When two oxygen ions are shared between neighbouring SiO_4 tetrahedra closed ring-groups of composition $(SiO_3)_n^{2n-}$, containing an indefinite number of members, can be formed. On the basis of Pauling's third rule the two-membered ring Si_2O_6 is not likely to occur in any structure since it would require the very close approach of two highly charged silicon ions, but the ring with three members, illustrated in Fig. 52c, p. 226, has been observed in benitoite, $BaTiSi_3O_9$ (Zachariasen, 1930b). The ring of six SiO_4 groups shown in Fig. 52d, p. 226, is found in beryl, $Be_3Al_2Si_6O_{18}$ (W. L. Bragg and West, 1926), a structure which we may describe in somewhat more detail as it is a particularly beautiful example of the characteristic features of silicate structures, and at the same time one of which the co-ordina-

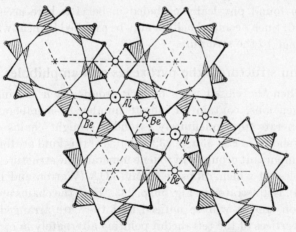

Fig. 54. The structure of beryl, $Be_3Al_2Si_6O_{18}$.

tion can be readily understood from a single diagram. A plan of the structure, projected on to the base of the hexagonal unit cell, is shown in Fig. 54. For clarity the SiO_4 groups are here shown as solid tetrahedra and only the beryllium and aluminium ions are separately indicated. The Si_6O_{18} rings are clearly revealed and it will be seen that these rings are bound together by the metallic cations. The oxygen co-ordination of these cations is that demanded by the radius ratio, and each beryllium ion is tetrahedrally surrounded by four oxygen ions belonging to four different rings. Similarly the aluminium ions occur between six different rings and are octahedrally co-ordinated by oxygen. The separate rings are thus bound together both laterally and vertically by the oxygen-cation bonds. The strength of each of these bonds, both from the aluminium and beryllium, is $\frac{1}{2}$, and the electrostatic valency rule is therefore satisfied in detail, since every oxygen ion not shared between two SiO_4 tetrahedra is linked to one silicon, one beryllium and one aluminium ion. A characteristic feature of the beryl structure is the wide, empty tunnels passing through the centres of the rings. No ions can be placed in these tunnels, since the valencies of the surrounding oxygen ions are already completely expended on their silicon neighbours, but it is possible that the helium so often found physically occluded in beryl is here accommodated. Such occluded helium may be expelled by heat without damage to the structure.

Chain structures: the pyroxenes and amphiboles.

When the closed rings of SiO_4 groups, each sharing two oxygen ions, contain an infinite number of members, they degenerate into indefinitely extended straight chains of the type shown in Fig. 55a, p. 232. Chains of this kind are found in the important group of pyroxene minerals, the structure of the simplest of which, diopside, $CaMg(SiO_3)_2$ (Warren and Bragg, 1928), is illustrated in Fig. 56, p. 233. Here the chains are seen end-on, and it will be noticed that they are arranged with the vertices of the tetrahedra pointing alternately in opposite directions. In the two directions normal to their length the chains are linked together by the oxygen-cation bonds. Each magnesium ion is 6-fold and each calcium ion 8-fold co-ordinated by oxygen.

In the amphibole minerals, closely related to the pyroxenes, a double chain of the type shown in Fig. 55b, p. 232, is found. This may be regarded as derived from the pyroxene chain by the operation of a reflection plane passing through the outermost oxygen ions. The oxygen:silicon ratio corresponding to this arrangement is 11:4. The structures of the amphiboles resemble very closely in their general features those of the pyroxenes, and will not be discussed in detail here. They differ from the pyroxenes, however, in containing hydroxyl or fluorine as an essential constituent, so that the idealized formula of tremolite may be written $(OH, F)_2Ca_2Mg_5Si_8O_{22}$. The hydroxyl and fluorine ions in such structures can never occur directly linked to silicon, since the single Si—OH or Si—F bond would completely saturate their valency and leave no other bonds available for their attachment to the rest of the structure. Accordingly, oxygen atoms contained in the hydroxyl group must be disregarded in deducing the characteristic oxygen:silicon ratio.

The structures of the pyroxenes and amphiboles not only reveal the long recognized crystallographic relationships between these two groups of minerals but also explain many of their physical properties. Thus, on account of the strong binding between silicon and oxygen ions such cleavages as take place are always parallel to the length of the chains. The fibrous character of many of the amphiboles is thus readily understood.

The crystal chemistry of pyroxenes and amphiboles. It is instructive to compare the now accepted formula of tremolite, $(OH, F)_2Ca_2Mg_5Si_8O_{22}$, with the composition $CaMg_3(SiO_3)_4 = Ca_2Mg_6Si_8O_{24}$ previously assigned on the basis of chemical analysis. The latter formula not only ignores the small quantity of water found as an essential constituent of the mineral, but also indicates a considerable excess of magnesium compared with the amount usually observed. Nevertheless, six magnesium ions are necessary to achieve electrical neutrality. In the light of the structure analysis it at once becomes clear that the characteristic oxygen:silicon ratio is 22:8 and not 24:8, and that there are only five magnesium

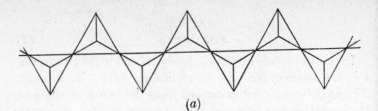

(a)

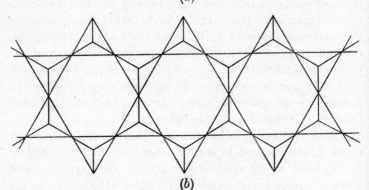

(b)

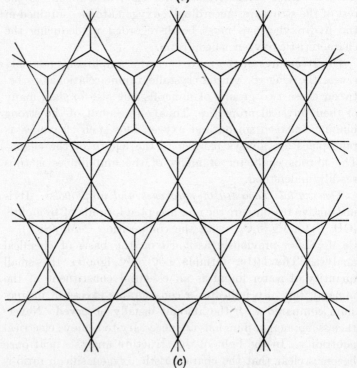

(c)

Fig. 55. Open silicon-oxygen groupings in silicates. (a) Tetrahedra sharing two oxygen atoms to form open chains, SiO_3, e.g. pyroxenes. (b) Tetrahedra sharing alternately two and three oxygen atoms to form open chains, Si_8O_{22}, e.g. amphiboles. (c) Tetrahedra sharing three oxygen atoms to form open sheets, Si_4O_{10}, e.g. micas.

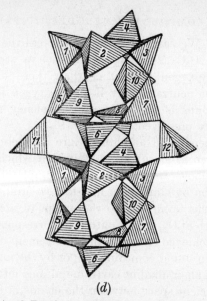

(d)

Fig. 55 (cont.). (d) Tetrahedra sharing four oxygen atoms to form open
frameworks, SiO_2, e.g. scapolite.

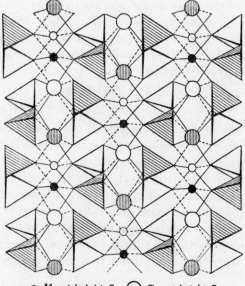

○ *Mg at height 0*   ◯ *Ca at height 0*

● *Mg at height ½*   ⊘ *Ca at height ½*

Fig. 56. The structure of diopside, $CaMg(SiO_3)_2$. The chains of Fig. 55a are
here seen end-on.

ions present. We cannot, however, express the composition in the form $O_2Ca_2Mg_5Si_8O_{22}$, since such a structure, containing two oxygen ions other than those in the silicon chains, is not neutral. Only if these oxygen ions occur as hydroxyl groups is the electrostatic valency rule satisfied and neutrality preserved.

The pyroxenes and amphiboles are characterized by the very extensive isomorphous substitution which they show. In the amphiboles we find our first example of the replacement of silicon by aluminium in 4-fold co-ordination, and in hornblende this occurs up to the extent of about $Si_6Al_2O_{22}$ compared with Si_8O_{22} in tremolite. The corresponding balance of charge is achieved either by the replacement of some Mg^{2+} ions by Al^{3+} in 6-fold co-ordination, or by the introduction of additional alkali or alkaline earth metal ions into the lattice. There is sufficient space between the chains in the structure to accommodate these additional ions. Even when no replacement of silicon occurs extensive substitution of cations by others of the same charge and comparable size may take place. Thus Fe^{2+} or Mn^{2+} may replace Mg^{2+}, the ions Fe^{2+}, Mg^{2+} or $2Na^+$ may replace Ca^{2+}, and F^- may replace OH^-. Berman and Larsen (1931) have proposed representing the amphiboles by the formula

$$(O, OH, F)_2(Ca, Na)_2(Na, K)_{0-1}(Mg, Fe^{2+})$$
$$(Mg, Fe^{2+}; Al, Fe^{3+})_4\{(Al, Si)_2Si_6O_{22}\},$$

but even this does not represent all the possibilities of substitution. In view of the complexities of these structures it is not surprising that their interpretation in terms of chemical analysis alone presented great difficulties. Even when we know what characteristic oxygen:silicon ratios to expect care must be taken in deducing such ratios to exclude from the oxygen ions any which occur in hydroxyl groups or as water, and to include with the silicon ions those aluminium ions which are in 4-fold but not those in 6-fold co-ordination.

Sheet structures: the micas.

If SiO_4 tetrahedra are linked together in such a way that three of the four oxygen ions are shared with neighbouring tetrahedra, a two-dimensional network of the type shown in Fig. 55c, p. 232, results. This arrangement corresponds to an oxygen:silicon ratio of 10:4 and is found in talc and the micas. The structure of muscovite mica, $(OH)_2KAl_2(Si_3Al)O_{10}$ (Jackson and West, 1930, 1933), is illustrated schematically in Fig. 57. Here the sheets of tetrahedra are seen edge-on and it will be observed that they are arranged in pairs with the vertices and bases of the tetrahedra alternately together. These vertices are strongly cross-linked by aluminium ions,

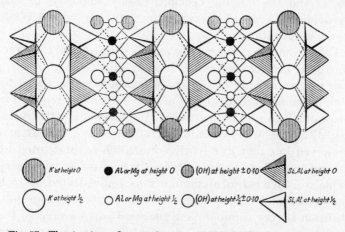

Fig. 57. The structure of muscovite mica, $(OH)_2KAl_2(Si_3Al)O_{10}$. The sheets of Fig. 55c, p. 232, are here seen edge-on.

each of which is octahedrally co-ordinated by four oxygen ions belonging to the sheets and by two hydroxyl groups. The bases of the tetrahedra are linked through potassium ions each co-ordinated by twelve oxygen neighbours. It is doubtful, however, if definite bonds can be regarded as reaching all these neighbours as a consideration of the electrostatic valency rule will show, for if we consider the oxygen ions forming the bases of the tetrahedra, it is clear that any linked to two silicon ions has its valency completely saturated and is thus rendered 'inactive'. Only in so far as silicon is replaced by aluminium can these oxygen ions become 'active', and every such oxygen ion which is bound to one silicon and one aluminium ion requires a further valency bond of strength $\frac{1}{4}$ to achieve saturation. We must therefore picture the potassium ion as electrostatically bound to only certain of its neighbours, but since the distribution of the aluminium ions in 4-fold co-ordination is purely statistical we cannot say which these active neighbours are. In talc, $(OH)_2Mg_3Si_4O_{10}$, there is no replacement of silicon by aluminium and all the oxygen ions in the bases of the sheets are inactive. It is accordingly impossible to accommodate any potassium ions between the sheets and the binding becomes closely analogous to that between the layers of a layer lattice with only van der Waals forces in operation.

Other common micas may be readily derived from the structure described for muscovite. In margarite, $CaAl_2(Si_2Al_2)O_{10}$, two instead of only one of the silicon ions are replaced by aluminium and the divalent Ca^{2+} ion is therefore required in place of K^+ to restore neutrality. In phlogopite, $(OH)_2KMg_3(Si_3Al)O_{10}$, the 4-fold co-ordinated aluminium of muscovite is preserved but that in 6-fold co-ordination is substituted by magnesium. Three magnesium ions are, of course, necessary in place of each pair of aluminium ions so substituted. As with the amphiboles and pyroxenes, however, isomorphous substitution is very common, and idealized compositions of the type just considered are rarely realized. Thus the extent to which silicon is replaced by aluminium is very variable, while the cations which may occur in 6-fold co-ordination include Al^{3+}, Fe^{3+}, Fe^{2+}, Mg^{2+}, Mn^{2+} and Li^+. The alkali metal, although most commonly K^+, may be Na^+ or Ca^{2+}, while finally OH^- may be replaced by considerable quantities of F^-. In spite of this complexity of composition, however, the structures can all be interpreted in terms of the simple idealized formula provided only that the primary significance of co-ordination number rather than valency is clearly appreciated. This point may be most readily illustrated by considering a number of actual analyses of mica structures.

The composition of the micas. In Table 52, the chemical analyses of some specimens of talc and of muscovite mica are shown. In the first column the composition is given in the conventional form as oxides, and in the second column the analyses are recalculated to show the relative number of atoms

TABLE 52

ANALYSES OF TALC AND MUSCOVITE MICA

Idealized formulae: talc $(OH)_2Mg_3Si_4O_{10}$; mica $(OH)_2KAl_2(Si_3Al)O_{10}$.

Talc

Composition by oxides		Composition by atoms			
MgO	30·22	Mg	2·92	— }	3·06
FeO	2·66	Fe	0·14	— }	
SiO$_2$	62·24	Si	4·05		
H$_2$O	4·94	OH	2·14		
	100·06	O	10·00		

Muscovite I

Composition by oxides		Composition by atoms			
Na$_2$O	0·90	Na	0·12	— }	1·03
K$_2$O	10·70	K	0·91	— }	
MgO	0·38	Mg	0·05	{1·93}	1·98
Al$_2$O$_3$	37·15	Al	2·90	{1·93}	
SiO$_2$	45·54	Si	3·03	{0·97}	4·00
H$_2$O	4·80	OH	2·13		
	99·47	O	10·00		

Muscovite II

Composition by oxides		Composition by atoms			
Na$_2$O	1·01	Na	0·12	— }	0·61
K$_2$O	6·05	K	0·49	— }	
MgO	0·50	Mg	0·05		2·08
CaO	0·27	Ca	0·02	{2·01}	
Al$_2$O$_3$	34·70	Al	2·61	{2·01}	
SiO$_2$	53·01	Si	3·40	{0·60}	4·00
H$_2$O	4·67	OH	1·99		
	100·21	O	10·00		

of each kind present, expressed on a basis of 10 atoms of oxygen. Oxygen in the hydroxyl group, which appears as water in the chemical analysis, is excluded from these 10 oxygen atoms and expressed separately as OH. The figures in the second column are therefore immediately comparable with the idealized formulae of the minerals.

The analysis of the talc shows that this particular specimen corresponds closely to the ideal composition $(OH)_2Mg_3Si_4O_{10}$. The O : Si ratio of 10 : 4 is closely satisfied, but there is some replacement of magnesium by iron. The total of $(Mg + Fe)$ slightly exceeds 3 and the resulting excess of positive charge is compensated by a corresponding excess of OH.

The analysis of muscovite I may be compared with the formula $(OH)_2KAl_2(Si_3Al)O_{10}$. The number of silicon ions is 3·03, so that 0·97 of the 2·90 aluminium ions must occur in tetrahedral co-ordination. The remaining 1·93 aluminium ions, together with 0·05 magnesium, are 6-fold co-ordinated. The loss of 0·97 unit of positive charge, brought about by the substitution of Al^{3+} for Si^{4+}, is compensated by the introduction of $(Na + K)$, and there is therefore a close correspondence between the amount of aluminium in 4-fold co-ordination and the total alkali content. In muscovite II an unusually low replacement of silicon occurs and only 0·60 aluminium ions per molecule are found in tetrahedral co-ordination. Corresponding to this the total alkali content is only 0·61 ion of $(Na + K)$ per molecule.

The physical properties of the micas. The very characteristic physical properties of the mica group of minerals find a ready explanation in the structure. The pseudo-hexagonal symmetry is an immediate consequence of the hexagonal form of the separate sheets and the eminent cleavage results from the rupture of the feeble oxygen-potassium bonds by which the sheets are held together. The optical properties may also be explained in terms of the structure but this point is discussed in more detail later.

A different kind of sheet structure has been found in apophyllite (W. H. Taylor and Náray-Szabó, 1931), where the SiO_4 tetrahedra are linked into four-membered rings. This is, however, the only sheet structure other than those of the mica type so far discovered.

Framework structures.

The final class of silicate structures is that which arises when the SiO_4 tetrahedra are so linked that every oxygen ion is shared between two tetrahedra. Such an arrangement gives rise to an indefinitely extended three-dimensional framework with an oxygen : silicon ratio of 2 : 1, and is, of course, found in its simplest form in the various modifications of silica already discussed. It is clear that no metallic silicate can be based on such a structure unless some of the silicon is replaced by aluminium, for only then does the framework acquire the negative charge required to balance that of the cations introduced.

In contrast to the other types of tetrahedron linkage already described, the three-dimensional frame-works commonly exist in a number of entirely different forms which give rise to several quite distinct families of petrologically important minerals. No silicates are based on the type of framework found in the various forms of silica, for these are all too compact to permit the insertion of other ions, but a portion of the essential structural framework of the mineral scapolite is illustrated in Fig. 55d, p. 233.

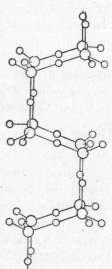

The felspars. Mineralogically by far the most important framework structures are the felspars (W. H. Taylor, 1933; W. H. Taylor, Darbyshire and Strunz, 1934), the basis of which is the very open framework illustrated in Fig. 58. In orthoclase, $K(Si_3Al)O_8$, one-quarter of the silicon in the structure is substituted by aluminium and for each silicon ion thus replaced one potassium ion is introduced. The potassium is accommodated in large interstices in the lattice and is surrounded by ten oxygen ions, but the co-ordination is irregular and the

O Oxygen

◯ Silicon or aluminium

Fig. 58. The silicon-oxygen framework of the felspars.

structure cannot conveniently be regarded as based on a packing of polyhedra. In albite, $Na(Si_3Al)O_8$, sodium replaces the potassium of orthoclase, and in anorthite, $Ca(Si_2Al_2)O_8$, two of the silicon ions are replaced by aluminium and a divalent cation is therefore required to restore neutrality. Complete solid solution occurs between albite and anorthite, but not between albite and orthoclase, in spite of their greater chemical similarity, on account of the difference in size between the sodium and potassium ions. The structures of the felspars provide a very satisfactory explanation of the numerous forms of twinning shown by these crystals.

The zeolites. A second group of minerals based on a framework structure are those of the zeolite family. The detailed features of these structures are primarily of mineralogical interest, but they also display certain important properties which call for mention here. A distinctive characteristic of the zeolites is that they all contain water, which, however, can be readily driven off by heat without destroying the structure, and can, moreover, be reversibly replaced or even substituted by other neutral substances such as ammonia, alcohol, mercury or iodine. The explanation of this behaviour lies in the very open nature of the zeolite framework, which is intersected by wide channels through which the water molecules can readily pass without disturbance to the structure as a whole (W. H. Taylor, 1930, 1934).

A second feature of the zeolites is the way in which even the cations can be similarly reversibly substituted by others, again without damage to the structure as a whole, and this base exchange is in fact the foundation of the permutite system of water softening. The substitution is found to be of two kinds: (1) a substitution similar to that found in the felspars with two ions replaced by two others of similar sizes and the same total charge, e.g. $K^+ + Si^{4+} \rightleftharpoons Ba^{2+} + Al^{3+}$, or $Na^+ + Si^{4+} \rightleftharpoons Ca^{2+} + Al^{3+}$; (2) a substitution in which the number of cations is altered, e.g. $Ba^{2+} \rightleftharpoons 2K^+$, $Ca^{2+} \rightleftharpoons 2Na^+$, or $Na^+ + 2Ca^{2+} \rightleftharpoons 3Na^+ + Ca^{2+}$. The structures contain sufficient open spaces to accommodate the additional ions taken up in the second type of substitution.

The zeolites provide another example of an incomplete defect structure, and in analcite, $NaAlSi_2O_6 . H_2O$, W. H. Taylor (1930) has shown that the 16 sodium ions in the unit cell are distributed at random over 24 equivalent positions. The readiness with which the cations can diffuse in and out of the zeolite structures would suggest, moreover, that the distribution is a statistical one both in space and in time, so that the sodium ions must be regarded as migrating freely through the structure in a fluid condition. The distribution of the water molecules in a partially dehydrated crystal must also be statistical.

The type of binding in the framework structures is reflected in their physical properties, and the strength of the silicon-oxygen bond, extending symmetrically in three dimensions, results in a characteristic lack of good cleavages. At the same time the symmetry of the framework gives rise to optical and mechanical properties which are very nearly isotropic and in

TABLE 53

SILICATE STRUCTURE TYPES

Structural arrangement	Examples	Oxygen: silicon ratio
Independent tetrahedra	Orthosilicates, e.g. olivine	4:1
Two tetrahedra sharing one oxygen atom	Thorveitite	7:2
Closed rings of tetrahedra each sharing two oxygen atoms	Benitoite, beryl	3:1
Infinite chains of tetrahedra each sharing two oxygen atoms	Pyroxenes	3:1
Infinite double chains of tetrahedra sharing alternately two and three oxygen atoms	Amphiboles	11:4
Infinite sheets of tetrahedra each sharing three oxygen atoms	Micas	5:2
Infinite framework of tetrahedra each sharing all four oxygen atoms	Felspars, zeolites	2:1

striking contrast to the platey character of the micas and the fibrous nature of the amphiboles.

This concludes our systematic description of the silicate structures, and for reference we give in Table 53, p. 241, a summary of the several classes of these structures together with the corresponding oxygen : silicon ratios. There remain a number of general points common to all the silicates which call for brief discussion.

The crystal chemistry of the silicates.

The nature of the SiO_4 *group.* Throughout our description of the silicates we have treated all the bonds as purely polar in origin and we have seen that the characteristic sizes and co-ordinations of the ions have all been in satisfactory agreement with such a picture. Although this treatment is undoubtedly justified as far as the metallic cations are concerned, it is very doubtful if the binding within the SiO_4 groups can be properly regarded as truly ionic. In the presence of such a small and highly charged ion as Si^{4+} the readily polarized oxygen ion must suffer considerable distortion, and in fact a measure of the extent of this polarization is provided by comparing the Al-O distance in 6- and 4-fold co-ordination. In sillimanite, where aluminium occurs in both states of co-ordination, Hey and Taylor (1931) have found the two distances to be about 1·9 and 1·7 A. respectively. When linked to silicon the polarization of the oxygen ion must be even larger, and in fact the characteristic Si-O distance of 1·62 A. is considerably smaller than the sum of the normal radii of the Si^{4+} and O^{2-} ions. Further evidence for regarding this binding as partially homopolar is provided by the argument, which we have already advanced in discussing the several structures of silica, that an oxygen ion linked to two silicon neighbours does not lie on the line joining these ions but is displaced so that the inter-bond angle is about 140°, indicating a compromise between the purely ionic binding with an angle of 180° and the purely homopolar with the tetrahedral angle of 109°. Fortunately, it is a matter of little practical moment whether we regard the

SiO_4 group as composed of a Si^{4+} ion co-ordinated by four O^{2-} ions or as a neutral silicon atom linked to each of four singly charged O^- ions by single homopolar bonds, for from either point of view the group appears as a discrete unit of the same characteristic shape and resultant charge. The Si—O bond has been discussed theoretically as an example of a resonance structure by Slater (1931 a) and by Pauling (1932 a).

The replacement of silicon by other ions. Although Al^{3+} is the only ion which commonly replaces Si^{4+} in tetrahedral co-ordination in the silicates, other ions occasionally appear in the same rôle. The most important of these is As^{5+} which is found in berzeliite, $Mg_2(Ca_2Na)As_3O_{12}$ (Bubeck and Machatschki, 1935). This mineral is isomorphous with the ortho-silicate garnet, of ideal composition $Al_2Ca_3Si_3O_{12}$, and it is seen from a comparison of the formulae that the three units of positive charge acquired by the substitution of As^{5+} for Si^{4+} are compensated by the replacement of 2 Al^{3+} by 2 Mg^{2+} and of Ca^{2+} by Na^+. Small but appreciable quantities of silicon are often found replacing arsenic in berzeliite.

Model structures of the silicates. Model structures of the silicates have been discussed by Goldschmidt (1926 b), who has instanced Li_2BeF_4 as a model of the structure of willemite, Zn_2SiO_4. The radii of the several ions in these two structures are

$$Li^+ \quad 0.78 \, A. \qquad Be^{2+} \quad 0.34 \, A. \qquad F^- \quad 1.33 \, A.$$
$$Zn^{2+} \quad 0.83 \, A. \qquad Si^{4+} \quad 0.39 \, A. \qquad O^{2-} \quad 1.32 \, A.$$

and the very close correspondence between the two sets of radii results in isomorphous structures with closely similar cell dimensions and crystallographic properties. On the other hand, the increased strength of the polar binding in the silicate is reflected in the physical properties, as the following data show:

	Li_2BeF_4	Zn_2SiO_4
Hardness	3·8	5·5
Melting point	470° C.	1509° C.
Solubility in water	Readily soluble	Insoluble

Similarly $NaLiBe_2F_6$ is a model of the structure of diopside, $CaMgSi_2O_6$.

The chemical classification of silicates. The purely structural classification of the silicates which we have here adopted naturally challenges comparison with older and more orthodox chemical classifications. Long before the application of X-ray structure analysis, the mineralogist had classed together, on purely morphological grounds, many silicates of very different constitution, while the chemical classification of substances of such uncertain and variable composition necessarily presented great difficulties. Nevertheless, we can now see that the failure of the chemical classification was due not so much to the inherent difficulty of the material as to the falsity of the principles on which it was based. On the one hand, the dual rôle of aluminium, which enables it to appear either as a normal metallic cation or in place of silicon, could only be detected by X-ray methods, and, on the other, the chemical classification sought always to refer all silicates to some corresponding acid. We cannot here emphasize too strongly that structurally there is no relation whatsoever between acids and their salts, and that in so far as acids exist it is a structural accident which does not represent any structural association. The properties of the strongly polarizing and vanishingly small H^+ ion are so entirely different from those of any other cation that they demand entirely separate treatment, and we deliberately refrain until Chap. x from discussing the structures of any acids or acid salts. In most of the silicates the disorganization of the structure which would result from the substitution of hydrogen for the other cations is so drastic that it is unthinkable that such an arrangement should be stable. The acids simply have no existence.

This concludes our discussion of the silicates. We repeat that no attempt has been made to give an account in any way adequate from the mineralogical point of view, but at the same time we have tried to discuss some of the more important chemical features of these structures. The reader who wishes for a more detailed account of the silicates is referred to the work of W. L. Bragg (1937), already mentioned. Other comprehensive reviews have been given by W. L. Bragg (1930), Machatsohki (1932), Schiebold (1932, 1933) and Berman (1937).

GERMANATES

The only other mesodesmic compounds which call for mention are the germanates. Here the radius of the Ge^{4+} ion, which is very nearly the same as that of Si^{4+}, again corresponds to a tetrahedral co-ordination by oxygen, and Goldschmidt (1931 b) has shown that there is a very close similarity between the germanates and silicates, and that germanates with analogous structures can be prepared corresponding to most of the classes of silicates we have discussed.

CHAPTER IX

IONIC COMPOUNDS: ANISODESMIC
STRUCTURES

INTRODUCTION

Anisodesmic ionic structures are intrinsically simpler than
the mesodesmic compounds discussed in the last chapter.
This greater simplicity arises primarily from the impossibility
in these structures of the indefinitely extended chains, sheets
and frameworks which occur in mesodesmic crystals. By
definition, anisodesmic structures contain some cation B
(usually of relatively high charge and small size) linked to its
co-ordinating anions by bonds of strength greater than one-
half the charge of these anions. It follows that no anion can
be linked to two B cations, and that therefore the ion B and its
anion neighbours constitute a discrete complex group in the
crystal bound together by forces very much stronger than
those binding it to the rest of the structure. Even when the
other bonds are disrupted in solution the complex group often
preserves its identity and continues to exist as a single unit.

This picture of the complex group as a coherent entity
enables anisodesmic structures to be described very simply in
terms of the disposition of these groups and of the remaining
cations. Often this arrangement is found to simulate closely
that observed in some very much simpler isodesmic structure,
and especially is this the case when the complex ion is in free
rotation and so acquires true spherical symmetry. The structures can then be considered as simple assemblages of cations
and large spherical anions.

In anisodesmic crystals the exact details of the structural
arrangement are of less interest than the shape of the complex
group, for, while the former is necessarily characteristic of
only a single substance, the latter is found to be practically the
same in all structures in which the given group occurs. Here,
therefore, we shall first describe the complex groups of com-

mon occurrence in ionic crystals, and then illustrate in detail, by only a few examples of some particular interest, typical structures in which they are found. As already explained, we exclude from this section the salts of organic acids since in them the structure is determined more by the polarity and shape of the molecule than by the mutual co-ordination of charged ions. We also defer until later any discussion of hydrated compounds.

THE STRUCTURE OF COMPLEX IONS

The majority of complex groups which we shall have to discuss are the anions of simple inorganic salts, and contain small, highly charged ions such as C^{4+}, N^{5+}, P^{5+}, As^{5+}, S^{6+}, Cr^{6+}, Mo^{6+}, Mn^{7+}, etc., co-ordinated by oxygen. A few ions of other types, however, and certain complex cations, also call for mention.

In all the complex ions occurring in anisodesmic structures the very strong polarizing power of the cation results in a pronounced tendency towards purely homopolar binding within the complex group, and this tendency is reflected in the structure by a considerable reduction in the interatomic distances compared with the values to be expected from a purely ionic linkage, and also in occasional departures in the shape of the group from the form to be expected on purely geometrical grounds.

Complex anions: diatomic ions.

Diatomic ions are necessarily linear and call for little discussion. The cyanide ion $(C \equiv N)^-$ is often found in free rotation, so that many cyanides have simple structures. Thus KCN has the sodium chloride arrangement. In AgCN, however, the stronger polarizing power of the silver ion prevents rotation and a more complex structure results. The carbide ion $(C \equiv C)^{2-}$ does not rotate but simple structures are nevertheless often formed, and that of CaC_2 may be considered as a sodium chloride structure in which elongated C_2 groups, all arranged parallel, distort the cubic unit cell into one with tetragonal symmetry. The same arrangement is found in a number of peroxides such as SrO_2 and BaO_2, in which the peroxide ion O_2^{2-} consists of two oxygen atoms strongly bound by a single homopolar bond $(O—O)^{2-}$. An illustration of the packing in these structures is given in Fig. 59, which reveals the extent of the polarization within the O_2 group and clearly shows that such structures can no longer be regarded as built of rigid spherical ions (Bernal, Djatlowa, Kasarnowsky, Reichstein and Ward, 1935). The structural distinction between these peroxides, containing O_2^{2-} ions, and those with the rutile and similar structures, in which separate

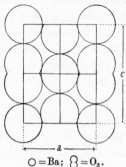

$O=Ba; \; \bigcirc\!\!\!\bigcirc =O_2.$

Fig. 59. The structure of barium peroxide, BaO_2.

O^{2-} ions occur, is chemically of interest as a confirmation of Mendeleef's classification of the peroxides into 'superoxides' (such as SrO_2 and BaO_2), in which the valency of the metal is not greater than in the normal oxide, and 'polyoxides' (such as MnO_2 and PbO_2, with the rutile structure), in which a higher metal valency obtains.

In KO_2 the singly charged O_2^- ion has a similar form but must here be regarded as a resonance between the neutral oxygen molecule $(O=O)^0$ and the doubly charged ion $(O—O)^{2-}$. In accordance with this the O-O distance is smaller than in SrO_2.

Triatomic ions.

The univalent ions N_3^-, CNO^-, CNS^-, Cl_3^-, Br_3^-, I_3^-, $ClICl^-$, etc., are all linear and form with small cations, such as Na^+, structures similar to the carbides with the groups all parallel. With larger cations, such as K^+ or Cs^+, different structures obtain in which the groups are all parallel to a plane but mutually inclined in two directions at right angles. The $Ag(CN)_2^-$ group in $K[Ag(CN)_2]$ is also linear.

A bent triatomic ion is found in the chlorite group, ClO_2^-, and in the nitrite group, NO_2^-, where the N—O bonds are inclined at an angle of $132°$. This structure may be regarded as derived from the symmetrical NO_3^- group by the removal of an oxygen atom followed by an increase in the interbond angle due to the repulsion between the oxygen ions. The extent of the polarization is indicated by the N-O distance of 1·13 A. which is considerably less than the normal radius of the oxygen ion alone. The PO_2 group in ammonium hypophosphite, $NH_4H_2PO_2$, is also bent, but this is due to the fact that the compound is not an acid salt but a neutral salt in which the radical must be more properly regarded as the tetrahedral $PH_2O_2^-$ group. This point is considered in more detail in the next chapter.

BX_3 ions.

BX_3 ions fall into two classes, according as to whether they have a plane or a pyramidal structure. The CO_3^{2-} and NO_3^- groups are the only common ions with the plane structure, and in both of them the cation is symmetrically surrounded by three oxygen neighbours at the corners of an equilateral triangle. In both groups the polarization is very strong and the C-O and N-O distances are 1·25 and 1·22 A. respectively. The increased compactness of the NO_3 group, although a measure of strong forces within the group, is also a measure of increased intra-ionic instability owing to the increasing contribution of the repulsive forces from the polarized oxygen ions. Corresponding to this the nitrates are as a class less stable than the carbonates. The extent of the polarization is also indicated by the fact that the molecular refractivity of the oxygen ions in the NO_3 and CO_3 groups is only about one-half that of the ion in the free state (Fajans and Joos, 1924). The NO_3^- group is frequently found in free rotation when it behaves as a spherical ion roughly equivalent in size to that of iodine.

The ions PO_3^{3-}, SO_3^{2-}, ClO_3^-, AsO_3^{3-}, SeO_3^{2-}, BrO_3^- and SbO_3^{3-} all have a low pyramidal structure in which the oxygen ions are arranged at the corners of an equilateral triangle but in which the cation is displaced from the plane of this triangle. In all cases these ions may be regarded as derived from the corresponding tetrahedral BX_4 ion by the removal of one oxygen atom, and the remaining B—O bonds are still directed roughly to three corners of a regular tetrahedron. The general stability relations of these ions resemble those of the plane groups except that a new source of instability is furnished by their unsaturated nature and consequent oxygen affinity.

Zachariasen's rule. The structure of BX_2 and BX_3 ions, and of molecules of the same composition, has been discussed theoretically by Zachariasen (1929a, 1931c, d), who, by treating these groups as bound by purely ionic forces, has argued that the complex $\begin{cases} BX_2 \\ BX_3 \end{cases}$ will have a $\begin{cases} \text{collinear} \\ \text{coplanar} \end{cases}$ configuration if the condition $\begin{cases} v = 2p \\ v = 3p \end{cases}$ is satisfied. Here v is the total number of valency electrons in the group and p the number of valency electrons in the inert gas following X in the periodic classification. The condition therefore demands that the total number of electrons available shall be just sufficient to enable the ions X to acquire an inert gas configuration by depriving B of all its valency electrons. If the total number of electrons is in excess of this number the surplus give rise to polarization effects which result in an unsymmetrical structure.

When applied to the various ions described above Zachariasen's rule leads to results in agreement with those experimentally observed. Thus the ClO_2^- and NO_2^- ions, with 20 and 18 valency electrons respectively, are not collinear, since the total number of electrons exceeds $2 \times 8 = 16$. Similarly the ions PO_3^{3-}, SO_3^{2-}, ClO_3^-, etc., in all of which the number of valency electrons exceeds 24, have a pyramidal structure. On the other hand, the structures of the CO_3^{2-} and NO_3^- ions, with exactly 24 electrons, are plane.

Although Zachariasen's generalization is based on the assumption of a purely ionic binding in the groups discussed, it has been pointed out by Slater (1931b) that the same conclusions can be reached when the more valid picture of the partially homopolar nature of this binding is adopted.

BX_4 ions.

The BX_4 ions are the most stable and also the commonest of complex ion groups. They fall into three classes according as the co-ordination round the B ion is tetrahedral, distorted tetrahedral, or plane.

The regularly co-ordinated tetrahedral ions are by far the most numerous and important and include PO_4^{3-}, SO_4^{2-}, ClO_4^-, CrO_4^{2-}, MnO_4^-, SeO_4^{2-} and BF_4^-. All these ions, with the exception of the coloured CrO_4^{2-} and MnO_4^- ions, are of substantially the same size, with a B-X distance of about 1·5 A., and within wide limits they may all be regarded as isomorphously replaceable. This is also true even of mixed complex ions such as PFO_3^{2-}, the salts of which are isomorphous with the corresponding sulphates. In such cases the isomorphism arises from the similarity in size of the two different kinds of X ion which must be regarded as statistically distributed to conform to the tetrahedral symmetry. The chemically much more closely related sulphate and thiosulphate ions, SO_4^{2-} and $S.SO_3^{2-}$, on the other hand, do not form isomorphous structures owing to the difference in size and polarizability of the oxygen and sulphur atoms.

The symmetrical form of the tetrahedral BX_4 groups makes the structures in which they occur nearly isotropic in their optical and mechanical properties. A great number of different structures are found among crystals containing these ions and a few of the more common will be considered below. Occasionally at high temperatures the BX_4 ions are found in free rotation.

The most common BX_4 ions with distorted tetrahedral co-ordination are MoO_4^{2-}, WO_4^{2-}, ReO_4^- and IO_4^-. Here the shape may be regarded as due to a compromise between an ionic binding with a regular tetrahedral co-ordination and a purely homopolar binding, which, for B ions of such high atomic number, can result in a plane square co-ordination (see p. 69). The distortion takes the form of a compression along a diad axis which, if continued, would finally produce a flat square of X ions. The shape and size of these ions prevent them from being isomorphous with the symmetrical tetrahedral ions, and at the same time confer on the structures in which they occur a more marked anisotropy of properties.

A plane square BX_4 group is formed by the ions $Ni(CN)_4^{2-}$,

$PdCl_4^{2-}$ and $PtCl_4^{2-}$. Here the planar arrangement may be regarded either as due to the purely homopolar character of the binding, or as arising from the octahedrally co-ordinated BX_6 groups by the removal of two X ions.

BX_6 ions.

All the complex BX_6 groups known have a regular octa-hedral co-ordination and the majority of them are halogen-containing ions. Oxygen ions are here excluded, since an anisodesmic structure could result only with a B ion of charge 7 or more and no such ion is sufficiently large to be 6-fold co-ordinated by oxygen. Octahedral co-ordination by oxygen in mesodesmic and isodesmic structures is, of course, very common. Among the octahedral BX_6 ions are SiF_6^{2-}, $TiCl_6^{2-}$, $SeCl_6^{2-}$, $ZrCl_6^{2-}$, $SnCl_6^{2-}$, $TeCl_6^{2-}$, $PtCl_6^{2-}$ and $PbCl_6^{2-}$, as well as most of the corresponding bromides. In addition the mixed groups $OsO_2Cl_4^{2-}$ and $OsNCl_5^{2-}$ appear to have a regular octahedral structure. Many trivalent ions such as AlF_6^{3-}, $Cr(CN)_6^{3-}$, etc., have the same arrangement but strictly are all mesodesmic.

From a structural point of view these highly symmetrical octahedral ions, whether in rotation or not, can be regarded as large spheres, and the structures to which they give rise are generally very simple ones determined by the packing of these spheres and the remaining cations. Such large anions, however, are very readily polarized, and the most stable structures are those in which only large and therefore weakly polarizing cations occur.

Polynuclear complex anions.

A number of polynuclear complex anion groups containing two or more cations B have been studied, and of these the most important are the ions of the several sulphur oxy-acids. The dithionate ion, $S_2O_6^{2-}$, consists essentially of two sulphur atoms each tetrahedrally co-ordinated by the other sulphur atom and by three oxygen neighbours, thus giving the very symmetrical group illustrated in Fig. 60a.

The trithionate ion, $S_3O_6^{2-}$, has the form and dimensions shown in Fig. 60b, and here again the co-ordination round the end sulphur atoms is tetrahedral. The significance of this structure has been discussed by Zachariasen (1934a,b) who has pointed out that the group may be regarded as bound

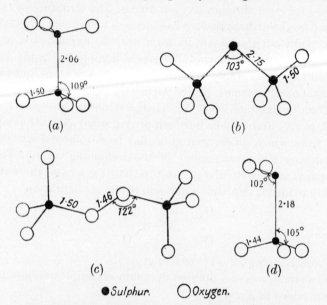

● Sulphur.   ○ Oxygen.

Fig. 60. The structures of some polynuclear complex groups.
(a) The dithionate ion, $S_2O_6^{2-}$.   (b) The trithionate ion, $S_3O_6^{2-}$.
(c) The persulphate ion, $S_2O_8^{2-}$.   (d) The pyrosulphite ion, $S_2O_5^{2-}$.

entirely by single homopolar bonds, thus explaining its characteristic form, if it is considered as consisting of six singly charged O^- ions, two S^{2+} ions and one neutral S atom, $(O_3^-S^{2+}SS^{2+}O_3^-)^{2-}$, corresponding to the electronic configuration

$$: \overset{..}{\underset{..}{O}} : \quad : \overset{..}{\underset{..}{O}} :$$
$$: \overset{..}{O} : \overset{.}{S} : \overset{.}{S} : \overset{.}{S} : \overset{..}{O} : \; .$$
$$: \overset{..}{\underset{..}{O}} : \quad : \overset{..}{\underset{..}{O}} :$$

The neutral sulphur atom in the centre of the group is saturated and clearly cannot be linked to any further atoms, so that the non-existence of such radicals as $S_3O_7^{2-}$ and $S_3O_8^{2-}$ is readily understood.

The persulphate group $S_2O_8^{2-}$ has the structure shown in Fig. 60c, p. 253, and may be regarded as two sulphate groups linked together through oxygen atoms. The structure of this group has been discussed by Zachariasen and Mooney (1934a) who point out that again its form may be explained if it is regarded as bound entirely by single homopolar bonds and as built up of six singly charged O^- ions, two S^{2+} ions and two neutral oxygen atoms, $(O_3^-S^{2+}OOS^{2+}O_3^-)^{2-}$.

The pyrosulphite ion $S_2O_5^{2-}$ has the structure shown in Fig. 60d, p. 253, and may be most simply regarded as a dithionate ion from which an oxygen atom has been removed without disturbing the arrangement of the remaining atoms. This structure is of particular interest in that it is a case where the X-ray evidence demands a revision of the configuration

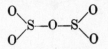

previously accepted on chemical grounds.

The structures of a number of common complex anions are summarized in Table 54.

TABLE 54

STRUCTURES OF SOME COMMON COMPLEX ANIONS

Type	Arrangement	Examples
XY	Linear	CN^-, O_2^-, O_2^{2-}, N_2^-
XYZ	Linear Bent	N_3^-, CNO^-, CNS^-, Cl_3^-, $ClICl^-$ ClO_2^-, NO_2^-
BX_3	Plane equilateral triangle Regular trigonal pyramid	CO_3^{2-}, NO_3^- PO_3^{3-}, SO_3^{2-}, ClO_3^-, etc.
BX_4	Regular tetrahedron Distorted tetrahedron Plane square	PO_4^{3-}, SO_4^{2-}, ClO_4^-, CrO_4^{2-}, MnO_4^-, SeO_4^{2-}, BF_4^- MoO_4^{2-}, WO_4^{2-}, ReO_4^-, IO_4^- $Ni(CN)_4^{2-}$, $PdCl_4^{2-}$, $PtCl_4^{2-}$
BX_6	Regular octahedron	SiF_6^{2-}, $TiCl_6^{2-}$, $SiCl_6^{2-}$, $ZrCl_6^{2-}$, $SnCl_6^{2-}$, $TeCl_6^{2-}$, $PtCl_6^{2-}$, $PbCl_6^{2-}$

Complex cations.

Compared with the complex anions, the number of complex cations is extremely small and is practically limited to the ammonium ion and its derivatives, and to the complex cations, such as $Ni(NH_3)_6^{2+}$, etc., which occur in the co-ordination compounds. The latter compounds are closely related to the hydrates and are most conveniently considered under that head.

In most structures the NH_4^+ ion can be treated as a spherical ion of radius 1·46 A. owing to the free rotation which takes place at temperatures above about 230° K. Most ammonium halides, therefore, have sodium chloride or caesium chloride structures. Ammonium fluoride, however, is interesting, for here the small fluorine ion exerts a sufficiently large attraction on the four tetrahedrally disposed hydrogen ions to prevent rotation and in consequence the 4-fold co-ordinated wurtzite structure results.

STRUCTURES CONTAINING COMPLEX IONS

Structures with plane BX_3 groups.

The calcite structure. The structure of calcite, $CaCO_3$, is common to a number of carbonates and nitrates, and may be most readily described in terms of its relation to the sodium chloride structure. If the sodium and chlorine ions of this latter structure are replaced by calcium and carbonate ions respectively, and the cubic structure is then distorted by compression along one triad axis, the calcite arrangement results. The planes of all the CO_3 groups are parallel and normal to the triad axis of the rhombohedral cell. The detailed co-ordination of the structure reveals that each Ca^{2+} ion is surrounded by a somewhat irregular octahedron of six O^{2-} neighbours, while each O^{2-} ion is bound to two Ca^{2+} ions as well as to the C^{4+} ion of the carbonate group. The electrostatic valency rule is therefore satisfied in detail.

The calcite structure is found in a number of compounds of the general type ABX_3, including the following carbonates and nitrates: $MgCO_3$, $CaCO_3$, $MnCO_3$, $FeCO_3$, $CoCO_3$, $ZnCO_3$,

$CdCO_3$, $LiNO_3$, $NaNO_3$. The appearance of the structure is conditioned primarily by the radius of the ion A, and if this radius exceeds about 1·1 A. the aragonite arrangement is generally preferred. Compounds, such as $CaCO_3$ itself, containing cations of radius near this critical value, are dimorphous and appear with both structures, the aragonite structure being generally the one stable at high temperatures since the influence of the thermal vibrations increases the effective size of the cation.

The aragonite structure. This structure may be regarded as derived from that of nickel arsenide by replacing arsenic by calcium and nickel by carbonate groups. As in calcite, all the CO_3 groups are parallel but the details of the co-ordination are different. Here the calcium ions are more highly co-ordinated, each being bound to nine O^{2-} neighbours, while each O^{2-} ion is bound to three Ca^{2+} ions as well as to the C^{4+} ion of the carbonate group. Again the electrostatic valency rule is satisfied in detail. The aragonite structure is found in the following salts: $CaCO_3$, $SrCO_3$, $BaCO_3$, $PbCO_3$, KNO_3, and it will be seen that in each case the cation is large.

When the radius of the cation exceeds about 1·45 A. the aragonite arrangement in its turn becomes unstable, and $RbNO_3$ and $CsNO_3$ have other structures. There is no divalent ion, however, sufficiently large for the corresponding transition to take place in any carbonates. With strongly polarizing cations the rubidium nitrate structure is apparently not stable, and, in spite of the close correspondence between the radii of the Tl^+ and Rb^+ ions, $TlNO_3$ has yet a different structure. Similarly $AgNO_3$ differs from $NaNO_3$ in not having the calcite structure.

Structures with pyramidal BX_3 groups.

This class includes a number of salts already listed, of which the commonest and most extensively studied are the sulphites, chlorates and bromates. All these salts have in common the characteristic low pyramidal form of the complex group with the B ion displaced about 0·5 A. from the plane of the oxygen ions. The exact details of the structural arrangements are, however, of little general interest, for there are many different structure types, depending on the size, charge and polariz ability of the cation, few of which are common to more than a small number of compounds. The structure of sodium sulphite, Na_2SO_3 (Zachariasen and Buckley, 1931), is typical of the general type of co-ordination which obtains in such structures and is illustrated in plan in Fig. 61. The SO_3 groups are all

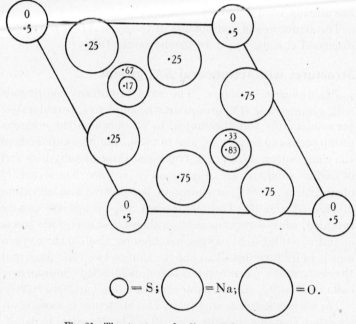

Fig. 61. The structure of sodium sulphite, Na_2SO_3.

arranged with the plane of the oxygen ions parallel to the base of the hexagonal unit cell. The Na^+ ions are of two kinds which respectively do and do not lie vertically above the centres of the SO_3 groups. Both kinds of Na^+ ions are octahedrally co-ordinated by oxygen, but the octahedra about those of the former type are considerably distorted. Each O^{2-} ion is linked to one S^{4+} ion and to four Na^+ neighbours so that the electro-static valency rule is satisfied.

The structure of potassium chlorate, $KClO_3$ (Zachariasen,

1929b), is closely related to that of calcite with K^+ instead of Ca^{2+} and ClO_3^- instead of CO_3^{2-} groups. The pyramidal structure of the ClO_3^- ion, however, as contrasted with the plane form of the CO_3^{2-} group, gives rise to an arrangement of only monoclinic symmetry, but physically the two structures are closely related with very similar properties. The transition from the anisodesmic structure of $KClO_3$ to the isodesmic perovskite structure of KIO_3, due to the increased size of the halogen ion, has already been noted.

The structures of compounds of the type ABO_3 have been discussed at some length by Zachariasen (1928a).

Structures with tetrahedral BX_4 groups.

The anhydrite structure. The most important compounds with symmetrical BX_4 groups are the sulphates, perchlorates, permanganates and chromates, in all of which the complex group proves to be very regular in form. Among compounds of the composition ABX_4 two structures, those of anhydrite and of barium sulphate, are of common occurrence. The structure of anhydrite, $CaSO_4$, is shown in perspective and elevation in Figs. 62 and 63. The tetrahedral SO_4 groups are clearly revealed, while careful inspection shows that each Ca^{2+} ion is co-ordinated by eight oxygen neighbours. Each of the oxygen ions is in its turn linked to one S^{6+} and to two Ca^{2+} ions, and the electrostatic valency rule is therefore satisfied. Sodium perchlorate, $NaClO_4$, has the same structure (Zachariasen, 1930c).

The barium sulphate structure. This structure is more complex than that of anhydrite and will not be described in detail. It appears to be formed whenever the size of the cation A is too large for the anhydrite structure to be stable. Thus, while $CaSO_4$ and $NaClO_4$ have the anhydrite arrangement, $SrSO_4$ and $KClO_4$ have the barium sulphate structure. Other substances with this structure are NH_4ClO_4, $RbClO_4$, $CsClO_4$, $TlClO_4$, $KMnO_4$ and $PbSO_4$.

A_2BX_4 *compounds.* With compounds of the type A_2BX_4 two different structures are again common, the appearance of one or the other being once more determined by the size of the cation A. When this ion is small the sodium sulphate

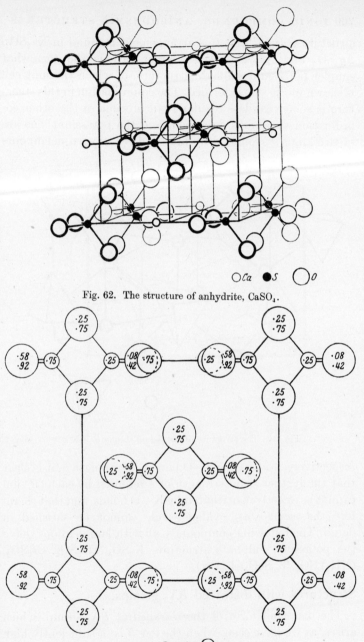

Fig. 62. The structure of anhydrite, CaSO₄.

○ = S; ○ = Ca; ◯ = O.
Fig. 63. The structure of anhydrite, CaSO₄.

structure obtains, and this arrangement is found in Na_2SO_4, Ag_2SO_4 and Ag_2SeO_4. With larger cations the somewhat simpler potassium sulphate structure, of which the unit cell is shown in Fig. 64, is formed. The co-ordination in this structure is somewhat less regular than in some of the other co-ordination structures described, and the potassium ions are of two kinds surrounded by nine and ten oxygen neighbours

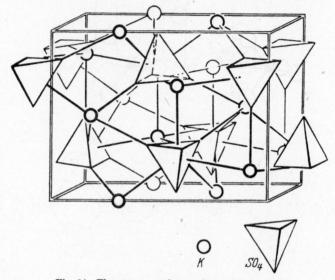

$$K \qquad SO_4$$

Fig. 64. The structure of potassium sulphate, K_2SO_4.

respectively. Since each S—O bond is of strength $\frac{3}{2}$, it is clear that the further bond strength of $\frac{1}{2}$ required by each O^{2-} ion cannot be exactly contributed by K—O bonds, and that therefore the electrostatic valency rule cannot be satisfied in detail. The following compounds, all with large cations, have the potassium sulphate structure: K_2SO_4, Rb_2SO_4, Cs_2SO_4, $(NH_4)_2SO_4$, K_2SeO_4, K_2CrO_4.

Structures with distorted BX_4 groups.

The distorted form of the tetrahedral BX_4 group, which arises, as we have seen, when the ion B is of sufficiently high atomic number, occurs, among common salts, in molybdates, periodates and tungstates. Two different structure types are common and the transition between them is determined primarily by the size of the metallic cation.

The unit cell of the structure of wolframite, $FeWO_4$, which is formed when the radius of the cation is less than about 0·95 A., is shown in Fig. 65. The flattened WO_4 tetrahedra and the deformed octahedra of O^{2-} ions co-ordinating the Fe^{2+} ions are both clearly seen. This structure is common to the tungstates of the following small cations: Mg^{2+}, Mn^{2+}, Fe^{2+}, Co^{2+}, Ni^{2+}, Zn^{2+}.

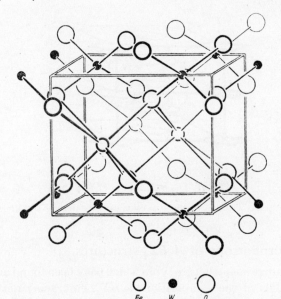

$\underset{Fe}{\bigcirc}$ $\underset{W}{\bullet}$ $\underset{O}{\bigcirc}$

Fig. 65. The structure of wolframite, $FeWO_4$.

In tungstates with large cations, and in certain molybdates and periodates, the structure of scheelite, $CaWO_4$, is found. In this structure the distorted WO_4 tetrahedra again appear, but the oxygen co-ordination round the cation is now 8-fold instead of 6-fold, and each O^{2-} ion is therefore linked to one W^{6+} and to two Ca^{2+} ions. The scheelite structure is common to the following compounds: $CaMoO_4$, $BaMoO_4$, $PbMoO_4$, $NaIO_4$, KIO_4, $CaWO_4$, $BaWO_4$, $PbWO_4$.

Structures with flat BX_4 groups.

An ionic structure in which flat BX_4 groups occur is that of potassium chloroplatinite, K_2PtCl_4, of which the tetragonal structure is illustrated in Fig. 66. Each $PtCl_4$ group is surrounded by eight potassium ions at the corners of a cube, and each potassium ion is co-ordinated by four $PtCl_4$ groups at the corners of a square. The flat form of the $PtCl_4$ group must be interpreted as implying a purely homopolar binding within the group. K_2PdCl_4 and $(NH_4)_2PdCl_4$ have the same structure.

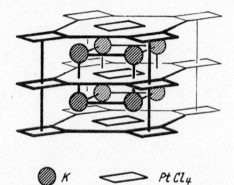

K $Pt Cl_4$

Fig. 66. The structure of potassium chloroplatinite, K_2PtCl_4.

The morphotropy of A_2BX_4 structures.

The numerous structure types which have been found among compounds of the composition A_2BX_4, embracing not only anisodesmic but also mesodesmic and isodesmic crystals, provide a particularly rich source of data for the study of the several factors governing morphotropic transitions between the different structures of chemically closely related compounds. It is of interest to consider these structures in some slight detail from this point of view.

The structures which are of common occurrence in A_2BX_4 compounds and which we have described are: among anisodesmic compounds, the potassium sulphate and sodium sulphate structures; among mesodesmic compounds, the olivine and phenacite structures; and among isodesmic compounds, the spinel arrangement. We have already seen that the transition from the potassium sulphate to the sodium sulphate structure, and again that from the olivine to the phenacite arrangement, is brought about by a decrease in the size of the ion A. In the case of the alkali sulphates the still further decrease in the size of this ion produces a transition to the phenacite and spinel structures, lithium sulphate having the former arrangement at low and the latter at high temperatures. In both these structures tetrahedral co-ordination about B is preserved so that the characteristic form of the SO_4 group is maintained and the structures are typically anisodesmic. The phenacite and spinel arrangements are therefore not confined to mesodesmic and isodesmic compounds respectively, but can also occur in anisodesmic crystals, so that the distinction between these three classes of structure is in some cases one rather of convenience than of fundamental significance.

The transition from the olivine to the phenacite structure with decreasing size of the ion A may be regarded as due to the increased 'contrapolarizing' influence of the small A ion on the tightly bound BX_4 group, which is thereby somewhat distended so that the binding within this group becomes qualitatively more nearly comparable with that throughout the whole structure. If this contrapolarizing influence is still stronger a transition to the spinel structure takes place. Thus Li_2MoO_4 has the phenacite arrangement, but Ag_2MoO_4, with the more strongly polarizing Ag^+ ion, has the spinel structure.

Similar considerations govern the olivine-phenacite transition, which may be regarded as due to the increased contrapolarizing influence of the smaller or more strongly polarizing ion A. Thus Mg_2SiO_4 has the olivine structure but Be_2SiO_4 and Zn_2SiO_4 the phenacite arrangement, the former due to the smaller size and the latter to the greater polarizing power of the metallic cation.

The transitions from the olivine and phenacite structures to that of spinel, corresponding to a looser binding within the BX_4 group, are brought about not only by the substitution of progressively smaller and more strongly polarizing A ions, as already described, but alternatively by the substitution of larger and less strongly polarizing B ions. Thus the olivine structures of Al_2BeO_4 and Mg_2SiO_4 give place to spinel structures in Al_2MgO_4 and Mg_2TiO_4, while the phenacite arrangement of Zn_2SiO_4 is similarly transformed to a spinel structure in Zn_2TiO_4.

The influence of temperature on the morphotropic transitions may be concisely expressed by saying that an increase in temperature is generally accompanied by a decrease in the tightness of binding of the BX_4 group, so that if any transition takes place with increasing temperature it is in the same direction as that brought about by an increase in the contrapolarizing power of the ion A. Thus Li_2SO_4 and Li_2MoO_4 have at low temperatures the phenacite structure and at high temperatures the spinel arrangement. Similarly K_2SO_4, Rb_2SO_4 and Cs_2SO_4 show a high temperature transition to the phenacite structure but at increasingly higher temperatures, due to the progressively smaller contrapolarizing power of the alkali ion.

The morphotropic transitions between the several A_2BX_4 structures are summarized schematically in Table 55. These transitions, and also those of ABX_4 compounds, have been discussed at greater length by Goldschmidt (1926 a, 1931 a).

TABLE 55

THE MORPHOTROPIC RELATIONSHIPS OF A_2BX_4 COMPOUNDS

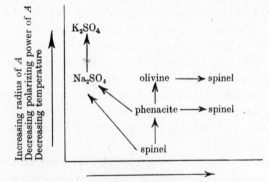

Increasing radius of B
Decreasing polarizing power of B
Increasing temperature

Structures with BX_6 groups.

In all structures containing BX_6 anions so far investigated the regular octahedral form of this group is preserved, and its high symmetry makes it possible to regard the group as a simple spherical ion of large size. When combined with sufficiently large cations these complex groups give rise to structures of very simple types. Thus many compounds such as K_2PtCl_6, K_2SnCl_6, Rb_2PdBr_6, Cs_2GeF_6, etc., all have in common the antifluorite structure, and quite generally this structure may be expected whenever the cation is large and of low polarizing power. With small cations the increased polarizing power may be expected to cause the breakdown of the BX_6 groups, but few such structures have as yet been investigated.

Structures with complex cations.

Apart from the ammonium compounds already discussed, the only structures containing complex cations which have been systematically investigated are the 'co-ordination compounds' of such ions as $Co(NH_3)_6^{2+}$, etc. These compounds are very closely related to the hydrates and are best discussed under that head.

THE CHEMISTRY OF ANISODESMIC STRUCTURES

The crystal structures of the anisodesmic compounds discussed above raise a number of points of general chemical interest, especially as these structures embrace many of the commonest compounds of inorganic chemistry. In the first place we see that purely geometrical conditions are again the primary factor in dictating the structure adopted, so that, for example, $CaCO_3$, as calcite, and $NaNO_3$ are isomorphous, whereas the chemically much more closely related $NaNO_3$ and KNO_3 have entirely different structures.

A second feature of the anisodesmic structures is that, no less than in the simple isodesmic crystals, all trace of any chemical molecule is lost. Thus in calcite each Ca^{2+} ion is co-ordinated by six O^{2-} ions and these oxygen neighbours belong to six different CO_3 groups. Similarly each O^{2-} ion is bound to one C^{4+} and to two Ca^{2+} ions, so that it is clearly impossible to represent the distribution of bonds within the framework of the material of a single molecule $CaCO_3$. In particular any 'structural formula' such as

$$Ca \underset{O}{\overset{O}{\diamondsuit}} C = O$$

is meaningless and misleading, for not only does it convey the impression that the single molecule has a real existence but it also suggests that some physical distinction exists between one oxygen atom and the other two: actually, as we have seen, they are all structurally equivalent and are all linked to both the carbon and the calcium ions. Such structural formulae arise from an attempt to interpret ionic structures in terms of chemical principles which are strictly only applicable to homopolar and molecular compounds. If a single molecule of calcium carbonate could exist, say as a gas, it might well have the structure represented above, but it is of little significance to discuss the structure of a body in a state in which it does not occur. If any formula is employed to represent the structure in the solid state, it must be one which simply expresses the co-ordination of each of the several ions in turn and which preferably also includes a statement of the electrostatic valency of the various bonds:

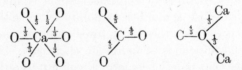

But it must be remembered that such a representation does not necessarily make any attempt to convey the geometrical disposition of the various bonds and that it is, in any case, characteristic not of the chemical compound but only of one particular structural modification of it: in calcium carbonate as aragonite the bond structure is entirely different.

Similar criticisms are applicable to numerous other formulae such as

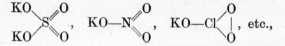

which bear no relation to the crystal structures described above for these compounds, and which can in fact convey nothing but an entirely erroneous impression of the bond distribution. It is only in purely molecular compounds that such formulae are of significance, and in all other cases a chemical formula based on the material of a single molecule can express little more than the relative numbers of the atoms of the several elements present.

This concludes our review of the anhydrous anisodesmic structures. Before passing on to an account of the hydrated compounds, however, it is appropriate to consider at this stage certain physical properties of crystal structures which may conveniently be described and interpreted in terms of the structures already discussed in this chapter.

SOME PHYSICAL PROPERTIES OF CRYSTALS

The free rotation of molecules and atom groups.

The conception of the free rotation of molecules in the solid state was first introduced by Pauling (1930a) to account for an anomaly in the entropy of solid hydrogen, and has since been found to be a phenomenon of frequent occurrence which enables a number of apparent inconsistencies in the structures of certain crystals to be satisfactorily explained. From the physical point of view free rotation is merely an extreme case of the normal energy of thermal agitation. In all solids at temperatures above the absolute zero the molecules possess energy of both vibration and rotation about the position of equilibrium, and the extent of the rotation depends upon the temperature and on the way in which the potential energy of the molecule varies with its orientation. If the potential energy in the equilibrium position is less than in other possible positions by an amount appreciably greater than kT per molecule, the rotation will be confined to small oscillations; but if the energy difference is never as large as kT, the kinetic energy of the molecule will be sufficient to bring about complete rotation. We see from this simple picture that free rotation will be most common with symmetrically shaped molecules of small moment of inertia in loosely-bound structures at high temperatures. The transition to the state of free rotation will in general extend over a finite temperature range, and it is clear that unsymmetrical molecules may have rotations about different axes excited successively at different temperatures. At the transition structural changes as well as anomalies in the physical properties are to be expected.

A quantitative treatment reveals that rotation may be expected in many structures at temperatures below their melting points. In hydrogen free rotation of the H_2 molecule occurs at the absolute zero, and the crystal structure down to the lowest temperatures at which it has been observed is one of hexagonal close-packing. In methane rotation sets in at about $20°$ K. and corresponding to the transition an anomalous increase in specific heat is observed between 18 and $22.8°$ K. Above the latter temperature the structure is a cubic close-packed one. Similarly in HCl and HBr transitions take place and the high temperature forms have close-packed structures, while at low temperatures more complex structures of lower symmetry obtain. In HBr, and also in HI, several successive transitions are observed and these may possibly be associated with the inception of rotation about different axes, but the point cannot be finally decided until the crystal structures of the intermediate forms are known.

The possibility of rotation in the solid state has led to the resolution of many apparent inconsistencies between the intrinsic symmetry of a molecule or complex group and that of the structure in which it occurs. The early investigations of the structures of the primary alkyl ammonium halides (Hendricks, 1928 a, b, c, 1930 a) appeared to indicate that the carbon chain in these compounds was linear with a C-C distance of 1.25 A. Such a conclusion was very difficult to reconcile either with the zigzag form of the chain found in the paraffins and other compounds or with the usual interatomic distance of 1·54 A. On the other hand, a zigzag chain was not consistent with the tetragonal symmetry of the structure. It is now found (Hendricks, 1930b) that in these structures the carbon chain is in free rotation about its length, due to its small moment of inertia about this direction, thus effectively acquiring a higher symmetry which enables it to be accommodated in the tetragonal structure and explains the observed spacing of 1·25 A. as the projection on to the axis of the chain of the inclined bonds of length 1·54 A.

Among inorganic compounds rotation of the anions CN^-, C_2^{2-}, O_2^{2-}, CO_3^{2-}, NO_3^-, ClO_3^-, ClO_4^- and SO_4^{2-} is frequently observed. In the case of such ions as CO_3^{2-}, NO_3^-, etc., the asymmetry of form results in free rotation being usually possible only about the triad axis, and in consequence such rotation often sets in without an increase in the symmetry of the structure as a whole. Thus in sodium nitrate (Kracek, 1931; Kracek and Posnjak, 1931; Kracek, Posnjak and Hendricks, 1931) the transition to the rotating form occurs gradually over an extended temperature range from 150 to 275° C. without alteration in the crystal structure but with a small change in the angle of the rhombohedral unit cell.

The ion NH_4^+ is found to rotate freely in many of its compounds and must do so in NH_4Cl, NH_4Br and NH_4I, all of which have the sodium chloride or caesium chloride structure at ordinary temperatures. In spite of its geometrical similarity to CH_4 the ammonium ion is, of course, much more strongly bound in the structures in which it occurs than is the methane molecule in the solid state, and free rotation is possible only at much higher temperatures. In ammonium fluoride at ordinary temperatures the binding is too strong to allow rotation and the wurtzite structure results.

The structure of ammonium nitrate is of particular interest because in this salt both cation and anion are capable of rotation. The system is one of considerable complexity, with six different crystalline modifications stable under different temperature conditions, and cannot be described in detail here, but it has been found by Hendricks, Posnjak and Kracek (1932) that the cubic form, stable above 125° C., has a caesium chloride structure in which both ions are in free rotation. The NH_4^+ and NO_3^- ions behave as spheres of radii 1·46 and 2·35 A. respectively. In the other forms, with more complex crystal structures, some or all of the rotational degrees of freedom of one or both ions are inhibited.

Examples of molecular rotation in organic compounds will be considered when these structures are discussed.

Fowler's theory. Molecular rotation in crystals has been discussed from a theoretical point of view by Fowler (1935a,b), who has pointed out that a close formal analogy exists between the transition from the fixed to the rotating state and the transition from the ordered to the disordered condition in alloy systems. Both transitions are essentially co-operative phenomena, for if we consider a structure in which some molecules are in rotation it is clear that the directive forces acting on any one molecule are themselves largely determined by the degree of rotation of its neighbours and vanish when these rotations are sufficiently intense. In this way we can see that rotation may be expected to set in with much greater suddenness than would otherwise be the case. We cannot here enter into details, but Fowler has considered particularly the application of the theory to the anomalously high specific heat which is observed at the transition to the rotating state.

The optical properties of crystals.

We have already seen in Chap. II that in many structures the optical properties, and in particular the refractivity, are simply those of the aggregate of ions, and it is clear that in such cases optical data can give no information concerning structure type or atomic arrangement. In structures in which considerable polarization occurs the extent of this polarization is often revealed by a reduction in the total refractivity, but once again little direct information concerning the atomic arrangement can be derived. We now proceed to consider under what conditions optical data can give more precise evidence of characteristic structural features.

The interaction of electromagnetic waves and matter arises from the polarization of the electronic structure of the individual atoms by the electric vector of the light waves, and a measure of the extent of this interaction is provided by the refractive index. In a gas the polarization of each atom is due solely to the influence of the electromagnetic wave, but in a solid this polarization is modified by the field due to the dipoles induced in neighbouring atoms, and in a crystal, in which these neighbours are disposed in some regular way, the extent of this secondary influence will in general depend upon the polarization direction of the light. Such structures will therefore have different refractive indices for light polarized in different directions, and so show double refraction. It is the magnitude and sign of this double refraction which reveal any characteristic features of the structural arrangement.

The relation between optical properties and crystal structure has been discussed quantitatively by W. L. Bragg (1924 a, b) for the particular case of a set of three atoms arranged at the corners of an equilateral triangle to form a complex group such as that found in the nitrates and carbonates, but his conclusions may be extended qualitatively to any molecule or group consisting of a planar or nearly planar arrangement of atoms of high refractivity. We then find that in such a group the resultant polarization of each atom, due to the combined influence of the electric vector of the light wave and the field of the dipoles induced on the neighbouring atoms, is greater than that due to the electric vector alone when this vector is polarized in the plane of the group, but is less when the plane of polarization is normal to the group, so that the refractivity of the group as a whole is greater in the former case than in the latter.

In the macroscopic crystal structure the resultant effect will depend upon the mutual orientation of the separate groups and also upon the other atoms or ions present. In many structures, however, the molecular refractivity of the ions of one type is so much greater than that of any of the other ions that for a purely qualitative treatment they alone need be taken into account. Especially is this the case in structures containing large anions such as the halogens or oxygen, in all of which the optical properties are determined primarily by the arrangement of these ions. Thus in all the anisodesmic compounds described in this chapter the optical properties reflect the form and arrangement of the complex anion groups.

In crystals containing planar atom groups, all with their planes parallel, a large negative birefringence is to be expected, with two high and comparable refractive indices for light polarized in the plane of the groups and one much lower index for vibrations at right angles to this plane. This is the effect which obtains in the calcite and aragonite structures, in which the BO_3 groups are parallel and in which a large negative birefringence is always found. The refractive indices of these particular minerals for sodium light are:

	Calcite		Aragonite
ϵ	1·486	α	1·531
ω	1·658	β	1·682
	—	γ	1·686

In the former case the crystal is uniaxial and vibrations in all directions in the plane of the CO_3 groups are propagated with the same velocity. In aragonite, although biaxial, the difference between the indices β and γ for light polarized in two directions at right angles in the plane of the groups is very much smaller than the difference between either of them and the third refractive index α, and the optic axial angle is correspondingly small.

When planar groups of strongly refracting ions are arranged in a structure all parallel to a line but no longer parallel to each other, we may expect strong positive birefringence since the single vibration direction parallel to all the groups will be associated with a much smaller velocity of propagation than any other direction. Such an arrangement is not found in any carbonate or nitrate structures, but is of common occurrence among molecular crystals. When the planar groups are inclined in all directions, no large birefringence is to be expected. This is the case in the structure of lead nitrate, which is cubic and therefore isotropic, due to the fact that the NO_3 groups are disposed normal to the four triad axes.

Similar arguments apply to rod-shaped molecules or atom groups. Here vibrations along the length of the group correspond to much greater interaction than vibrations in any other direction, and in a structure in which all the groups are parallel a large positive birefringence is therefore to be expected. This is the case in the structure of selenium, for which $\omega = 3\cdot0$ and $\epsilon = 4\cdot04$, and also in the paraffins and other structures to be discussed later. When the groups are no longer parallel to each other but remain parallel to a plane, a large negative birefringence results with the one small refractive index corresponding to the vibration direction normal to this plane. If the groups are inclined in all directions, no large birefringence is to be expected.

In structures in which the arrangement of the strongly

TABLE 56

RELATION BETWEEN OPTICAL PROPERTIES AND CRYSTAL STRUCTURE

	Shape and arrangement of atom groups or molecules	Optical properties	Conclusions	Examples
1	Roughly spherical	Almost isotropic	None	Quartz Felspars, etc. Sulphates
2	Rod-shaped			
	(a) All parallel to one direction	Large positive birefringence	Molecules parallel to direction of greatest refractive index	Selenium Paraffins, etc.
	(b) All parallel to a plane but not to each other	Large negative birefringence	Plane of molecules normal to direction of least refractive index	$C_{18}H_{37}NH_3Cl$
	(c) Inclined in all directions	Almost isotropic	Arrangement cannot be either 2 (a) or 2 (b)	CO_2
3	Flat			
	(a) Planes parallel	Large negative birefringence	Planes of molecules normal to direction of least refractive index	Layer lattices Micas, etc. Calcite 1.3.5 triphenylbenzene
	(b) Planes all parallel to a line but not to each other	Large positive birefringence	Planes of molecules all parallel to direction of greatest refractive index	Urea Benzene
	(c) Planes inclined in all directions	Almost isotropic	Arrangement cannot be either 3 (a) or 3 (b)	Resorcinol

refracting atoms or ions is very symmetrical low double refraction is to be anticipated. Thus all sulphates and other structures with tetrahedral BO_4 groups have only small birefringence, and the same is true of those silicates based on a framework structure of SiO_4 tetrahedra and of those in which a nearly close-packed arrangement of oxygen ions is found.

The above arguments are summarized in tabular form in Table 56, p. 273, where other examples, both from structures already discussed and from others to be considered later, are given. The optical properties of a number of substances have been reviewed and interpreted in terms of their structures by Wooster (1931).

HYDRATED ANISODESMIC STRUCTURES

Introduction.

It is not in general possible for neutral molecules to be bound in ionic structures, but that of water, and to a lesser extent that of ammonia, prove exceptions to this general rule. The reason for this anomalous behaviour lies primarily in the electrical polarity and small size of these molecules. The particular relevance of these two factors will appear as our discussion proceeds.

In many hydrates the function of water is simply to co-ordinate the cations and thereby effectively surround them with a neutral shell which increases their radius and enables their charge to be distributed over a greater number of anions. In most ionic structures, and particularly in those containing complex anions, the disparity in radius between the anion and cation is too great for simple structures of high co-ordination to obtain and a tendency towards layer lattices or even purely molecular arrangements often results. This tendency becomes the more marked the higher the ionic charges and therefore the greater the discrepancy in radii. The possibility of co-ordinating the cations by water molecules, however, completely alters this state of affairs, for a small and strongly polarizing cation can be thereby transformed into a feebly polarizing ion with a size comparable with that of many complex anions. Thus the 6-fold co-ordination of the aluminium ion by water changes this ion of radius 0.57 A. into the $[Al(H_2O)_6]^{3+}$ complex of approximate radius 3.3 A., which is considerably larger than that of the I^- or even SO_4^{2-} anions. Such large cations may be expected to give rise to stable structures of much less complexity than the small ions of the unco-ordinated element. For the same reason we may expect hydrates to be commonest and most stable among salts with small cations. Thus sodium salts show a much greater tendency to contain water of crystallization than do the corresponding compounds of potassium.

The function of water in the hydrates, however, is not quite as simple as such an elementary picture would suggest, for we cannot regard the water molecules merely as neutral conducting spheres whose function is to distribute more widely the cation charge. Indeed, if they could be so regarded, the forces of attraction between the neighbouring ions and the induced charges on the water molecules would be insufficient to give coherence to the structure and hydrates would not exist. We shall see in the next chapter that there is ample evidence, both from the structure of ice and from the behaviour of water itself in the liquid state, that the very large dipole moment of this substance is due to a tetrahedral distribution of charge over the surface of the spherical molecule. If a tetrahedron be imagined inscribed within the molecule, two corners of this tetrahedron are regions of positive and the remaining two corners regions of negative electrification. It follows from this structure that the packing of water molecules into a crystal must satisfy certain physical requirements, for a structure can only be stable if these molecules are so disposed that their charged areas are approximately directed towards ions of opposite sign. This condition often precludes simple structural arrangements which would otherwise be possible.

A second consequence which arises from the tetrahedral structure of the water molecule is the possibility of such molecules being linked not only both to cations and to anions but also to each other, for provided that two water molecules are so arranged that oppositely charged regions are in juxta-position attraction will take place. In many structures water molecules do occur linked in this way.

Hydrates in which the primary function of the water molecules is, as described above, to co-ordinate the cations and so increase their effective size and distribute more widely their electric charge, may be described as containing co-ordinated water. In such structures the water molecules play an essential part in determining the stability of the lattice as a whole and cannot be removed without the complete break-down of the structure. The anhydrous salt, if it exists, neces-sarily can bear no structural relation to the hydrate. A second class of hydrate compounds exists, however, in which the water molecules play a less fundamental part and merely occupy interstices in the structure where they can add to the electrostatic energy without upsetting the balance of charge. In some cases the rôle of these water molecules is so trivial that they can be expelled from the lattice without any breakdown of the crystal or alteration in its structure, but although this is not always the case the corresponding dehydrated compound is often structurally closely related to the hydrate. Hydrates of this kind may be said to contain structural water. In many cases, as we shall see below, water molecules of both kinds occur simultaneously in a single compound. In a few struc-tures the water molecules assume an intermediate rôle and classification is more difficult.

HYDRATES CONTAINING CO-ORDINATED WATER

The detailed features of hydrate structures may be best illus-trated by discussing at length only one typical such compound and by then considering very briefly a number of others which have been studied. A structure which is particularly convenient for such a discussion is that of $NiSO_4 . 7H_2O$.

The structure of $NiSO_4 . 7H_2O$.

The structure of $NiSO_4 . 7H_2O$, projected on to the face (001) of the orthorhombic unit cell, is represented in Fig. 67 (Beevers and Schwartz, 1935). In this diagram the tetrahedral SO_4 groups are clearly revealed and also the octahedral groups of six water molecules around each nickel ion. In addition to the six water molecules thus co-ordinated, a seventh, marked 11 in the figure, is linked to no cation but only to oxygen ions of SO_4 groups and to other water molecules. Not all of the six water molecules co-ordinating any nickel ion are the same. Four of these molecules, numbered 5, 7, 8 and 10, which may

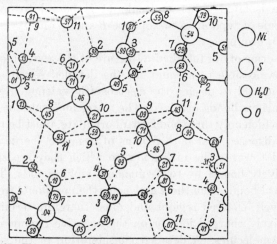

Fig. 67. The structure of nickel sulphate heptahydrate, $NiSO_4.7H_2O$.

be described as of type A, make two contacts external to the $[Ni(H_2O)_6]$ group and these molecules have their three bonds roughly in a plane. The other two water molecules, 6 and 9, which are at opposite corners of the octahedron and may be called type B, make three external contacts, and the four bonds to these molecules are arranged tetrahedrally, as are also those to the isolated water molecule 11. The detailed co-ordination round all the water molecules of one type is not, however, the same and may be summarized thus:*

Molecules 5, 7 and 8 of type A are each bound externally to one oxygen ion in each of two different SO_4 groups.

* There are four molecules of composition $NiSO_4.7H_2O$ in the unit cell and the symmetry therefore requires that every atom or ion of each kind shall be repeated four times. Corresponding water molecules in Fig. 67 have the same numbers.

Molecule 10 of type A is bound externally to one water molecule of type B and to the isolated molecule 11.

Molecule 6 of type B is bound externally to one oxygen ion in each of two different SO_4 groups and to the isolated water molecule 11.

Molecule 9 of type B is bound externally to one oxygen ion of an SO_4 group, to one water molecule of type A and to the water molecule 11.

The isolated water molecule 11 is bound to one water molecule of type A, to two of type B and to one oxygen ion of an SO_4 group.

In terms of our tetrahedral picture of the water molecule it is now possible to account for the detailed features of this binding and to discuss the electrostatic valency strength of the various bonds involved. The water molecules of type A, from which only three bonds in all originate, must be regarded as so disposed that both regions of negative charge are presented towards the nickel ion, to which they are therefore effectively bound by two coincident single bonds. The two outward bonds from these molecules then originate from their positively charged regions and must therefore terminate on negatively charged ions or on the negative regions of other water molecules. A detailed consideration of the structure reveals that this is so. The two water molecules of type B must be so arranged that only one of their negative charges is adjacent to a nickel ion, to which they are therefore bound by only a single bond. A second incoming bond reaches these ions from the positively charged region of an adjacent water molecule and the two outgoing bonds are satisfied by the negative charges on the oxygen ions of SO_4 groups or on neighbouring water molecules.

The bond strengths of the various ions may be most simply deduced by considering first the co-ordination round the nickel ions. We have seen that each such ion is effectively bound by $2 \times 4 + 2 = 10$ single bonds so that the strength of each is $\frac{2}{10} = \frac{1}{5}$. This, therefore, must also be the strength of each outward bond from the various water molecules, and it is easy to complete the bond structure in the manner shown in

Fig. 68. This diagram also shows figuratively the co-ordination of all the ions of each type and should be compared carefully with the actual structure diagram and with the description in the preceding paragraphs. The bond-structure diagram reveals how exactly the electrostatic valency rule is satisfied by the structure and also how the neutrality of each water molecule is achieved by the distribution of its tetrahedral bonds between cations, anions and other water molecules.

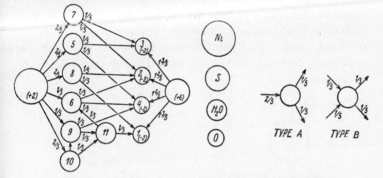

Fig. 68. The electrostatic valency bond structure of nickel sulphate heptahydrate, $NiSO_4 . 7H_2O$.

The structure of $NiSO_4 . 7H_2O$ has been discussed in some detail because it is a particularly beautiful example of the principles underlying the formation of hydrate structures, and because it also illustrates very clearly the way in which water is bound in these structures and may appear either co-ordinating the cations or situated in interstices where it is not directly bound to any cations at all. While a rough description of such structures may often be given in terms of the packing of the anions, complex or simple, and of the co-ordinating polyhedra of water molecules round the cations, it is clear from this example that the packing must be carried out in such a way that the somewhat exacting demands of the tetrahedral form of the water molecule are satisfied. This condition often necessitates arrangements of much greater complexity than would otherwise be expected. We may now proceed to consider very briefly certain other hydrates as further examples of the general principles which we have advanced.

Other hydrates.

In $NiSO_4.6H_2O$ (Beevers and Lipson, 1932a; Beevers and Schwartz, 1935) the octahedral co-ordination of six water molecules round each nickel ion is found exactly as in $NiSO_4.7H_2O$, but the additional isolated water molecule is, of course, absent. The similarity in co-ordination moreover extends beyond the purely geometrical form of the group, for again four of the six water molecules are of type A with two external contacts and two are of the 'tetrahedral' type B with three such contacts. This structural resemblance between the hexa- and heptahydrates emphasizes the relatively unimportant function of the additional water molecule in the latter salt.

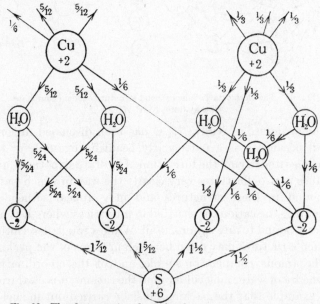

Fig. 69. The electrostatic valency bond structure of copper sulphate pentahydrate, $CuSO_4.5H_2O$.

The structure of $CuSO_4.5H_2O$ (Beevers and Lipson, 1934) is analogous to that of $NiSO_4.7H_2O$ inasmuch as the water molecules are of two kinds. The detailed bond structure is shown in Fig. 69, and it will be seen that four of the water molecules co-ordinate Cu^{2+} ions. Each of these ions is octahedrally surrounded by four water molecules and two O^{2-} ions belonging to SO_4 groups. The fifth water molecule is co-ordinated only by other water molecules and by oxygen ions. The structure thus explains the distinction previously recognized on chemical grounds between one water molecule and the other four. The structure also provides our first example of one in which the cations are co-ordinated partly by water molecules and partly by oxygen ions.

In $NiSnCl_6.6H_2O$ (Pauling, 1930b) an octahedral co-ordination round nickel is again observed while the tin ions are similarly co-ordinated by chlorine. The whole structure is built up by the packing together of these octahedral $[Ni(H_2O)_6]^{2+}$ and $[SnCl_6]^{2-}$ groups and in this case the arrangement is quite simple and may be described as a slightly deformed caesium chloride structure. Many other isomorphous salts of the general type $A^{2+}B^{4+}X_6^-.6H_2O$, where A is Mg, Mn, Zn, etc., B is Si, Sn, Pd, Pt, etc., and X is F, Cl, Br, I, probably have the same structure.

In $MgCl_2.6H_2O$ and $MgBr_2.6H_2O$ (Andress and Gundermann, 1934) the magnesium ions are octahedrally co-ordinated by water molecules and these structures are of particular interest in that the size of the complex $[Mg(H_2O)_6]$ groups compared with that of the halogen ion is such that a fluorite structure might be anticipated. Such an arrangement, however, would necessitate each water molecule being in contact with four chlorine ions and is clearly not compatible with the tetrahedral water structure, which would allow only two such contacts. The actual structure observed is closely related to the fluorite arrangement and may be described as a distortion of that structure whereby the number of chlorine contacts of each water molecule is reduced from four to two. In $AlCl_3.6H_2O$ (Andress and Carpenter, 1934) the cations are again octahedrally surrounded by water and the arrangement may be roughly regarded as a co-ordination structure of $[Al(H_2O)_6]^{3+}$ and Cl^- ions. The chief interest of this structure lies in its relation to that of $[Al(NH_3)_6]Cl_3$ to be discussed below.

In the structures of the alums $A^+B^{3+}(SO_4)_2 . 12H_2O$ (Lipson and Beevers, 1935; Lipson, 1935) both cations are surrounded by six water molecules but the detailed features of the complex groups thus formed are quite different. In $KAl(SO_4)_2 . 12H_2O$, to take a specific example, the water molecules co-ordinating the Al^{3+} ion are all doubly bound to that ion and make only two external contacts. Those co-ordinating the K^+ ions, however, are all of the tetrahedral type and make three external contacts, two with oxygen ions of SO_4 groups and one with a water molecule of an $[Al(H_2O)_6]$ group. Moreover, the co-ordination round the K^+ ion must be regarded as governed solely by the external contacts of the water molecules and not by the potassium : water radius ratio, which would demand a much higher co-ordination, so that these six water molecules may be regarded as fulfilling a structural rather than a co-ordinating function in the lattice. The arrangement of the $[A(H_2O)_6]^+$, $[B(H_2O)_6]^{3+}$ and SO_4^{2-} groups in all the alums is not the same, but gives rise to three different structures, the transition between which is determined by the size of the univalent ion. The alums are therefore not all isomorphous, but since the three structures are all cubic we have here a case where the lack of isomorphism can be revealed only by X-ray methods.

When the cation in a hydrate is very small the cation : water radius ratio is not large enough for 6-fold co-ordination and instead a tetrahedral disposition of water molecules round the cation is found. Such an arrangement obtains in $BeSO_4 . 4H_2O$ (Beevers and Lipson, 1932b) which is tetragonal but pseudo-cubic and may be regarded as a slightly deformed caesium chloride structure built of $[Be(H_2O)_4]^{2+}$ and SO_4^{2-} complex ions. In this structure all the water molecules are of the same type, each having only two external bonds to one oxygen ion in each of two different SO_4 groups. These water molecules must therefore be regarded as all directed with their negatively charged regions turned towards the beryllium ions. The resulting roughly uniform distribution of positive charge over the outer surface of the $[Be(H_2O)_4]$ groups no doubt accounts for the simplicity of the structure. A similar tetrahedral co-ordination round the cations is found in $Li_2SO_4 . H_2O$ (Ziegler, 1934), but here each lithium ion is surrounded by only one water molecule and by three oxygen ions belonging to SO_4 groups.

HYDRATES CONTAINING STRUCTURAL WATER

The hydrates containing only structural water of which the crystal structures have been investigated are far fewer in number than those in which the water molecules play the more fundamental rôle of co-ordinating the metallic cations, and it would in fact appear that the co-ordination type of hydrate is the one of more widespread and common occurrence, and that compounds in which the water occurs solely in a structural capacity are rare. On the other hand, in many structures, as in the alums described above, some water molecules of each type are found, while in the other compounds the water molecules, although directly linked to the cations, appear, on account either of the low or irregular co-ordination, to be present in a structural rather than in a co-ordinating capacity.

The zeolites.

The most outstanding examples of hydrates containing only structural water are those which comprise the zeolite family of silicates already briefly described. In all these minerals the stability of the structure is due to the three-dimensional framework of linked SiO_4 tetrahedra, and the rigidity of this framework is so great, and the contribution of the water molecules to its stability so trivial, that the latter can be reversibly expelled from the crystals, or even substituted by other molecules such as those of alcohol, mercury or ammonia, without change or damage to the structure as a whole (Lengyel, 1932). Nevertheless, the total number of water molecules which can be accommodated in the unit cell is rigidly limited, and W. H. Taylor (1934) has shown that the arrangement of these molecules is always one which is strictly in conformity with their tetrahedral structure.

Gypsum.

Another hydrated mineral containing structural water is gypsum, $CaSO_4 \cdot 2H_2O$ (Wooster, 1936), but in this structure the water molecules play a far more important part than in the zeolites, and in fact the coherence of the structure in one direction is entirely due to bonds from these molecules. The structure is illustrated in Fig. 70, and may be described as a layer lattice in which sheets of Ca^{2+} and SO_4^{2-} ions are so arranged that each cation is surrounded by six O^{2-} ions and by two water molecules. Each water molecule is linked to one Ca^{2+} ion, to one O^{2-} ion in its own sheet and to one O^{2-} ion in a neighbouring sheet, and these last-mentioned bonds are the only ones holding the sheets together. The perfect cleavage arises from the rupture of these weak bonds, and their weakness is also revealed by the very much greater coefficient of thermal expansion normal to the sheets than in any other direction.

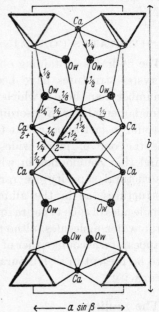

$\bullet = Ca$; $\bullet = H_2O$; $\triangle = SO_4$

Fig. 70. The structure of gypsum, $CaSO_4 \cdot 2H_2O$.

COMPLEX CO-ORDINATION COMPOUNDS

The rôle of the ammonia molecule in the numerous co-ordination compounds such as $Co(NH_3)_6Cl_2$, etc., is very closely analogous to that of water in the hydrates, and its primary function may be again regarded as that of artificially increasing the effective size of the cation so that this ion may readily form simple stable structures when combined with anions of large size. The great majority of the co-ordination compounds whose structures have so far been investigated are of the general type $A(NH_3)_6X_2$, where A is one of the divalent elements Mg, Ca, Zn, Cd, Mn, Fe, Co, Ni, and X is a large univalent anion, being most commonly Cl^-, Br^- or I^- but occasionally a complex group such as ClO_4^-, PF_6^-, SO_3F^-, etc. In all these compounds, with very few exceptions, the structure is one which may be described very simply as a fluorite arrangement of the ions $[A(NH_3)_6]^{2+}$ and X^-, and in each case the ammonia molecules are found in regular octahedral co-ordination about the metallic cation.

The function of ammonia in effectively increasing the radius of the cation is still more clearly brought out by a comparison of the structures of the above compounds with those of the corresponding bodies containing no ammonia. Thus $Mg(NH_3)_6I_2$, $Co(NH_3)_6I_2$, etc., have the very symmetrical fluorite structure just described, but in MgI_2, CoI_2, etc., the small size and correspondingly greater polarizing power of the cations result in the appearance of a layer lattice. And, in fact, it immediately follows from the critical value of the radius ratio that no simple iodide of the type AI_2 can have the fluorite structure since no divalent cation exists with a radius as great as $1 \cdot 61$ A., the critical value which must be exceeded if this structure is to be formed.

The close analogy between the parts played by the water and ammonia molecules in co-ordinating metallic cations is further illustrated by the fact that in certain structures these two molecules can replace each other statistically to form internal mixed crystals. Thus Hassel (1928) found that $Co(NH_3)_6SO_4Br$ and $Co(NH_3)_5H_2O.SO_4Br$ both have the same structure, so that in the latter compound the NH_3 and H_2O molecules must be distributed at random. Similarly, the complex cyanides $Co(NH_3)_4(H_2O)_2.Co(CN)_6$, $Co(NH_3)_5H_2O.Co(CN)_6$ and $Co(NH_3)_6.Co(CN)_6$ are probably structurally isomorphous (Pauling, 1930b). This analogy of structure, however, is not always found between hydrates and ammoniates, and in certain cases the latter compounds have decidedly simpler structures due to the less pronounced polarity of the ammonia molecule. We have already seen that in some hydrates a simple structure which might be expected on general grounds is not found because it is inconsistent with the tetrahedral form of the water molecule, and in such cases the corresponding ammoniate often has this simple structure. This is the case, for example, in $Al(NH_3)_6Cl_3$ which has the yttrium fluoride structure although that of the corresponding hydrate $Al(H_2O)_6Cl_3$ is far more complex (Andress and Carpenter, 1934).

CHAPTER X

IONIC COMPOUNDS CONTAINING HYDROGEN

INTRODUCTION

We have already briefly referred to the unique part played by the H^+ ion in ionic structures, which arises from its vanishingly small size and correspondingly great polarizing power. The particular characteristics of this ion confer on the structures in which it is found properties so different from those of the generality of ionic crystals that its compounds are best discussed separately. The chief classes of ionic chemical compound containing the hydrogen cation are acids, acid salts, hydroxides and water, and the crystal structures of such of these as have been studied will now be considered. We exclude from our discussion hydrides and all other compounds containing the hydrogen anion H^-, for this anion behaves as a normal ion of characteristic radius about 1·54 A. resembling F^- in many of its properties. Thus Zintl and Harder (1931) have shown that all the alkali hydrides have the sodium chloride structure, while in hypophosphites such as $NH_4H_2PO_2$ (Zachariasen and Mooney, 1934b) the complex anion consists of a nearly regular tetrahedral co-ordination of phosphorus by the ions O^{2-} and H^- to form the complex group $(H_2^-P^{5+}O_2^{2-})^-$. The hypophosphites are not acid salts but normal salts in which the hydrogen atoms are part of the acid radical.

THE HYDROGEN BOND

The hydrogen bond in chemistry.

The conception of a binding between two atoms as being possible through the medium of a hydrogen ion was first advanced by Huggins in 1919 and by Latimer and Rodebush (1920), and has since been widely applied, especially in organic chemistry. Thus the tendency to polymerization shown by compounds containing the groups $-NH_2$, $-OH$, $-COOH$, $=NOH$, $=NH$, etc., has been attributed to hydrogen-bond formation between two or more molecules, and in the case of formic acid (Pauling and Brockway, 1934) electron diffraction measurements show that the bimolecular polymer has the structure

$$H-C\begin{array}{c} O-H-O \\ \\ O-H-O \end{array}C-H.$$

The fact that polymerization does not occur in these compounds when the hydrogen is replaced by other atoms or groups reveals that hydrogen plays some essential part in the polymerization process. Hydrogen-bond formation is also possible between two atoms within a single molecule, but here we cannot discuss the purely chemical implications of this bond, for which the reader is referred to the recent survey of Lassettre (1937).

From a structural point of view the characteristic features of the hydrogen bond arise from the vanishingly small size of the H^+ ion, as a result of which it can appear only in 2-fold co-ordination. The bond has been discussed theoretically by Pauling (1931a) who has shown that it is essentially ionic and not homopolar in nature and is only to be expected binding atoms of high electron affinity. Among substances of common occurrence it is therefore in practice confined to the binding between oxygen, fluorine and nitrogen atoms. In compounds containing two oxygen ions linked by a hydrogen bond we may picture the bond as yielding the complex group $(O^{2-}H^+O^{2-})^{3-}$, in which the drastic polarization of the O^{2-} ions results in the very small O-O distance of about $2 \cdot 55$ A. It is, however, probable that this simple picture is not a very faithful representation of the physical reality, and that actually the hydrogen proton enters one of the atoms with which it is combined to form a pseudo-atomic molecule or molecular ion, so that in the case just considered the binding is rather of the form (OH)(O). The bond is, however, definitely symmetrical, and must therefore be regarded as a resonance between the two configurations (OH)(O) and (O)(HO), so that for practical purposes the elementary description is adequate.

The hydrogen bond in crystal structures.

Potassium dihydrogen phosphate. Among compounds in which the existence of the hydrogen bond has been directly established by structure analysis one of the first to be investigated was potassium dihydrogen phosphate, KH_2PO_4 (West, 1930). This structure, which is represented schematically in Fig. 71, consists of hydrogen ions, tetrahedral PO_4 groups and

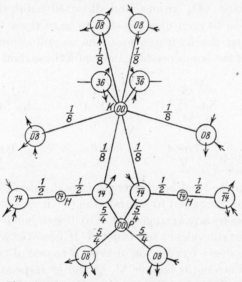

Fig. 71. The structure of potassium dihydrogen phosphate, KH_2PO_4.

somewhat irregular KO_8 groups. The complex groups are so arranged that every O^{2-} ion belongs to one PO_4 group and to two KO_8 groups, and the electrostatic bond strength reaching each O^{2-} ion from its P^{5+} and K^+ neighbours is therefore $\frac{5}{4} + 2 \times \frac{1}{8} = \frac{3}{2}$. This total is less than the bond strength of 2 required to saturate the oxygen ion and the valency of this ion can only be satisfied if it is in addition bound to one H^+ ion by a bond of strength $\frac{1}{2}$. If the hydrogen ions are arranged in the way figuratively represented in Fig. 71, every oxygen ion is bound by a hydrogen bond to one other and its valency demands are thus satisfied. In confirmation of this distribution of the hydrogen ions the oxygen atoms linked by hydrogen bonds are found to be separated by the characteristic distance of 2·54 A., a distance considerably less than that between oxygen atoms, belonging to different PO_4 groups, between which no hydrogen bond occurs.

Sodium bicarbonate. In the structure of sodium bicarbonate, $NaHCO_3$ (Zachariasen, 1933), the presence of the hydrogen bond is again clearly shown. A plan of this structure is given in Fig. 72, and it will be seen to consist of hydrogen atoms, plane CO_3 groups and distorted octahedral NaO_6 groups. The oxygen ions are seen to be of three types and, disregarding the hydrogen ions, the co-ordination and the strength of the bonds reaching the ions of the several types are:

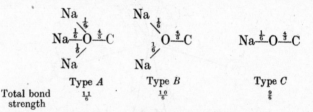

	Type A	Type B	Type C
Total bond strength	$\frac{11}{6}$	$\frac{10}{6}$	$\frac{2}{6}$

Here again the total bond strength in each case falls short of the total of 2 required to saturate the O^{2-} ions, but it is now not possible by any arrangement of hydrogen bonds to satisfy the electrostatic valency rule in detail. If, however, a hydrogen bond links every oxygen ion of type *B* to one of type *C* the total bond strengths become $\frac{11}{6}$, $\frac{13}{6}$ and $\frac{12}{6}$ respectively, and the rule is almost satisfied. Such a distribution of hydrogen bonds is just the one to be expected on structural grounds, for it corresponds to the actual number of hydrogen atoms present and also explains the close approach of the oxygen ions of types *B* and *C* with a separation of only 2·55 A.

Ammonium halides. The structures of the ammonium halides are interesting in that they reveal that hydrogen-bond formation is restricted to atoms of high electron affinity. In NH_4F the binding between nitrogen and fluorine may be regarded as due to hydrogen bonds, so that the co-ordination of each atom is necessarily limited to four neighbours and the wurtzite structure results. In the other halides, however, the electron affinity of the halogen ion is too small for hydrogen-bond formation and the structures must be regarded as purely ionic co-ordination compounds of the NH_4^+ and halogen ions, in which, in consequence, higher co-ordination prevails. In the structure of ammonium hydrogen fluoride, NH_4HF_2 (Pauling, 1933), FHF^- ions, bound within themselves by hydrogen bonds, tetrahedrally co-ordinate the nitrogen atoms, to which they are linked by further hydrogen bonds. In the corresponding potassium salt, KHF_2, a much less 'open' structure is found due to the higher co-ordination arising from the purely ionic binding between the FHF^- and K^+ ions.

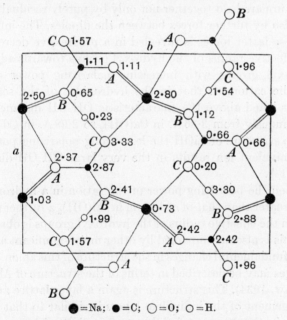

● = Na; ● = C; ◯ = O; ◯ = H.

Fig. 72. The structure of sodium bicarbonate, $NaHCO_3$.

THE HYDROXYL BOND

The structure of hydroxides.

The function of hydrogen in interatomic binding, with special reference to hydroxide structures, has been discussed by Bernal and Megaw (1935). The majority of hydroxides whose structures have been analysed are of the type $A(OH)_2$, but in addition the structures of LiOH, $Al(OH)_3$, $B(OH)_3$ and of a few other hydroxides are known. Of the hydroxides of divalent elements those of the metals Ca, Mg, Mn, Zn, Co, Ni, Fe and Cd have been studied, and all are found to have layer lattices of the cadmium iodide type, in which, therefore, the cation is octahedrally co-ordinated by hydroxyl groups. In these structures the hydroxyl group may be treated to a first approximation as a spherical ion OH^-, but the asymmetrical co-ordination of the layer lattice produces considerable polarization of this ion so that neighbouring layers of the structure are held together not only by purely residual forces but also by further forces between the dipoles. The influence of these latter forces is revealed in a progressive decrease in the effective radius of the hydroxyl groups towards adjacent hydroxyl groups with increasing polarizing power of the metallic cation, so that in the hydroxides of the series of metals listed above the characteristic OH-OH distance falls continuously from 3·36 A. in $Ca(OH)_2$ to 2·98 A. in $Cd(OH)_2$. In the structure of LiOH the less strong polarizing power of the univalent ion results in the very large OH-OH distance of 3·61 A.

When the polarizing power of the cation in a hydroxide is still greater than that of cadmium in $Cd(OH)_2$ a further reduction in the effective radius of the hydroxyl groups is observed, but this is also accompanied by other more significant and far more fundamental changes in the structure of this anion. These changes may be described in terms of the structure of $Al(OH)_3$ (Megaw, 1934). This structure is again a layer lattice and the arrangement of the individual layers is similar to that of the layers in the cadmium iodide structure but with one out of every three cation sites vacant. Each OH group is therefore co-ordinated in its own layer by two Al^{3+} ions and by one 'hole'. The mutual disposition of the adjacent layers is, however, quite different from that in other layer lattices, for these are so superposed that the OH groups fall directly above one another instead of being arranged in the usual close-packed manner common to most layer lattices of the AX_2 and AX_3 types. Moreover, the binding between successive layers in $Al(OH)_3$ is exceptionally strong, as is revealed by the very small OH-OH distance of 2·78 A. and also by the relatively small coefficient of thermal expansion normal to the plane of the layers (Megaw, 1933).

The structure of $Al(OH)_3$ reveals that the drastic polarization of the hydroxyl group results in a change far more profound than a mere increase in its dipole moment, for if the structure of the group were that of a simple dipole the structure of $Al(OH)_3$, with such groups arranged end to end, would clearly be unstable and give rise to repulsion instead of particularly strong attraction between the layers. The problem has been discussed at length by Bernal and Megaw (1935), who conclude that with increasing polarization the cylindrical structure of the polar OH groups must ultimately break down and give place to a structure of tetrahedral symmetry from which the bonds are characteristically directed in a manner analogous to that which we have already seen to obtain in the case of the water molecule. From the point of view of electrostatic valency the hydroxyl group may be pictured as a tetrahedral complex, three corners of which are occupied by concentrations of negative charge, each of value $\frac{1}{2}$, while the fourth, occupied by the hydrogen ion, is the seat of a positive charge of the same value.

With such a picture of the structure of the hydroxyl group it is clear that two such groups can attract each other provided that they are so disposed that regions of opposite charge are adjacent:

The binding which arises in this way Bernal and Megaw have termed the *hydroxyl bond*. It differs essentially from the hydrogen bond in that here hydrogen is a constituent of both the groups that are linked, and in that it is not a resonance phenomenon since there is no possibility of either hydrogen atom migrating from the group to which it belongs. It is, moreover, less strong than the hydrogen bond, as is revealed by the larger characteristic O-O distance of about 2·70 A.

It is now easy to see under what conditions we may expect to find the hydroxyl bond in crystal structures. The tetrahedral symmetry must be satisfied and also the electrostatic valency principle, so that each OH group must be bound to two other OH groups by the hydroxyl bonds and in addition either to two cations by bonds of strength $\frac{1}{2}$ or to one cation by a single bond of strength unity. In the former case the coordination round each OH group must be roughly tetrahedral and in the latter case a planar arrangement is to be expected. When the electrostatic valency of the cation-OH link is less than $\frac{1}{2}$ the polarization of the hydroxyl group is insufficient to give rise to the characteristic tetrahedral structure and no hydroxyl bond can be formed.

Structures containing hydroxyl bonds.

These conclusions are in agreement with the evidence derived from the crystal structures of the hydroxides. In all the hydroxides of divalent metals having the cadmium iodide structure the cation-OH bond strength is $\frac{2}{6} = \frac{1}{3}$, so that no hydroxyl bond is possible and the OH group behaves as a simple dipole with a radius towards other hydroxyl groups of 1·5–1·8 A. Of the hydroxides of divalent metals so far studied $Zn(OH)_2$ alone shows a hydroxyl bond, for this substance is dimorphous and in addition to the cadmium iodide structure has an orthorhombic variety in which the cations are coordinated by only four OH groups and in which, therefore, the Zn—OH bonds are of strength $\frac{1}{2}$. Each OH group is bound to two other such groups and to two zinc ions, and the tetrahedral distribution of its bonds is satisfied. In $Al(OH)_3$ the higher charge of the cation makes an octahedral co-ordination of OH groups still consistent with a hydroxyl bond, and in this structure each OH group is bound to two Al^{3+} ions and to two other OH groups, one in its own layer and one in the adjacent layer. This particular structure has been discussed at length by Bernal and Megaw (1935) who have been able to account completely for the detailed features of the symmetry and the interatomic distances in terms of the hydroxyl bond.

Boric acid. The structure of boric acid, $B(OH)_3$ (Zachariasen, 1934c), is formed by the superposition of plane sheets of boron and oxygen atoms each of the type shown in Fig. 73. The structure is of interest in that the 3-fold co-ordination of the B^{3+} ions results in a B—OH bond of strength unity, so that a hydroxyl binding is to be expected in which each OH group is linked only to a single cation and in which, therefore, the three

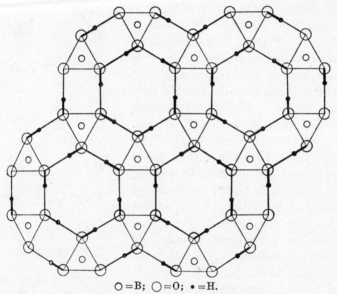

○ = B; ◯ = O; ● = H.

Fig. 73. The structure of boric acid, $B(OH)_3$.
The structure is formed by the superposition of layers of the type shown.

bonds from each OH group must all lie in a plane. The structure will be seen to satisfy these requirements in a very beautiful manner, and in the diagram the polarity of each hydroxyl bond is schematically illustrated by representing the hydrogen ion. The forces between the sheets must be purely residual in character and the distance of 3·18 A. between hydroxyl groups in different sheets is considerably greater than that between the groups bound by hydroxyl bonds. The structure of boric acid was originally interpreted in terms of hydrogen bonds between the OH groups in place of the hydroxyl bonds here described. Bernal and Megaw (1935) pointed out, however, that the observed separation of 2·71 A. between OH groups is far greater than the value of 2·55 A. normally associated with the hydrogen bond, and that, moreover, in all other structures in which hydrogen bonds are known no oxygen atom is ever found bound by a hydrogen bond to more than one other.

Other compounds. Hydroxyl bonds are also found in the mineral lepidocrocite, FeO(OH) (Goldsztaub, 1935), the structure of which is shown in Fig. 74. It is essentially a layer lattice in which each layer is composed of four planes of atoms. The two inner planes contain Fe^{3+} and O^{2-} ions, while the two outer planes contain only OH groups. Each hydroxyl group is tetrahedrally co-ordinated by two cations in its own layer and by two OH groups, to which it is bound by hydroxyl bonds, in the adjacent layer. In this structure the hydroxyl bonds are therefore exerted only between OH groups in different layers. It is interesting to compare the structure of lepidocrocite with that of the closely related FeOCl. The separate layers of this latter structure are identical with those in FeO(OH), but the packing of the layers is completely different, for the Cl⁻ ions do not have to satisfy the tetrahedral

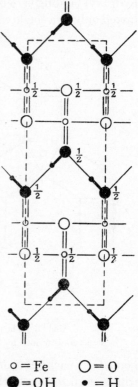

o = Fe   O = O
● = OH   • = H

Fig. 74. The structure of lepidocrocite, FeO(OH).

distribution of bonds characteristic of the OH groups, and in adjacent layers are therefore close-packed.

The hydroxyl bond has also been observed in a number of other compounds, some of which will be discussed in the chapter devoted to molecular structures and others of which are considered below. Apart from its occurrence in solids, however, it must also be responsible for the polymerization of many alcohols in the liquid state or in solution, just as the hydrogen bond is responsible for the polymerization of acids. Thus Zachariasen (1935) has shown that in methyl alcohol there is a tendency towards polymerization which is doubtless due to hydroxyl-bond formation:

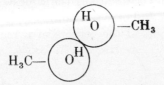

This interpretation is confirmed by the electric moment of the resultant double molecule which proves that the association is not a symmetrical dipole effect.

The chemistry of the hydroxyl bond.

The progressive transition from the hydroxyl group of cylindrical form found in the alkaline hydroxides to the tetrahedral structure of this group which obtains in the amphoteric and acidic hydroxides is part of a continuous transition towards hydrogen-bond formation, for, with increasing polarization, the energy required to remove the hydrogen ion completely from the oxygen atom becomes progressively less, and ultimately the possibility of migration into a neighbouring oxygen atom arises. This, however, can only happen in hydroxy-oxides of the general type $AO_n(OH)_m$, where an oxygen ion as opposed to a hydroxyl group is available to receive the migrating hydrogen ion. The hydrogen bond is therefore to be expected only in oxy-acids and oxy-acid salts such as H_2SO_4, KH_2PO_4, etc., but not in hydroxy-acids $A(OH)_n$, such as $B(OH)_3$, etc. Hydroxides of the type $A(OH)_n$ in which the cation A is of exceptional polarizing power, as, for example, in AgOH, will be expected to be unstable since the tendency towards hydrogen-bond formation cannot be satisfied.

The transition between the hydroxyl and hydrogen bonds

has been discussed from a wave mechanical point of view by Gillette and Sherman (1936).

The structure of ice.

The structure of ice has been studied by W. H. Bragg (1922) and by Barnes (1929), and the distribution of the molecules in the hexagonal unit cell is shown in Fig. 75. The arrangement of these molecules is essentially the same as that of the silicon ions in the structure of β-tridymite and each is co-ordinated by four neighbours at the corners of a regular tetrahedron.

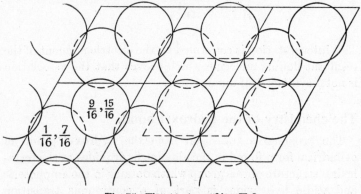

Fig. 75. The structure of ice, H_2O.

Alternatively the arrangement may be described as one in which the water molecules occupy the positions of both the zinc and sulphur atoms in the wurtzite structure. The intermolecular distances correspond to a radius of the water molecule of $1\cdot38$ A., a value very close to that found in hydrates. It is not, of course, possible by X-ray means to determine the positions of the hydrogen ions in the molecule but this point is discussed further below.

From the chemical point of view the most important feature of the ice structure is that it reveals no trace of any associated molecules so that the properties of ice cannot be attributed to the existence of any molecular complexes such as H_4O_2, H_6O_3, etc. From a purely geometrical point of view the most striking feature is the low co-ordination and corresponding 'open' character of the molecular arrangement, which is in

marked contrast to the close-packing of the atoms in, say, the
structures of the true metals, and which clearly indicates a
directed binding more analogous to that found in diamond.
The constitution of the water molecule has been discussed at
length by Bernal and Fowler (1933), and by Fowler and Bernal
(1933), who have shown, both from the observed dipole
moment and from spectroscopic and other physical properties,
that the distribution of charge in the molecule is of the form
shown in Fig. 76. Here the hydrogen protons are deeply
embedded in the oxygen ion, the nucleus of which is in consequence displaced from the centre of the molecule by the

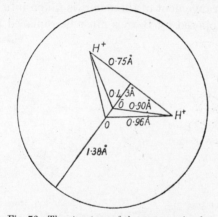

Fig. 76. The structure of the water molecule.
H⁺ are the hydrogen nuclei, O the oxygen nucleus and O⁻ the
centre of negative charge and of the molecule.

repulsion of these protons. As far as its external field is concerned this picture of the molecule may be somewhat simplified
into a tetrahedral distribution of two regions of positive and
two regions of negative charge each of amount about $\frac{1}{2}e$, the
small value of this charge compared with the unit charge on
the protons being due to the partial screening of the hydrogen
nuclei. This form of the water molecule may alternatively be
regarded as arising from the combination of a H⁺ ion and an
OH⁻ group. Due to the great polarizing power of the hydrogen
ion the tetrahedral structure of the hydroxyl group is developed
and the H⁺ ion with unit charge is then absorbed and trans-

forms one of the concentrations of charge $-\frac{1}{2}e$ to a region of positive charge $+\frac{1}{2}e$.

It is clear that such a structure of the water molecule must impose limitations on the way in which these molecules can pack together, and that, in fact, we shall expect the structure of ice to be one in which each molecule is tetrahedrally surrounded by four others so disposed that regions of opposite charge are adjacent, and in which, therefore, the binding is essentially similar to the hydroxyl bond already described. In this way it is possible to deduce the positions of the hydrogen ions in the structure, and Bernal and Fowler have shown that when the arrangement of these ions is taken into account the structure proposed by Barnes must be replaced by one with

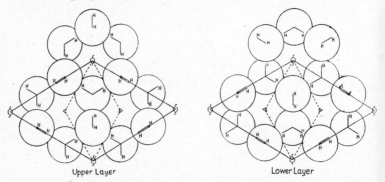

Upper Layer   Lower Layer

Fig. 77. A possible structure of ice taking account of the arrangement of the hydrogen atoms. The structure is formed by the superposition of the two layers shown. The true unit cell is marked by full lines. Dotted lines indicate the pseudo-unit cell corresponding to the structure shown in Fig. 75, p. 298.

exactly the same distribution of the oxygen atoms but in which the unit cell is larger. The choice of a larger unit cell can be made in more than one way, the simplest of which gives the structure shown in Fig. 77, with a unit cell three times the size of that of Barnes and containing 12 molecules. This structure is polar. An alternative non-polar arrangement is possible with a still larger unit cell containing 96 molecules, but it is, of course, impossible to discriminate between these two structures, or to distinguish either from that proposed by Barnes, by X-ray methods alone.

The various polymorphous forms of ice stable at low temperatures or high pressures have been studied by McFarlan (1936 a, b), and the two forms whose structures have been completely determined again show the characteristic tetrahedral co-ordination of each molecule by its neighbours. In both cases, however, the tetrahedra are considerably distorted from the regular form found in ordinary ice.

THE STRUCTURE OF LIQUIDS, LIQUID CRYSTALS AND GLASSES

We cannot here make any attempt to give an adequate account of the structure of these phases which are, in any case, not strictly within the province of crystal chemistry. Nevertheless, certain general features of these systems are so intimately connected with conceptions based on the structures of crystalline solids that they can be properly understood only in terms of such conceptions and so warrant brief mention in this place.

Liquids.

The characteristic feature of what we may term an 'ideal liquid' is a close contact between spherical molecules, leading to a relatively dense, approximately close-packed structure, but one in which any regularity of packing is confined to only a few molecular diameters. We may illustrate this structure by its analogy to a sack full of spheres: there is no regularity extending over large distances, so that it is not possible to deduce the arrangement of spheres in one region given that in another, but the assemblage as a whole has a density not very different from that of a close-packed structure, and there is a high probability that the immediate environment of any given sphere is nearly the same as in a close-packed crystal. Ideal liquid structures of this type are found in the molten metals (Tarasov and Warren, 1936), including the metals of the B sub-groups of which the structures in the solid state are not close-packed. Thus in bismuth the directional tendency of the binding in the crystal is lost in the liquid, which is in consequence denser than the solid so that a contraction in volume occurs on melting.

In liquids in which the molecules depart considerably from spherical symmetry, or in which the molecules are strongly polar, a less regular packing of lower co-ordination is found, and in methyl alcohol Zachariasen (1935) has shown that the distribution in the liquid indicates a tendency towards the formation of clusters of molecules bound by hydroxyl bonds. Such clusters, however, do not have any permanent existence in the liquid but are in a continuous state of formation and disintegration, and must not be regarded as in any way indicative of chemical association. Similar departures from the ideal close-packed liquid structure are found in a number of benzene derivatives (Skinner, 1930), in some of which a change of structure with temperature takes place due apparently to molecular rotation or to a change in molecular shape. In compounds, such as acids and alcohols, which contain active groups the structure of the liquid must be determined both by the directed character of the intermolecular forces and by the shape of the molecules, but in neutral compounds, such as the hydrocarbons, the latter factor alone can operate.

The structure of water. By far the most important liquid, however, in which a departure from a close-packed arrangement is found is water, the structure of which has been discussed at length by Bernal and Fowler (1933) and by Fowler and Bernal (1933). The density of water reveals immediately the very open nature of its structure, for a close-packed liquid consisting of molecules of the known size of the water molecule would have a density of approximately 2·0. At the same time the X-ray diffraction from liquid water (Stewart, 1931) is entirely different from that from a close-packed liquid, and instead reveals a structure in which there is a pronounced tendency for each molecule to be surrounded by only four neighbours tetrahedrally disposed at a distance of about 2·8 A. We are thus led to a picture of water as a pseudo-crystalline liquid consisting of small regions in which a more or less regular tetrahedral arrangement of molecules obtains. Such a tetrahedral arrangement is not, however, sufficient completely to specify the structure of the liquid, for the tetrahedra can be linked in a number of different ways just as the SiO_4 tetrahedra in silica can give rise to the different structures of cristobalite, tridymite and quartz. In ice, as we have seen, the arrangement of the water molecules is the same as that of the silicon ions in tridymite, but the same structure cannot occur in liquid water since the density would in that case be lower than that of ice. If, however, the structure of water is a pseudo-crystalline arrangement based on the more compact quartz structure the higher density can be understood, and Bernal and Fowler have in fact shown that the observed X-ray diffraction curves for water at room temperatures can be explained only in terms of a 'quartz-like' arrangement and are not consistent with a 'tridymite-like' structure. At high temperatures, however, the diffraction effects approximate more and more closely to those of an ideal liquid so that between, say, 150° C. and the critical temperature water has a pseudo-close-packed structure. Similarly at temperatures below about 4° C., and in super-cooled water, a change in structure again occurs, and a transition towards a tridymite- or ice-like arrangement is found. We may thus recognize in all three different forms of water, between which a continuous transition with temperature takes place:

Water I	$\rightleftharpoons$	Water II	$\rightleftharpoons$	Water III
Ice-like		Quartz-like		Close-packed
Stable below		Stable between		Stable above
about 4° C.		4° C. and about 150° C.		about 150° C.

It is not to be considered, however, that the liquid is ever in any way heterogeneous, consisting of a mixture of regions of different structure, but only that the average mutual arrangement of the molecules resembles more closely water I, II or III according to the temperature.

In terms of this picture the anomalous contraction in volume with increasing temperature between 0 and 4° C. is readily understood, for in this temperature range the ice-like arrangement is rapidly breaking down to give place to the more compact quartz-like structure, and the normal expansion of the latter is completely masked by the larger volume change accompanying the morphotropic transformation. Only when the ice-like arrangement is completely transformed does the normal expansion become apparent.

The pseudo-crystalline structure of water discussed above has been applied by Bernal and Fowler (1933) to account either quantitatively or qualitatively for many other of its chemical and physical properties. We cannot, however, here give any account of this work, for which the reader is referred to the original papers.

General accounts of recent works on the theory of liquids have been given by Stewart (1929, 1930), Randall (1934), Herrmann (1936), Bernal (1937), Herzfeld (1937), Warren (1937) and Randall (1938).

Liquid crystals.

In substances consisting of molecules of very unsymmetrical shape, and particularly in substances in which very long molecules occur, a tendency to preserve a pseudo-crystalline structure above the melting point is revealed by the appearance of a liquid crystalline phase stable between this temperature and that at which an isotropic liquid is formed. In such compounds the asymmetry of the molecules results in melting taking place in two or more stages, in the first of which the lateral attractions between the molecules are not broken down. In the *smectic* state the molecules are all arranged with their axes parallel and are restricted in their movement to motion in a series of regularly spaced parallel sheets, within each of which, however, there is no regularity of arrangement. This condition is represented schematically in Fig. 78c, and may be compared with the arrangement of the isotropic liquid shown in Fig. 78a. In the *nematic* state, shown in Fig. 78b, the molecules still have their axes parallel but are otherwise arranged quite irregularly and are free to move at random. In the case of substances with molecules of sufficient length it is possible to imagine such a condition existing also in solution, and in tobacco mosaic virus (Bawden, Pirie, Bernal and Fankuchen, 1936) this is indeed the case. A strong solution of this substance has the properties of a nematic liquid crystal but a dilute solution, in which the molecules have room to rotate freely, is isotropic. Even the dilute solution, however, becomes anisotropic if the molecules are constrained to assume a preferred orientation by flow through a tube.

The smectic and the nematic phases represent two of a number of geometrically possible intermediate states between solid and liquid, and we can in fact recognize a series of conditions of matter, corresponding to progressively more

(a) Isotropic liquid. Neither orientation nor periodicity.

(b) Nematic. Orientation without periodicity. Above, viewed perpendicular to molecular axis; below, parallel to molecular axis.

(c) Normal Smectic. Orientation and molecules in equispaced planes with no internal periodicity. Above, viewed perpendicular to molecular axis; below, parallel to molecular axis.

Fig. 78. Symbolical representation of the structures of liquid crystals.

regular molecular arrangements, between the ideal liquid and the crystalline solid:

Ideal close-packed liquid, e.g. Na, CCl_4.
Associated liquid, e.g. H_2O, $CH_3.OH$.
Nematic liquid crystal.
Smectic liquid crystal.
Crystalline solid.

We cannot here give any further account of the nature of liquid crystals. They have been discussed briefly by Bernal and Wooster (1932) and by Randall (1934), and have been the subject of a long series of papers in the *Zeitschrift für Kristallographie* (Friedel and Friedel, and others, 1931) and of a symposium of the Faraday Society (Oseen, and others, 1933).

Glasses.

The structure of a glass is formally closely analogous to that of an associated liquid. The mechanical properties of glasses, and particularly their mechanical strength, show that the forces responsible for their coherence must be essentially the same as in a crystal, and that the atoms must be linked together to form an extended, continuous three-dimensional network. In this network the immediate environment of each atom is the same as, or similar to, that in a crystal, but any long-distance regularity or periodicity is lacking. The distinction between a crystal and a glass has been illustrated by Zachariasen (1932) by the two-dimensional example shown in Fig. 79. Here there is seen to be no regularity in the lattice of the glass but the type of binding and co-ordination is essentially the same in the two cases.

The structure of silica glass and of BeF_2 in a vitreous state has been investigated by Warren (1933, 1934) and by Warren and Hill (1934), who have found that the X-ray diffraction patterns from these substances are in complete accord with the picture of the glass as an irregular network of SiO_4 or BeF_4 tetrahedra. Thus in silica glass the atomic distribution is such that any given SiO_4 tetrahedron has four neighbouring tetrahedra at a distance of $3 \cdot 2$ A., and, on the average, twelve second nearest neighbours at about $5 \cdot 2$ A., but beyond this distance the irregularity of the network makes the distribution of more remote neighbours completely random.

Zachariasen's picture of the structure of glasses enables many of their characteristic physical properties to be explained. Thus the gradual and indefinite melting of a glass arises from the irregularity of the structure, for, since all the atoms are structurally inequivalent, the energy required to detach an atom from the network is different for each individual atom. With increasing temperature, therefore, an increasing number of atoms become free, so that the break-down is a continuous rather than an abrupt phenomenon. The low thermal expansion of silica glass also arises from its

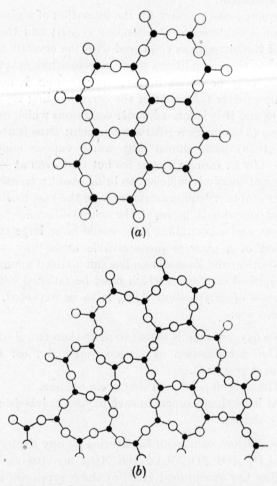

(a)

(b)

Fig. 79. Zachariasen's picture of the structure of a glass: (a) the regular structure of the crystal; (b) the corresponding glass structure.

structure, for the interatomic distances increase on heating but at the same time the strain due to the irregularity of the structure is partly relieved and a closer packing results, so that the glass, so to speak, expands into itself. The process is closely analogous to the zero expansion of water near 4° C. due to the transition from the ice-like to the more closely packed quartz-like arrangement.

The conditions necessary for the formation of a glass have also been considered by Zachariasen (1932); and the great rarity of the vitreous as compared with the crystalline state shows that these conditions must be somewhat exacting. A glass can only be stable if its energy content is not substantially greater than that of the corresponding crystalline structure and if it is formed under conditions which hinder a transition to this more regular arrangement. Thus Burton and Oliver (1936) have shown that water vapour condensed below $-110°$ C. forms vitreous ice but that even at $-80°$ C. the thermal energy is sufficient to bring about a transition to the more stable crystalline structure. In the vast majority of chemical compounds, however, the energy difference between a vitreous and a crystalline state would be so large that the formation of a glass is inconceivable under any possible circumstances, and Zachariasen has summarized a number of semi-empirical conditions which must be satisfied before an oxide glass of composition A_mO_n is to be expected. These conditions are:

(1) No oxygen atom is bound to more than two A atoms.
(2) The co-ordination of oxygen round A must be low (usually 3 or 4).
(3) The oxygen polyhedra share only corners.
(4) At least three corners in each oxygen polyhedron must be shared.

These conditions cannot all be satisfied by any oxides of the types A_2O, AO, AO_3, A_2O_7 and AO_4: no vitreous oxides (excluding the exceptional H_2O) of these types are known. On the other hand, the conditions can be satisfied by oxides A_2O_3 if the oxygen atoms form triangles round each A atom, and by oxides AO_2 and A_2O_5 if the oxygen atoms co-ordinate the cations tetrahedrally. From these conditions, by taking into account the characteristic oxygen co-ordination of various cations, Zachariasen concludes that only the following oxides are to be expected to occur in vitreous forms: B_2O_3, SiO_2, GeO_2, P_2O_5, As_2O_5, P_2O_3, As_2O_3, Sb_2O_3, V_2O_5, Sb_2O_5, Cb_2O_5, Ta_2O_5, and among fluorides only BeF_2.

General accounts of recent work on the structure of glasses have been given by Warren (1937) and Randall (1938).

This concludes our account of the crystal chemistry of ionic compounds. It will be seen how wide a part of the whole field of inorganic chemistry is included in their study. A survey of recent work on ionic crystals has been published by Machatschki (1938 a, b).

CHAPTER XI

MOLECULAR COMPOUNDS

INTRODUCTION

Molecular compounds are those in which definite chemical molecules can be recognized as having a more or less discrete existence in the crystal structure. In such compounds the molecules are generally bound within themselves by forces considerably stronger than those linking adjacent molecules together, so that all such structures are heterodesmic. The intermolecular forces, however, are not necessarily only residual in nature, and molecular structures also exist in which the molecules are linked by metallic or ionic bonds. Thus the structures of selenium and bismuth already described are, strictly speaking, molecular in this sense in that they are built up of separate molecules, each of infinite extent in one and two dimensions respectively, bound together by metallic forces. Similarly, the chains in the stibnite structure and the sheets in the various layer lattices and also in talc and boric acid are essentially single molecules, but any attempt to separate these compounds from the other closely associated structures with which they were discussed would be largely artificial. The classification of molecular compounds is therefore less precise than that of the other types of structures which we have considered, and is one which is in part arbitrary and in part determined by practical convenience. The only structures which unambiguously call for discussion in this chapter are those in which molecules, of whatever size, are bound together by purely residual bonds, but we shall also consider here certain other structures in which the intermolecular linking is more or less polar in nature but in which the shape of the individual molecules no less than the type of binding has an important influence in determining the structure.

By far the most important molecular structures are those which embrace the whole field of organic chemistry, but in this field the use of X-ray methods has developed relatively slowly, and it is only in recent years that they have been sufficiently extensively applied for important and significant results to have emerged. In part this is due to the practical problems presented by organic compounds, the analysis of which is technically more difficult than that of inorganic structures, owing, on the one hand, to the scarcity of good crystals and, on the other, to the closely comparable scattering powers of the carbon, nitrogen and oxygen atoms. More particularly, however, is it due to the fact that in organic chemistry chemical evidence alone had already enabled a fairly accurate picture of the structures of most simple compounds to be formed. As a result, the early structure analyses were all primarily verifications of the molecular configurations long accepted by the chemist, and in each case the chemist's structure was in fact confirmed. But even in the simplest structures X-ray analysis can give additional information on three important points outside the scope of direct chemical experiment, namely, (a) the dimensions of the molecule and of the individual interatomic bonds within it, (b) the shape of the molecule as a whole, as distinct from merely the angles between the bonds from any given atom, and (c) the mutual arrangement of the different molecules in the structure and the nature of the binding forces between them. We may consider these points separately.

The dimensions of the molecule. We have already emphasized that in homopolar compounds the conception of the atoms as spheres of characteristic radii is only of limited significance, and, in particular, is not valid in structures of low or irregular co-ordination where drastic polarization results in considerable departures in the shape of the atoms from the spherical form. Especially is this true in molecular structures, on account of the completely unsymmetrical co-ordination, and in these only interatomic distances, and not individual radii, are significant. It is found, however, that the distance between two given atoms linked by a given type of bond is closely constant throughout the whole range of organic compounds, so that characteristic bond-lengths can be tabulated, which, together with a knowledge of the interbond angles, enable accurate models of the molecules to be constructed. A number of such bond-lengths are summarized in Table 57, and it will be seen that for a given bond the interatomic distance is closely constant in a wide range of chemically dissimilar compounds. On the other hand, the lengths of single, double and triple bonds between the same atoms are significantly different, so that a detailed study of interatomic distances can give direct evidence of the type of binding in the structure: and especially in complex structures, where chemical evidence alone cannot provide such information, is this method of approach very fruitful.

Molecular shape. Although the characteristic interatomic distances and interbond angles are very closely or exactly preserved in all molecular compounds, a knowledge of these quantities is not sufficient to determine completely the molecular shape on account of the flexibility arising from free rotation about each single bond. Detailed structure analyses reveal that in many compounds this flexibility of the molecule is in fact very marked, so that, although some molecular types have certain general characteristic shapes, the precise configuration of the molecule cannot usually be predicted on chemical grounds alone and is determined by the detailed distribution of the neighbouring molecules in the structure.

Intermolecular binding. No less important than the information which X-ray methods give concerning the nature of the interatomic binding within the molecule is the light they throw on the type of force responsible for the coherence of different molecules, and in this field the results are the more valuable because the purely chemical evidence is here less direct and unambiguous. In some structures these forces are of strength scarcely less than that of the homopolar bonds within the molecule and are scarcely less entitled to be regarded as definite chemical bonds, while in others they are purely residual in character. For practical convenience in the classification of molecular compounds the intermolecular forces may be divided into three more or less distinct types determined by their strength and origin. The strongest are the

TABLE 57

Bond-lengths in molecular structures

Compound	Bond type*	Length
Diamond	C—C aliphatic	1·54
Paraffins	C—C aliphatic	1·54
Dibenzyl	C—C aliphatic	1·58
Benzoquinone	C—C in ring	1·50
Ethylene	C=C	1·34
Benzoquinone	C=C in ring	1·32
Carbon suboxide	C=C	1·30
Acetylene	C≡C	1·20
Tolane	C≡C	1·19
Graphite	C—C	1·42
Benzene	C—C aromatic	1·42
Hexamethylbenzene	C—C aromatic	1·42
Naphthalene	C—C aromatic	1·41
Anthracene	C—C aromatic	1·41
Durene	C—C aromatic	1·41
Dibenzyl	C—C aromatic	1·41
Chrysene	C—C aromatic	1·41
p-Diphenylbenzene	C—C aromatic	1·42
Diphenyl	C—C aromatic	1·42
Hexamethylbenzene	C—C al.-ar.	1·48
Durene	C—C al.-ar.	1·47
Dibenzyl	C—C al.-ar.	1·47
p-Diphenylbenzene	C—C between rings	1·48
Diphenyl	C—C between rings	1·48
Polyoxymethylene	C—O	1·49
Methyl ether	C—O	1·42
Benzoquinone	C=O	1·14
Urea	C=O	1·25
Oxalic acid dihydrate	C=O ⎱ resonance C—OH ⎰	⎱1·24 ⎰1·30
Resorcinol	C—OH	1·36
Pentaerythritol	C—OH	1·46
Urea	C—N	1·37
Thiourea	C—N	1·37
Hexamethylenetetramine	C—N	1·42
Phthalocyanine	C—N ⎱ resonance C=N ⎰	1·34
Thiourea	C=S	1·64
Hexachlorbenzene	C—Cl	1·86
Hexabrombenzene	C—Br	1·94
Iodoform	C—I	2·10
Di-iodocyclohexane	C—I	2·12
	N—O	1·38
Nitric oxide	N=O	1·15
p-Dinitrobenzene	N=O	1·20
Nitrogen	N≡N	1·06
Oxalic acid dihydrate	⎱O—O hydrogen bond ⎰O—O hydroxyl bond	2·52 2·85

* Very few of the bonds have strictly the unique structure indicated and in most cases a resonance structure, with greater or less contributions from one or more other configurations, obtains.

purely ionic forces which arise in the structures of organic
acids, bases and salts. These structures, strictly speaking, are
ionic, but for reasons already discussed are most conveniently
classified with the molecular crystals. Less strong than the
purely ionic binding is the polar linkage which occurs between
molecules possessing local dipoles, such as are produced by
—OH, =NH or =O groups. In structures with this type of
binding the molecules are packed in such a way that adjacent
dipoles neutralize each other locally as far as possible, thus
producing a system of minimum electrostatic energy. The
weakest type of intermolecular linkage is the purely residual
bond which arises between neutral molecules devoid of any
active polar groups.

The classification of molecular structures.

The different types of intermolecular binding forces described in the last paragraph provide a convenient basis for
the classification of molecular structures. But cutting across
such a classification is a second classification in terms of the
shape of the individual molecules, for in molecular structures
we are no longer concerned with the packing of spherical atoms
under the influence of different types of force, but instead with
the packing of complex units of irregular shape. For this
purpose it is convenient to assign all molecules to one of four
somewhat arbitrarily defined groups. In the first are all the
small symmetrical molecules which may be regarded as very
roughly spherical in shape. This group includes a number of
inorganic molecular structures as well as many simple organic
compounds most of which are liquids or gases at ordinary
temperatures. In this group the structures correspond to an
approximately close-packed arrangement of the molecules.
A second group includes long molecules, and here the structures are primarily ones in which these molecules are packed
together like sticks in a bundle, although the presence of
active groups often introduces complexities in the arrangement. The third group embraces structures containing more
or less flat molecules, and these are generally found to be
packed so that they are all parallel to a line but not to each

other. For completeness, a fourth group may be recognized containing large, complex, three-dimensional molecules, but few representatives of this class have as yet been investigated.

A classification of molecular structures in terms of inter-molecular binding force and molecular shape is summarized in Table 58, which is an amplified presentation of the van der Waals section of Table 6, p. 43. It is scarcely necessary to emphasize that such a classification, especially as regards molecular shape, is to a large extent arbitrary and that no rigid dividing lines can be recognized between the

TABLE 58

THE CLASSIFICATION OF MOLECULAR STRUCTURES

Molecular shape	Type of intermolecular binding force		
	Apolar	Polar	Ionic
Simple symmetrical molecules	Inert gases Diatomic gases, H_2, O_2, etc. Hydrides, NH_3, CH_4, etc. Polyhalides, CCl_4, etc. Simple hydro-carbons Basic beryllium acetate	Urea and thiourea Hexamethylene-tetramine Pentaerythritol	Oxalic acid and oxalates Simple amino-acids Simple alkyl-ammonium salts
Long molecules	Long-chain ali-phatic hydro-carbons Cycloparaffins	Long-chain al-cohols, ketones and esters	Fatty acids and soaps Long-chain alkyl-ammonium salts
	Plastic sulphur Rubber	Cellulose	Fibrous protein
Flat molecules	Orthorhombic sulphur Aromatic hydro-carbons Phthalocyanines Cyanuric triazide	Halogen, nitro- and amino-derivatives of aromatic hydrocarbons Phenols Quinones Sugars Sterols	Aromatic acids and their salts Aromatic bases and their salts Methylene blue halides
Complex three-dimensional molecules	—	—	'Globular' proteins?

several different structure types. Nevertheless, the classification is convenient in providing a general basis for our
discussion of individual structures.

The number of organic compounds whose structures have
been determined is still much smaller than that of inorganic
substances studied, and this fact, together with the much
greater complexity of organic crystals, make general principles in this field more difficult to advance. Each substance
has its own characteristic structure and only in the most
general terms is it possible to point to structural features of
widespread occurrence among compounds of a given type. The
choice of substances investigated has, moreover, often been
somewhat capricious, so that numerous isolated analyses, in
some cases of compounds of considerable complexity, are
available, while the structures of many other and simpler
bodies are still unknown. For all these reasons our discussion
of molecular compounds must be primarily a descriptive
account of some of the structures analysed, in the course of
which any general principles which these structures illustrate
will be emphasized. As always, no attempt will be made to
cover the whole field of published analyses, but instead a few
representative examples characteristic of various different
types of compound will be described.

We shall consider first only compounds of which a complete
structure analysis is available, and then pass on to review very
briefly certain more complex compounds of which no detailed
analyses have yet been made but of which a merely superficial X-ray examination has sufficed to furnish a valuable
indication of the general features of the structural arrangement.

COMPOUNDS WITH SMALL SYMMETRICAL MOLECULES

Apolar intermolecular binding.

The characteristic feature of all structures of this class is an
approximately close-packed arrangement of the molecules,
which arises from their roughly spherical form and the

symmetrical, undirected distribution of the intermolecular bonds.

The inert gases. All the inert gases which have been investigated are found to have a cubic close-packed arrangement in which the atoms must be bound by purely residual forces. The formal resemblance, discussed in Chap. II, between the metallic and residual bonds is emphasized by the close-packed structure of these gases, while their low melting points reveal the weakness of this latter type of linkage. The atomic radii of these elements are:

Ne	A	Kr	Xe
1·60 A.	1·91 A.	2·01 A.	2·20 A.

Diatomic molecular structures. A number of compounds consisting of diatomic molecules have cubic close-packed structures due to free molecular rotation. This is the case with N_2, CO, HCl and HBr, but most of these substances are polymorphous and occur with one or more other and more complex structures at lower temperatures when rotation is inhibited. In HI rotation never takes place, due to the large moment of inertia, and a more complex structure persists up to the melting point. In solid hydrogen the H_2 molecules are arranged as in hexagonal close-packing, and free rotation probably occurs even at the absolute zero. Rotation is not found in any of the halogens, in the structures of which the diatomic molecules occur relatively widely separated from their neighbours. Thus in chlorine the Cl-Cl distance within the molecule is 1·99 A. and between adjacent molecules 2·79 A. In iodine the corresponding distances are 2·70 and 3·54 A. respectively. The weakness of the intermolecular binding in these structures is revealed by a comparison of the low melting point of the solid with the stability of the diatomic molecule of the gas, or by a comparison of the heat of evaporation of the solid with the heat of dissociation of the molecule. In the case of chlorine these quantities are 4·5 and 58·5 kcal. per gram molecule respectively.

Other simple structures. A number of other simple molecular compounds, especially compounds of hydrogen with one other atom, have cubic close-packed structures. Among these are

CH_4, NH_3, PH_3, AsH_3, SH_2, SeH_2, etc. In N_2O and CO_2 the linear N—O—N and O—C—O molecules are still arranged at the points of a cubic face-centred lattice, but are not in free rotation, being disposed with their axes permanently parallel to the triad axes of the cube. The symmetry is, therefore, that not of the holohedral but of the pyrites class of the cubic system. In a number of structures of compounds such as CBr_4, SiI_4, $TiBr_4$, TiI_4, SnI_4, etc., consisting of symmetrically shaped molecules of large atoms, the distribution of the molecules is one which leads to a nearly close-packed arrangement of these atoms.

Basic beryllium acetate. The structure of $Be_4O(CH_3COO)_6$ has been elucidated by Pauling and Sherman (1934) and is found to be a purely molecular arrangement and not a co-ordination structure. The structure of a single molecule is shown in Fig. 80. Each beryllium ion is tetrahedrally sur-

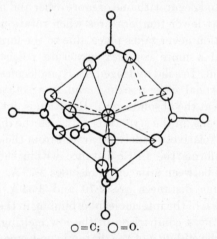

$\bigcirc = C$; $\bigcirc = O$.

Fig. 80. The structure of the molecule of basic beryllium acetate, $Be_4O(CH_3COO)_6$. Only the carbon and oxygen atoms are shown. The beryllium atoms are situated at the centres of the tetrahedra of oxygen atoms. One acetate group at the back of the molecule is omitted for clarity.

rounded by four oxygen atoms, three of which are contributed by the acetate groups and the fourth of which is the central basic oxygen atom. The four BeO_4 tetrahedra therefore all have a common corner in this atom. The two oxygen atoms of the carboxyl group are geometrically equivalent and structurally indistinguishable, and the electrostatic valency rule is satisfied if each such atom is held to carbon by a resonating single-double bond:

$$CH_3 . C \overset{O}{\underset{O^-}{\diagup}} \rightleftharpoons CH_3 . C \overset{O^-}{\underset{O}{\diagup}}$$

The roughly tetrahedral molecules are packed in the cubic unit cell as are the atoms in diamond, and the volatility and other physical properties of the substance reveal that the inter-molecular binding is relatively weak.

Polar intermolecular binding.

The number of detailed structure determinations among compounds of this class is very small and is practically confined to a few amines and alcohols.

Urea and thiourea. The shape of the molecule of urea, $(NH_2)_2CO$, and the arrangement of the molecules in the tetragonal unit cell are shown in Fig. 81, which reveals the

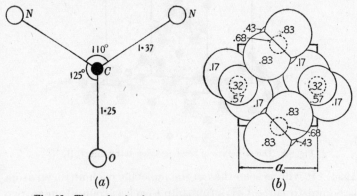

(a) (b)

Fig. 81. The molecule of urea, $(NH_2)_2CO$, and the packing of the molecules in the unit cell.

characteristic packing of the flat molecules with their planes at right angles but all parallel to the *c* crystallographic axis (Hendricks, 1928*d*; Wyckoff and Corey, 1934). The detailed interatomic distances within the molecule are of interest since the length 1·37 A. for the C—N bond is considerably shorter than the normal value of 1·42 A. for this link and may imply a resonance between the forms

$$\underset{NH_2}{\overset{NH_2}{\diagdown}}C{=}O, \quad \underset{NH_2}{\overset{NH_2}{\diagdown}}C{\to}O \text{ and } \underset{NH_2}{\overset{NH_2}{\diagdown}}C{\to}O,$$

with the first predominating. In thiourea (Wyckoff and Corey, 1932) plane molecules of similar shape occur, but the structure is orthorhombic and the arrangement of the molecules somewhat less symmetrical.

Hexamethylenetetramine, $C_6H_{12}N_4$. The very symmetrical molecule of this substance and the symmetrical packing of the separate molecules in the cubic unit cell are illustrated in Fig. 82 (Dickinson and Raymond, 1923; Wyckoff and Corey,

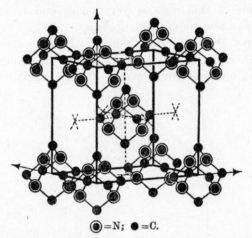

$\textcircled{\bullet} = N; \quad \bullet = C.$

Fig. 82. The structure of hexamethylenetetramine, $C_6H_{12}N_4$.

1934). It will be seen that in the molecule each nitrogen atom is bound to three CH_2 groups and each carbon atom to two nitrogen and two hydrogen atoms. In this structure the C—N bond has its characteristic length of 1·42 A. The closest distance of approach between the CH_2 groups of different molecules is 3·72 A. The symmetrical nature of the structure suggests that any dipole interaction can here play only a very small part in determining the packing of the molecules.

Pentaerythritol, $C(CH_2OH)_4$. The structure of pentaery-

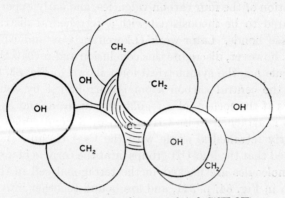

Fig. 83. The molecule of pentaerythritol, $C(CH_2OH)_4$.

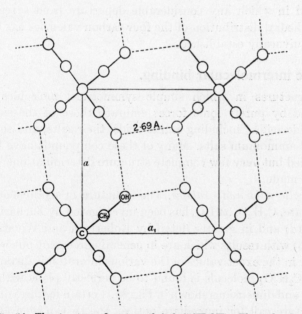

Fig. 84. The structure of pentaerythritol, $C(CH_2OH)_4$. The molecules of Fig. 83 are here seen in plan.

thritol has been extensively studied to determine the configuration of the four carbon valencies, and early experiments appeared to be inconsistent with a tetrahedral distribution of these bonds. Later work (Llewellyn, Cox and Goodwin, 1937), however, discredits this conclusion and reveals that the molecule has the symmetrical form shown in Fig. 83, p. 321. Here the central carbon atom is surrounded by four CH_2 groups at the corners of a regular tetrahedron, and each OH group is attached to its CH_2 group by a bond which makes a nearly tetrahedral angle with the C—CH_2 link and is so directed that the four OH groups lie at the corners of a square. The molecules are packed in the tetragonal cell in the way shown in Fig. 84, p. 321, and are bound together into sheets by hydroxyl bonds of length 2·69 A.

It is probably true to say that no structure has yet been found in which any considerable departure from a regular tetrahedral distribution of the four carbon valencies has been unequivocally established.

Ionic intermolecular binding.

Structures in which simple symmetrical molecules are linked by purely ionic forces embrace those of the simple organic acids,* including amino-acids, their salts, and simple alkyl-ammonium salts. Many of these compounds have been studied but very few complete structure determinations have been made.

Oxalic acid and oxalates. The structure of oxalic acid dihydrate, $C_2H_2O_4 . 2H_2O$, has been investigated by Zachariasen (1934d) and in greater detail by Robertson and Woodward (1936) with results which are in general agreement but which differ in the exact values of the various interatomic distances. The $C_2H_2O_4$ molecule is found to be perfectly plane with the form and dimensions shown in Fig. 85. Certain features of this structure call for immediate notice. The two oxygen atoms attached to each carbon atom are not precisely equivalent

---

* Acids are included in this section of the classification since the hydrogen bond, which is normally responsible for the intermolecular binding, has been treated as purely ionic in nature.

since there is a significant difference between the two C-O distances of 1·24 and 1·30 A. On the other hand, this difference is far too small to represent the distinction between a C=O and a C—OH bond, and it must therefore be concluded that there is a partial but incomplete resonance between the two bindings. The plane form of the molecule is also noteworthy for it might be anticipated on general grounds that an arrangement with the planes of the two hydroxyl groups at right angles would be more stable. The very small C·O distance of 1·43 A., however, compared with the normal single bond distance of 1·54 A., reveals that this link is not a true single bond but

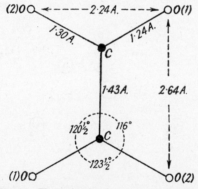

Fig. 85. The molecule of oxalic acid, (COOH)₂.

possesses some considerable amount of double-bond character due to conjugation between double bonds in the two carboxyl groups. In this case free rotation about the C—C bond is, of course, excluded.

The mutual arrangement of the $C_2H_2O_4$ and water molecules in the monoclinic structure is shown in Fig. 86, p. 324. In this plan the two different kinds of oxygen atom are distinguished as (1) and (2) to correspond to the structure of the molecule in Fig. 85, so that these oxygen atoms may be roughly associated with the =O and —OH groups respectively. In Fig. 86, p. 324, the larger C—O(2) bonds of length 1·30 A. are considerably foreshortened due to the inclination of the plane of

2I-2

the molecule to that of the paper, and appear shorter than the
C—O(1) bonds of length 1·24 A. It will be seen that the
binding between the oxalic acid molecules is entirely through
the medium of the water molecules, each of which is linked to
two O(2) and to one O(1) atom from three different molecules.
These three H_2O—O bonds, however, differ significantly in
their length, the two H_2O—O(2) and the H_2O—O(1) distances
being approximately 2·85 and 2·52 A. respectively. This latter
distance is closely the same as that which we have seen to

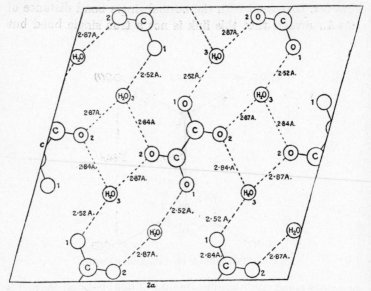

Fig. 86. The structure of oxalic acid dihydrate, $(COOH)_2.2H_2O$.

exist between oxygen atoms bound by a hydrogen bond, and
clearly indicates hydrogen-bond formation between each
water molecule and an =O atom. The other distances are far
too large for hydrogen bonds, and are characteristic rather of
only weak hydroxyl bonds between the water molecules and
—OH groups. It is significant that the O(1) atoms which take
part in the hydrogen bonds are linked to only one water molecule, thus confirming the general principle derived from the
study of other structures containing these bonds. The binding
in oxalic acid has been discussed by Bernal and Megaw (1935),

but since their arguments are based on the structure determination of Zachariasen they require slight modification in the light of the more accurate analysis of Robertson and Woodward.

We have discussed the structure of oxalic acid in some detail because it provides a particularly clear example of the type of information which X-ray methods may be expected to yield when applied to molecular compounds, and especially of the extent to which these methods can provide information on detailed molecular configuration and intermolecular binding which is beyond the scope of direct chemical experiment. Our arguments reveal how important in such discussions is a detailed and exact knowledge of interatomic distances, and how imperative, therefore, are precision structure analyses.

The structures of two modifications of anhydrous oxalic acid have been studied by Hendricks (1935) and in both the form of the molecule is closely the same as in the dihydrate and the molecules are directly linked together by hydrogen or hydroxyl bonds. The same form of molecule is also found in the salts $K_2C_2O_4.H_2O$, $Rb_2C_2O_4.H_2O$, KHC_2O_4 and $RbHC_2O_4$ (Hendricks, 1935), but in $(NH_4)_2C_2O_4.H_2O$ (Hendricks and Jefferson, 1936) the oxalic acid molecule appears definitely to have a different form. The carbon atoms are separated by the exceptionally large distance of 1·58 A., indicating that the link between these atoms no longer has any double-bond character, and in consequence rotation about this bond occurs so that the two CO_2 groups are not coplanar but are inclined to one another at an angle of about 28°.

Acetates. The structures of $NaUO_2(CH_3COO)_3$ and $AgUO_2(CH_3COO)_3 . ?H_2O$ have been studied by Fankuchen (1935, 1936) and in each case a co-ordination structure is formed with complete equivalence between the two oxygen atoms of the carboxyl group.

Substituted ammonium salts. The structures of a number of substituted ammonium halides have been analysed, but only those of the $N(CH_3)_4^+$ ion have complex groups sufficiently small and symmetrical to be discussed in this section. Other salts with more complex substituents will be considered below.

In $N(CH_3)_4Cl$, $N(CH_3)_4Br$ and $N(CH_3)_4I$, the $N(CH_3)_4^+$ ion has a symmetrical tetrahedral form and builds with the halogen ions a purely ionic co-ordination structure which may be regarded as a slightly deformed caesium chloride arrangement (Wyckoff, 1928; Zachariasen, 1928 b).

Amino-acids. The structure of glycine, NH_2CH_2COOH (Kitaigorodski, 1936), and of a number of other simple amino-acids (Bernal, 1931 b) have been considered. In these compounds the packing of the molecules is determined primarily by their strongly dipolar or polypolar character.

COMPOUNDS WITH LONG MOLECULES

The most important compounds of this class are the long-chain paraffins and their related alcohols, esters, ketones, fatty acids, etc. In addition a few other isolated bodies of less importance also call for mention.

Apolar intermolecular binding.

The paraffins. The long-chain paraffins have been the subject of considerable study and the structure of the member $n\text{-}C_{29}H_{60}$ has been completely determined by Müller (1928). The molecule is of the type shown in Fig. 87, and consists

Fig. 87. The structure of a normal paraffin chain.

of a plane zigzag chain of carbon atoms with the characteristic tetrahedral interbond angle of $109\frac{1}{2}°$ and a C-C distance of $1\cdot54$ A. The distribution of these molecules in the orthorhombic unit cell is shown in Fig. 88 in two plans projected on to the basal plane. The carbon chains are all arranged parallel to the c crystallographic axis but have their planes mutually inclined in two different directions, thus giving rise to an approximately close-packed arrangement. The repeat distance in the structure embraces the length of two molecules and those in the upper and lower halves of the unit cell are distinguished as *AA* and *BB* respectively. The terminal atoms of the *AA* and *BB* molecules are separated vertically by a gap of about 4 A.

A number of other long-chain *n*-paraffins have been studied in less detail* and all show the same characteristic form of the carbon chain. The detailed features of the arrangement are, however, not always the same, and in some cases a monoclinic structure is found with the carbon chains parallel to each other but inclined obliquely to the base of the unit cell. Certain paraffins appear to be polymorphous and in some instances structural changes are observed at high temperatures. This point is discussed more fully below.

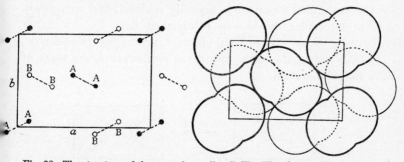

Fig. 88. The structure of the normal paraffin, $C_{29}H_{60}$. The chains of Fig. 87 are here seen end-on. The molecules *A* and *B* are mutually displaced vertically through one half of the height of the unit cell. The second figure emphasizes the packing.

The physical properties of the paraffins are in satisfactory accord with the structures. The strong forces within the chains compared with the feeble lateral binding between them results in a very pronounced anisotropy of thermal expansion (Müller, 1930). The optical properties also reflect the structural arrangement, and the strong positive birefringence corresponds to the distribution of long molecules with their axes parallel.

The structures of a number of paraffins at temperatures up to their melting points have been investigated by Müller (1930, 1932), who has found a progressive transition with increasing temperature towards a hexagonal structure, corre-

* For references, see Müller (1927).

sponding to the close-packing of freely rotating cylindrical molecules. This transition may be followed by a study of the change in cell dimensions, for, although the thermal expansion coefficient is very much greater in any direction normal to the axis of the chain than along that axis, there is nevertheless a pronounced anisotropy of the lateral expansion as between the a and b crystallographic directions. The sense of this anisotropy is such as to decrease the angle ψ, Fig. 89, with increasing temperature until it approaches the value of 60° for the hexagonal structure, but in most paraffins this freely rotating form would be reached only at temperatures above the melting point. In $C_{21}H_{44}$—$C_{27}H_{56}$ and in $C_{29}H_{60}$, however, the hexagonal structure is actually realized, and completely free molecular rotation is established both by the X-ray investigations and by the optical properties (Yannaquis, 1933), which, above the transition temperature, are those of a uniaxial crystal.

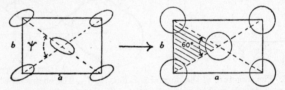

Fig. 89. The influence of molecular rotation on the structures of the paraffins.

The structures of the paraffins are of theoretical importance in that they provide an ideal example of a C—C single aliphatic bond uncomplicated by the possibility of resonance or by the presence of active groups and strong inter-molecular forces. The C-C distance of 1·54 A. observed in these compounds is therefore probably the most reliable estimate of the length of this bond. This distance is very closely the same as that found in diamond, emphasizing once again the essentially identical nature of the binding in the two cases, while similarly the heat of dissociation of the bond is closely comparable with the value deduced from the heat of evaporation of diamond.

Cycloparaffins. A series of cycloparaffins from $C_{12}H_{24}$ to $C_{30}H_{60}$ has been studied by Müller (1933), and in them the ring is found to have the same zigzag form and the same inter-atomic distances as in the straight-chain paraffins. The ring, however, is not circular but consists of a double chain, of cross-section almost exactly twice that of the simple paraffin molecule, bridged at each end by a small ring of 1–3 carbon atoms. In cyclohexane, C_6H_{12}, and its derivatives (Dickinson and Bilicke, 1930; Hassel and Kringstad, 1930; Hassel, 1931) the number of carbon atoms is insufficient to form such a double chain, and instead a regular puckered ring with trigonal symmetry results.

Polar intermolecular binding.

Compounds in which the molecules are bound partly or wholly by polar forces stronger than the normal residual bonds are those containing active groups such as —OH, =O, —NH$_2$, etc. Among long-chain structures some alcohols and ketones have been studied in detail.

Aliphatic alcohols. In the normal primary aliphatic alcohols the carbon chain has the same characteristic form and dimensions as in the paraffins, and the chains are again arranged parallel to one another in the unit cell. In some cases these parallel chains are normal to the base of the cell and in others they are inclined to this plane, while certain alcohols are di-morphous and occur with both structures (Malkin, 1930; D. A. Wilson and Ott, 1934). The presence of the active hydroxyl

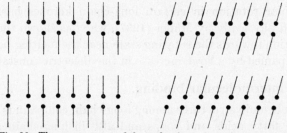

Fig. 90. The arrangement of the molecules in long-chain alcohols.

group at the end of the molecule leads to an association of molecules in pairs to form double layers, giving rise to the structural arrangements represented schematically in Fig. 90.

Rotation of the carbon chain in alcohols has been observed by Bernal (1932 a, b) in $C_{12}H_{25}OH$. This compound solidifies from the melt at 24° C. in a hexagonal form which transforms to the normal monoclinic structure on cooling below 16° C. The transition is not, however, reversible and the hexagonal form cannot be reproduced without melting. In this structure the transition to the rotating state involves not only the rotation of the molecules about their length but also a change in their angle of tilt, and this no doubt accounts for the irreversible character of the transformation.

Aliphatic ketones. Measurements of the cell dimensions of a number of long-chain ketones show that the carbon chain is again of the same form as in the paraffins (Saville and Shearer, 1925). The length of a molecule containing a given number of carbon atoms is found to be independent of the position of the CO group, but in methyl ketones, $R . CO . CH_3$, the presence of the active group near the end of the molecule results in an association into double layers analogous to that found in the alcohols. When the group is further removed from the end of the molecule no such association takes place and single-layer structures are formed. In all cases the linear form of the molecule is preserved and there is no evidence of any 'folded' molecule of the type

$$CH_3—\ldots\ldots\!\!\!\!\diagdown$$
$$\qquad\qquad\qquad\!\!\!\!C{=}O.$$
$$CH_3—\ldots\ldots\!\!\!\!\diagup$$

Molecular rotation in certain long-chain ketones has been studied physically by Müller (1937), who has shown that the transition towards the rotating state near the melting point is accompanied by a large increase in the dielectric constant.

Ionic intermolecular binding.

Purely ionic structures among long-chain compounds occur in the fatty acids and soaps and also in long-chain alkyl-ammonium salts. Few soaps have been studied, but the other two classes of compound call for brief discussion.

Fatty acids. A number of fatty acids have been studied by X-ray methods (Piper, Malkin and Austin, 1926; Müller, 1927;

Francis, Piper and Malkin, 1930) and, although in most cases the investigation has been confined to little more than a determination of cell dimensions, the general features, if not the precise details, of the structures of these compounds are now known. Many of the fatty acids are polymorphous but in all cases the characteristic form of the carbon chain is preserved, and these chains are arranged parallel to each other but inclined to the base of a monoclinic unit cell. The presence of the active carboxyl group at the end of the chain results in an association of pairs of molecules:

$$CH_3—\ldots—C \overset{O}{\underset{OH}{\Big\langle}} \qquad \overset{HO}{\underset{O}{\Big\rangle}} C—\ldots CH_3,$$

and so gives rise to a double-layer structure similar to that of the long-chain alcohols and methyl ketones. The binding between the pairs of molecules in the double layers is thus primarily polar or ionic, but the lateral binding between adjacent molecules and also that between neighbouring layers is still largely residual in character.

Alkyl-ammonium halides. The structures of a number of long-chain primary alkyl-ammonium halides have been investigated and are historically of interest as being the first structures in which molecular rotation in the solid state was clearly established. Thus Hendricks (1928c, 1930a) found that the compounds $C_4H_9NH_3Cl$, $C_5H_{11}NH_3Cl$, $C_6H_{13}NH_3Cl$ and $C_7H_{15}NH_3Cl$, as well as the corresponding bromides and iodides, had a tetragonal structure in which the carbon atoms of each alkyl group seemed to lie on a straight line with a C-C separation of only 1·26 A. It is now established that this structure is due to the free rotation of the relatively short carbon chain about its length, as a result of which an apparent C-C spacing of 1·26 A. arises from the projection on to the chain axis of the inclined bond of length 1·54 A. This conclusion is confirmed by the fact that at liquid air temperatures a larger unit cell of lower symmetry appears (Hendricks, 1930b), while thermal measurements similarly indicate a polymorphous transition (Southard, Milner and Hendricks, 1932). The corresponding compounds with longer chains do not rotate at room temperatures, and $C_{18}H_{37}NH_3Cl$ has an orthorhombic structure with a zigzag chain of the usual form (Bernal, 1932 a, b). This particular structure is of exceptional interest, however, because the mutual arrangement of the molecules is quite different from that so far found in any other long-chain compounds. The molecules associate through their active groups to form double layers, as in the alcohols and fatty acids, and are inclined at about 48° to the plane of these layers. In adjacent double layers, however, the molecules are not parallel but slope in opposite directions in the manner shown in Fig. 91. This struc-ture gives rise to a strong negative birefringence, in con-trast to the positive birefringence associated with the parallel arrangement of molecules found in other long-chain com-pounds.

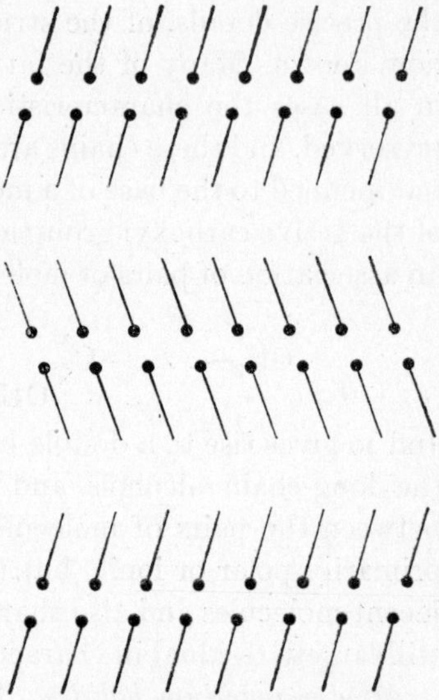

Fig. 91. The arrangement of the molecules in $C_{18}H_{37}NH_3Cl$.

COMPOUNDS WITH FLAT MOLECULES

The number of molecular compounds containing molecules more or less flat in shape of which complete structure analyses are available is greater than that of any other class of molecular compound. This is primarily due to the intrinsic chemical interest presented by the problem of the configuration of the benzene ring, as a result of which numerous extensive and detailed studies of the structures of aromatic compounds have been carried out. There are, however, also certain inorganic molecular structures which properly must be considered here. We have already emphasized that many structures, such as those of bismuth, cadmium iodide, boric acid, etc., are, strictly speaking, molecular inasmuch as more or less well defined, albeit infinitely extended, molecules can be clearly recognized. In such cases, however, the metallic or ionic intermolecular binding has determined, purely as a matter of convenience, the classification adopted. There remain for consideration among inorganic structures those of sulphur and graphite, in which the intermolecular binding is purely residual in character.

Apolar intermolecular binding.

Sulphur. The structure of orthorhombic sulphur (Warren and Burwell, 1935) is of importance in that it provides a direct confirmation of the presence in the solid state of an S_8 molecule, the existence of which is strongly suggested by chemical evidence. The S_8 molecule has the puckered ring form illustrated in Fig. 92, with interatomic distances and bond angles closely the same

Fig. 92. The structure of the sulphur molecule, S_8.

as in the S—S—S binding of the trithionate group. Sixteen such molecules are arranged in the orthorhombic unit cell in the way shown in Fig. 93, p. 334. The molecules lie approximately in four layers perpendicular to the *c* axis and the planes of all the molecules are parallel to this axis but not to each other. In conformity with this structure the crystals have a large positive birefringence with the *c* axis as the acute bisectrix. The closest distance of approach between the atoms of different molecules is 3·3 A.

Graphite. The hexagonal structure of graphite, C (Bernal, 1924; Hassel and Mark, 1924), is shown in Fig. 94, p. 334. The carbon atoms lie in a series of parallel sheets in each of which they are arranged at the corners of a set of plane regular hexagons. The sheets are so superposed that only one-half of the atoms in each sheet lie vertically above atoms in the sheet below, so that the carbon atoms are of two kinds in respect of their environment, and the repeat distance along the *c* axis of the cell is therefore twice the distance between adjacent sheets.

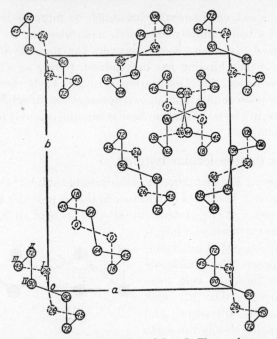

Fig. 93. The structure of orthorhombic sulphur, S. The numbers are the c co-ordinates of the atoms expressed in degrees. Some of the sixteen molecules in the unit cell are omitted for clarity.

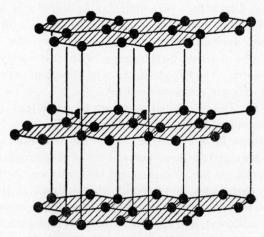

Fig. 94. The structure of graphite, C.

Within each sheet the C-C distance is 1·42 A. but the closest distance of approach between separate sheets is 3·40 A. The structure is essentially a molecular one in which each sheet constitutes a single molecule indefinitely extended in two dimensions. The characteristic C-C distance of 1·42 a. is intermediate between the distances corresponding to a single and a double bond, so that the bond distribution in each sheet corresponds to a resonance structure in which each link is equivalent to 1⅓ single bonds. The binding between successive sheets must be purely residual, and the characteristic mechanical properties of graphite arise immediately from the weakness of this binding. Similarly the thermal expansion is very much greater in a direction normal to the sheets than in their plane.

Benzene. On account of the particular chemical significance of the configuration of the benzene ring the structures of a considerable number of aromatic compounds have been studied in some detail. Apart from their particular chemical importance the earlier of these structure determinations are also historically of interest as being the first analyses which did more than confirm a molecular arrangement already well established on chemical grounds, by providing unambiguous evidence on the form of a molecule previously in dispute.

For practical reasons the structure of benzene itself was not determined until several of its derivatives had been analysed. The first complete structure determination of an aromatic compound was that of hexa-methylbenzene, $C_6(CH_3)_6$ (Lonsdale, 1928, 1929 *a, b*), and this analysis revealed unequivocally that in this compound the benzene ring has a plane regular hexagonal form, resulting in a molecule with the shape and dimensions shown in Fig. 95. Any form of puckered ring for the benzene nucleus, such as that found in cyclo-

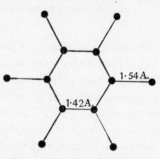

Fig. 95. The molecule of hexa-methylbenzene, $C_6(CH_3)_6$.

hexane or in diamond, is wholly inadmissible, while the C-C distance of 1·42 A. similarly excludes the possibility of an aliphatic binding in the ring. On the other hand, the substituent CH_3 groups are linked to the benzene nucleus by normal single bonds of length 1·54 A.

In the structure of benzene itself (Cox, 1932d) the ring is again found to have the same planar hexagonal form with the same characteristic interatomic distance of 1·42 A. The mutual arrangement of the molecules in the orthorhombic unit cell is shown in Fig. 96, and it will be seen that they are all disposed

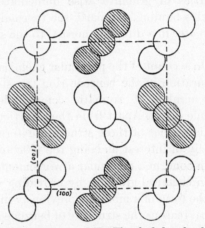

Fig. 96. The structure of benzene, C_6H_6. The shaded molecules are displaced vertically relative to the others through one half of the height of the unit cell.

with their planes almost parallel to the b crystallographic axis but otherwise inclined in two directions nearly at right angles. The structure is relatively loosely knit, the closest distance of approach between the carbon atoms of neighbouring molecules being about 3·8 A. The characteristic arrangement of the molecules with their planes all nearly parallel to a line but not to each other explains the large positive birefringence.

From the chemical point of view the structural investigations of benzene and its derivatives throw immediate light on the distribution of valencies in the benzene ring. The symmetrical form is sufficient to exclude any static model of alternate double and single bonds, but the detailed study of interatomic distances further shows that the C-C separation of 1·42 A., intermediate between the values 1·54 and 1·33 A. for a single and double bond respectively, must correspond to a resonance structure in which the bonding is intermediate between these two types. The same conclusion is indicated by the value of the heat of dissociation of the aromatic bond which lies between those of the C—C and C=C links. As we have already seen (p. 70), however, a rigid treatment shows that the resonance structure is not solely between the two

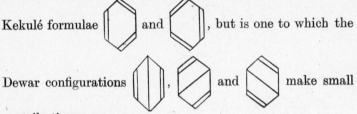

Kekulé formulae ⬡ and ⬡ , but is one to which the

Dewar configurations ⬡ , ⬡ and ⬡ make small

contributions.

Naphthalene and anthracene. The structures of naphthalene, $C_{10}H_8$, and anthracene, $C_{14}H_{10}$, have been completely determined by Robertson (1933 a, b). The shapes and dimensions of the two molecules are shown in Fig. 97. In each case the carbon

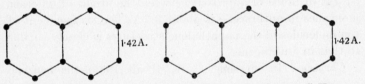

Fig. 97. The molecules of naphthalene, $C_{10}H_8$, and anthracene, $C_{14}H_{10}$.

atoms are arranged at the corners of quite plane regular hexagons with the same interatomic distance as in benzene. The disposition of the molecules in the monoclinic unit cell of anthracene is shown in Fig. 98, p. 338, from which it will be seen that they lie with the long axes all nearly parallel to the *c* crystallographic axis, but with their planes mutually inclined in two different directions. Such an arrangement is similar to that found in the paraffins and in a number of other structures already described, and is to be expected whenever more or less flat, elongated molecules devoid of active groups are packed together under the influence of purely residual forces. The

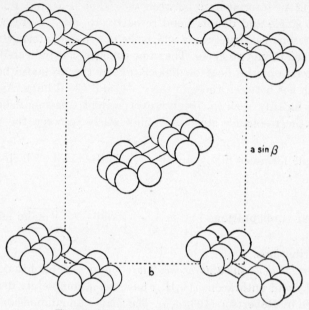

Fig. 98. The structure of anthracene, $C_{14}H_{10}$.

closest distance of approach between the atoms of different molecules in anthracene is about 3·7 A. The arrangement of the molecules in the naphthalene structures is closely similar to that in anthracene.

Chrysene. In chrysene, $C_{18}H_{12}$ (Iball, 1934), the benzene

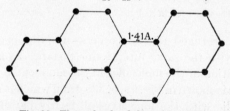

Fig. 99. The molecule of chrysene, $C_{18}H_{12}$.

rings again have the same regular hexagonal structure with the characteristic C-C distance of about 1·41 A., and are linked to give the plane symmetrical molecule shown in Fig. 99.

These molecules are packed in the monoclinic unit cell in a manner similar to that in the naphthalene and anthracene structures. The closest distance of approach between the atoms of different molecules is 3·42 A.

Substituted benzenes. The structures of a number of substituted benzene hydrocarbons have been studied, including those of diphenyl (Dhar, 1932), *p*-diphenylbenzene (Pickett, 1933), *p*-diphenyldiphenyl (Pickett, 1936), *o*-diphenylbenzene (Clews and Lonsdale, 1937), 1.3.5-triphenylbenzene (Orelkin and Lonsdale, 1934) and 1.2.4.5-tetramethylbenzene (Robertson, 1933c, d). The mole-

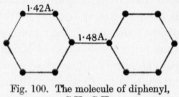

cule of *diphenyl*, $C_{12}H_{10}$, has the form and dimensions shown in Fig. 100. The two benzene rings lie in the same plane and have the usual symmetrical shape. The distance between the carbon

Fig. 100. The molecule of diphenyl, $C_6H_5:C_6H_5$.

atoms linking the two rings is significantly less than the usual single-bond length of 1·54 A. and must imply some degree of conjugation in this bond. This is in conformity with the planar structure of the molecule, for with a single bond between the rings free rotation about this bond would be possible and a structure with the planes of the molecules inclined to one

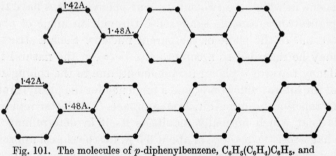

Fig. 101. The molecules of *p*-diphenylbenzene, $C_6H_5(C_6H_4)C_6H_5$, and *p*-diphenyldiphenyl, $C_6H_5(C_6H_4)_2C_6H_5$.

another would be expected to be more stable. In p-*diphenylbenzene* and p-*diphenyldiphenyl* the molecules are precisely analogous in form to those of diphenyl, as shown in Fig. 101,

and in fact the three compounds form a series of closely
related monoclinic structures differing little except in the
cell dimension parallel to the length of the molecule:

	a	b	c	β
Diphenyl	8·22 A.	5·69 A.	9·5 A.	94·8°
p-Diphenylbenzene	8·08 A.	5·60 A.	13·59 A.	91·9°
p-Diphenyldiphenyl	8·05 A.	5·55 A.	17·81 A.	95·8°

It is clear from our description of the structures of naphthalene, anthracene, chrysene and the three benzene derivatives just discussed that the molecules in these bodies are
characterized no more by their flatness than by their length,
and that, in fact, in all these structures the molecular packing
is closely similar to that found in the long-chain compounds
already described. This point serves to emphasize once again
that our classification is largely arbitrary and that practical
convenience no less than rigid geometrical principles must
ultimately be allowed to dictate the form it assumes.

The structure of o-*diphenylbenzene* is of interest because
here the contiguity of the two large substituent groups introduces important differences in the molecular form as compared with the corresponding compound with the substituent
groups in the *para* position. In this case no complete X-ray
analysis has yet been made, but magnetic measurements are
sufficient definitely to exclude the possibility of a planar
molecule, and to suggest that the probable molecular structure
is one in which the two substituent phenyl groups have their
planes turned in the same sense through an angle of about
50° out of the plane of the parent nucleus. Such a structure
may be regarded as a compromise between the natural tendency towards a planar arrangement, due to the conjugation
of the interatomic bonds, and a tendency for the phenyl groups
to repel one another on close approach. This latter repulsion
is that which normally manifests itself in determining the
characteristic distance of about 3·5 A. for the closest approach
between the atoms of different molecules, but even with the
proposed structure different atoms in neighbouring phenyl
groups approach within 2·9 A. of each other, so that the forces
tending to produce a plane molecule must be strong enough
to balance a considerable repulsion between the groups.

In 1.3.5-*triphenylbenzene* the molecule is more nearly plane, and its symmetrical shape results in a structure in which the packing is entirely different from that found in compounds with elongated molecules. The arrangement is essentially a layer structure in which each layer is built up of molecules closely packed in the way shown in Fig. 102. The superposition of these layers produces a crystal of pseudo-hexagonal symmetry with large negative birefringence. In this compound magnetic measurements (Lonsdale, 1937) again reveal that the molecule is not planar, but that the sub-

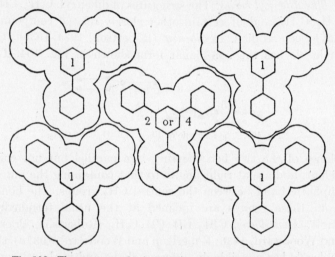

Fig. 102. The structure of 1.3.5-triphenylbenzene, $C_6H_3(C_6H_5)_3$. The structure is formed by the superposition of layers of the type shown.

stituent groups are all rotated in the same sense through an angle of about 25° out of the plane of the central nucleus. As is to be expected, the departure from the planar arrangement is not as great as in *o*-diphenylbenzene, but the structure serves to reveal that substituent groups even in the *meta* positions can exert a considerable influence on one another if they are large enough.

The effect of repulsion between substituted methyl groups is shown in the structure of 1.2.4.5-*tetramethylbenzene*, the molecule of which is illustrated in Fig. 103, p. 342. In this case

X-ray evidence alone is sufficient to reveal a small but significant displacement of the methyl
groups away from each other towards
the unsubstituted positions in the
ring. The molecules are packed in the
structure in a way similar to that
found in benzene, but entirely different from the arrangement in
hexamethylbenzene, where the molecules are all parallel.

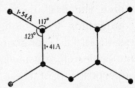

Fig. 103. The molecule of
$1.2.4.5$-$C_6H_2(CH_3)_4$.

The dibenzyl series. The structures of dibenzyl, $C_6H_5 . CH_2 .$
$CH_2 . C_6H_5$, and of certain other closely related compounds
have been studied. In *dibenzyl* (Robertson, 1934, 1935a) the
molecule has the non-planar form shown in Fig. 104. The

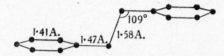

Fig. 104. The molecule of dibenzyl, $C_6H_5(CH_2)_2C_6H_5$.

planes of the two benzene rings are parallel but not coincident, and are at right angles to that containing the purely
aliphatic bond between the central CH_2 groups. The bonds
from these groups are inclined at the usual tetrahedral
angle. In *stilbene*, $C_6H_5 . CH : CH . C_6H_5$ (Robertson, Prasad
and Woodward, 1936; Robertson and Woodward, 1937a), the
molecule has a strikingly different shape and is almost completely planar with the dimensions shown in Fig. 105. This

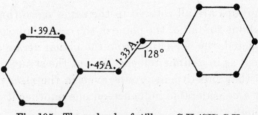

Fig. 105. The molecule of stilbene, $C_6H_5(CH)_2C_6H_5$.

structure throws important light on the nature of the chemical
binding in the molecule, for the length of the C_6H_5—CH bond

is very appreciably less than the normal single-bond distance
and clearly indicates a considerable degree of double-bond
character, corresponding to a resonance between the structures

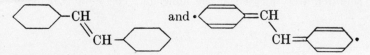

The existence of such resonance is confirmed by the planar form
of the molecule, for if the former configuration alone occurred
a structure similar to that of dibenzyl would be expected: on
the other hand, with the latter configuration a planar molecule
is demanded on stereochemical grounds owing to the impossibility of free rotation about a double bond. A molecule
of very similar form is found in *tolane*, $C_6H_5.C:C.C_6H_5$
(Robertson and Woodward, 1938), with a $C\equiv C$ bond of
length 1·19 A. Resonance in such compounds has been
discussed theoretically by Pauling and Sherman (1933*a*),
and by Penney and Kynel (1938).

The phthalocyanines. A number of other isolated structure
analyses on compounds with flat molecules have been made
and those of the phthalocyanines and of cyanuric triazide may
be briefly discussed here.

The structure of phthalocyanine and its metallic derivatives
(Robertson, 1935*b*, 1936*a*; Robertson and Woodward, 1937*b*)
provides a particularly beautiful example of a complete structure analysis of a compound of considerable complexity,
although for technical reasons the method of analysis applied
in this case is unfortunately not always possible. The molecule
is found to be quite plane and to have the shape and dimensions
shown in Fig. 106, p. 344. The atoms may be identified by
the 'structural formula' shown below, but this formula cannot
be considered to give a true representation of the molecule
for reasons now to be considered.

The inner system of sixteen carbon and nitrogen atoms
forms a very regular arrangement with a practically constant
interatomic distance of 1·34 A., which must represent an equivalence between all the C—N bonds, and therefore a single-
double-bond resonance in each case, instead of the fixed

distribution of bonds implied by the formula. Similarly, the four benzene rings are all structurally precisely equivalent and cannot be interpreted as three benzenoid and one *o*-quinonoid ring definitely located in the molecule. The same conclusion

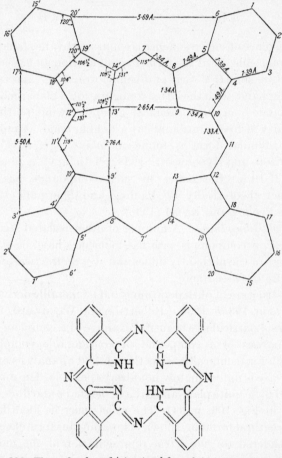

Fig. 106. The molecule and 'structural formula' of phthalocyanine.

is compelled by the equality of the eight C—C bonds of length 1·49 A. linking these rings to the inner system, so that the structure must be regarded as one in which the whole molecule is one continuously conjugated system.

In spite of this free resonance in the structure there is, however, a significant departure in the shape of the molecule from true tetragonal symmetry, and this appears as a small but real difference between the distances 2·65 and 2·76 A. separating different nitrogen atoms of the inner system. The attraction between the nitrogen atoms 2·65 A. apart is probably to be interpreted as implying hydrogen-bond formation between these atoms, and if this is the case the phthalocyanine molecule is the first example of an internal hydrogen bond directly established by X-ray means.

In the metallic phthalocyanines the metal atom is located in the centre of the molecule which preserves its form substantially unaltered. We cannot, however, here discuss the purely chemical significance of these compounds, for which the reader is referred to the original papers quoted.

Cyanuric triazide. The structure of cyanuric triazide, $(C_3N_3)(N_3)_3$, has been completely determined (Knaggs, 1935)

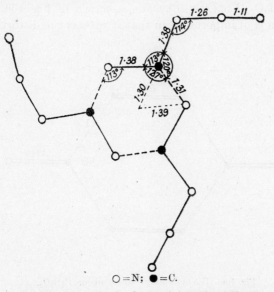

$O = N;$ ● $= C.$

Fig. 107. The molecule of cyanuric triazide, $(C_3N_3)(N_3)_3$.

and has established the shape of the azide group, N_3, in this compound. The molecule has the plane form shown in Fig. 107, and the N_3 group is accurately linear but unsymmetrical, the distance between the central nitrogen atom and that attached to the ring being 1·26 A., while that between the two outer nitrogen atoms is 1·11 A. This structure lends support to Sidgwick's view that the group is a resonance between the configurations —N=N⇒N and —N←N≡N (Sidgwick, 1934). The unsymmetrical form of the cyanuric ring, with alternate bonds of lengths 1·38 and 1·31 A., evidently corresponds to fixed single and double bonds with little or no resonance between them.

Polar intermolecular binding.

Molecular compounds containing flat molecules bound by polar intermolecular forces comprise chiefly aromatic compounds containing active groups. Of these a few alcohols, ketones and nitro- derivatives have been studied.

Benzoquinone. The structure of the molecule of benzoquinone, $C_6H_4O_2$ (Robertson, 1935c), is shown in Fig. 108. This structure is of importance in that it reveals the distortion of

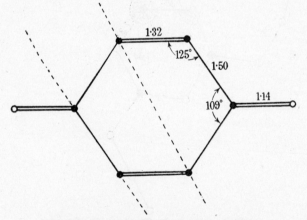

Fig. 108. The molecule of benzoquinone, $C_6H_4O_2$.

the regular form of the benzene ring which arises when the possibility of a resonance structure is excluded. The distortion takes the form of a lengthening of C—C bonds adjacent to the C=O group to 1·50 A. and a shortening of the other ring bonds to 1·32 A. corresponding to the appearance of definite single and double bonds.

p-*Dinitrobenzene.* In p-dinitrobenzene, $C_6H_4(NO_2)_2$ (James, King and Horrocks, 1935), a distorted molecule, of the form shown in Fig. 109, is again found. The benzene ring is no longer

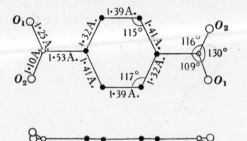

Fig. 109. The molecule of p-dinitrobenzene, $C_6H_4(NO_2)_2$.

exactly plane and the two oxygen atoms of the NO_2 groups are not equivalent, being separated by different distances from the nitrogen atom. There appears also to be a very marked interaction between the NO_2 groups and the benzene nucleus, resulting in a considerable shortening of one of the two bonds adjacent to each of these groups. This same inter-action is reflected in the way the mole-cules are bound together, for each oxygen atom of any molecule is closely associated with three CH groups of adjacent molecules, and the strength of this intermolecular binding results in a structure of relatively high density and great hardness.

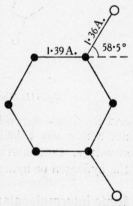

Resorcinol. The structure of the molecule of resorcinol, m-dihydroxy-benzene, $C_6H_4(OH)_2$ (Robertson, 1936b), is shown in Fig. 110, and the arrangement of these molecules in the orthorhombic unit cell in Fig. 111, p. 348. The significant feature of this

Fig. 110. The molecule of resorcinol, $C_6H_4(OH)_2$.

structure is the binding of the molecules through hydroxyl groups which are directed towards each other and approach within distances of about 2·7 A. This close approach clearly corresponds to hydrogen- or hydroxyl-bond formation, and the structural arrangement is of interest in that this binding is achieved without the carbon atoms of different molecules approaching nearer than the usual distance of about 3·5 A. The molecules in Fig. 111 are not all at the same height,

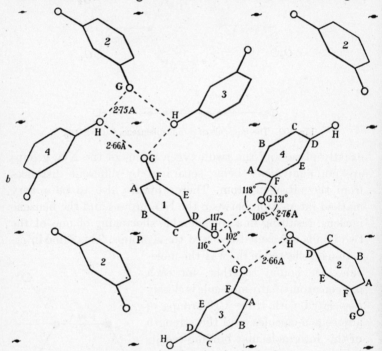

Fig. 111. The structure of resorcinol, $C_6H_4(OH)_2$.

and the bonds shown between hydroxyl groups actually form not a ring but a helix extending indefinitely through the structure. Both lateral and vertical coherence is thus due to the hydrogen or hydroxyl bonds.

Ionic intermolecular binding.

Molecular structures containing flat molecules bound by

purely ionic forces presumably include aromatic acids and their salts, but, although preliminary investigations of many of these compounds have been carried out, no complete analyses seem to be available. As an isolated example of structures of this type we may consider the methylene blue halides.

Methylene blue halides. The chemical formula of these salts is usually written in one of the two forms

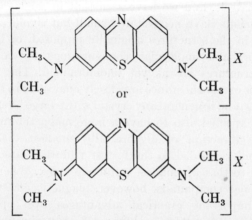

and the halogen atom is supposed to be bound to the sulphur atom in the former arrangement or to the $=N(CH_3)_2$ group in the latter. The structure analysis of the iodide (W. H. Taylor, 1935 *a, b*) confirms the general form of the molecule as a long planar arrangement with dimensions consistent with the usual interatomic distances, but indicates no sharp distinction between the two ends of the molecule, and shows, moreover, that the iodine ion is not bound to any particular part of the chain but acts solely as a unit in the packing of the structure, just as in inorganic ionic compounds.

COMPOUNDS WITH COMPLEX THREE-DIMENSIONAL MOLECULES

Complex three-dimensional molecules occur in certain proteins and probably also in such compounds as strychnine and camphor. No complete analyses of any such structures have,

however, been made, and an account of the results of preliminary investigations is deferred until a later section.

THE MAGNETIC PROPERTIES OF
MOLECULAR CRYSTALS

We have already alluded in our discussion of several of the
structures described above to the value of magnetic measurements in confirming the structural arrangements deduced by
X-ray analysis, and we have seen that in some cases these
measurements have necessitated small but significant modifications in the structures originally proposed, or have suggested probable molecular configurations for compounds
whose structures are as yet undetermined. The magnetic
properties of any substance are closely analogous to its optical
properties, and in general any crystal with a large birefringence
may be expected also to have a large magnetic anisotropy,
with the direction of algebraically smallest diamagnetic
susceptibility parallel to the fastest vibration direction and
therefore to that of smallest refractive index. When applied
to molecular compounds, however, magnetic measurements
possess important practical advantages over optical investigations, for while the latter can only give qualitative
information about molecular arrangement, since the strong
mutual influence of the molecules upon one another makes
any quantitative treatment impossible, the magnetic properties of any compound are to a very close approximation
the vector sum of those of the separate molecules.

The magnetic susceptibilities of a number of molecular
crystals have been studied by Krishnan, Guha and Banerjee
(1933), Krishnan and Banerjee (1935) and by Lonsdale and
Krishnan (1936), and, from those of known structure, the
individual molecular susceptibilities necessary to give rise to
the observed crystal susceptibilities have been deduced. The
susceptibilities of a number of molecules derived in this
way are given in Table 59, where the corresponding crystal
susceptibilities are also quoted. In each case the susceptibility
κ_1 is that along the length of the molecule and κ_3 that normal
to its plane. A comparison of these susceptibilities with the

crystal susceptibilities χ_1, χ_2 and χ_3 shows a close correspondence between κ_1 and χ_1 in each case, since in the four compounds the lengths of the molecules are parallel to each other and to the direction of crystal susceptibility χ_1. There is, however, no similar correspondence between the other susceptibilities, and, moreover, in each case $(\chi_2 \sim \chi_3)$ is considerably less than $(\kappa_2 \sim \kappa_3)$ due to the fact that the planes of the molecules are not all parallel and the lateral anisotropy of the individual molecules is to a large extent compensated in the crystal as a whole by their mutual inclination.

TABLE 59

THE MAGNETIC SUSCEPTIBILITIES OF CERTAIN
MOLECULAR COMPOUNDS

Compound	Observed crystal susceptibilities $\times 10^6$			Deduced molecular susceptibilities $\times 10^6$		
	χ_1	χ_2	χ_3	κ_1	κ_2	κ_3
Naphthalene	$-56\cdot0$	$-146\cdot4$	$-76\cdot6$	$-56\cdot1$	$-53\cdot9$	$-169\cdot0$
Anthracene	$-75\cdot5$	$-211\cdot8$	$-102\cdot9$	$-75\cdot8$	$-62\cdot6$	$-251\cdot8$
Diphenylbenzene	$-96\cdot8$	$-214\cdot0$	$-145\cdot4$	$-96\cdot8$	$-88\cdot1$	$-271\cdot3$
Diphenyldiphenyl	$-122\cdot0$	$-290\cdot0$	$-192\cdot0$	$-122\cdot0$	$-110\cdot0$	$-372\cdot0$

The study of the magnetic properties of molecular compounds is likely to become increasingly important in the future, for as more and more complex structures are investigated more and more supplementary information must be invoked before a complete X-ray analysis becomes possible: and the most effective and economical analyses are those which draw most widely on all the available data. At the same time the physical method of approach must not be regarded as replacing the formal X-ray analysis, which alone can give detailed information on molecular configuration, interatomic distances and interatomic binding. The over-enthusiastic interpretation of magnetic measurements has more than once in the past led to the proposition of erroneous structures when it has been overlooked that several alternative molecular configurations have been equally consistent with the observed data.

This concludes our discussion of molecular compounds of which detailed analyses are available. General accounts of the application of X-ray methods in this field have recently been given by Robertson (1937, 1938a,b) and by Mark and Schossberger (1937). We now pass on to a brief consideration of compounds of which no complete analyses have yet been made, but of which even only a partial or preliminary investigation has been sufficient to throw valuable light on many features of the structure and to suggest the probable form of the molecules and their disposition in the lattice.

INCOMPLETE STRUCTURE ANALYSES

It must always be the ultimate aim of any structure analysis to provide a complete description of the exact position of every atom in the unit cell, but in many cases such a detailed analysis is technically extremely difficult, and as progressively more and more complex bodies are studied, the difficulties are likely to become increasingly great. When no complete analysis is possible, however, it does not necessarily follow that even the most superficial X-ray investigation is without profit, and frequently no more information than the cell dimensions and the space group enables important conclusions to be drawn. Especially is this true when the evidence can be supported by arguments of a purely chemical nature or by information derived from optical, magnetic or other physical properties. In this section we shall give a number of examples of substances in which the general features, if not the precise details, of the structures have been determined in this way. Here, even more than elsewhere in this book, we make no attempt to give an account of all the compounds studied, for in many cases they are bodies of considerable complexity and of specialized interest and often any adequate account of the structures deduced would demand lengthy arguments of a purely chemical kind. We shall, therefore, confine ourselves to a somewhat arbitrary selection of bodies, chosen to illustrate rather the type of problem which may be solved and the kind of information which may be expected than the specific results which have been achieved. References will enable the reader to pursue in more detail subjects of particular interest.

As with the molecular compounds already discussed, it is convenient to classify those about to be described in terms of the general molecular shape, and we may recognize three separate classes containing long, flat, and three-dimensional molecules respectively. Again the classification is largely arbitrary, and rather than separate substances closely related it may be convenient occasionally to transgress its strict interpretation.

Compounds with long molecules: fibre structures.

Among compounds with long molecules those which have been most extensively studied are the biologically important structures of naturally occurring fibres such as cotton, silk, wool, hair, feather, quill, muscle, etc. These substances have a number of general features in common which may be briefly described here.

Cellulose. The structure of cellulose in the form of cotton and artificial silk has been investigated by Meyer and Mark (1928) who have shown that fibres of these substances give X-ray photographs which indicate that they are composed of bundles of elongated crystallites all arranged with their axes parallel to the length of the fibre but otherwise twisted relative to each other in a random fashion. Each of these crystallites is very small, with linear dimensions of the order of $600 \times 50 \times 50$ A., and contains only a few thousand unit cells.

The probable shape of the molecules and their arrangement in the unit cell can only be deduced with the help of chemical arguments, and the formation of cellobiose by the partial hydrolysis of cellulose suggests for the latter a structure built of an indefinite chain of glucose residues joined by oxygen atoms:

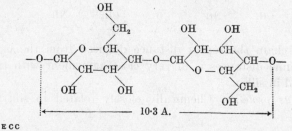

Such an arrangement is confirmed by the observed repeat distance of 10·3 A. along the fibre axis, which is in close agreement with that to be expected from the usual interatomic distances. The fact that the repeat distance embraces two residues shows that alternate rings are related to one another by rotation through 180° about the chain length so that the chain has the symmetry of a screw diad axis. The chains must be disposed in the unit cell with their lengths parallel to the fibre axis, but the detailed features of the structure cannot be regarded as established, although many tentative suggestions have been advanced. Comprehensive accounts of the works on cellulose have been given by Meyer and Mark (1930), Hess and Trogus (1934) and by Cox (1938).

Silk. In its physical features the structure of silk is qualitatively similar to that of cellulose, which it resembles in being a fibre structure built up of a large number of small, elongated crystallites arranged nearly parallel to the fibre axis. The detailed features of the two structures are, however, entirely different, and in silk the characteristic repeat distance along the length of the fibre is only 7·0 A. compared with 10·3 A. in cellulose. Moreover, the two substances are chemically quite unrelated, the essential constituent of silk being the polypeptide fibroin. This substance is produced by the repeated condensation through peptide linkages of the two α-amino-acids glycine and alanine to form an indefinitely extended chain:

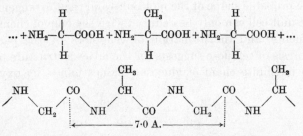

In this chain the repeat distance deduced from the usual interatomic distances is in very close agreement with that observed in silk.

Fibrous proteins. Chemically closely related to silk are

numerous other naturally occurring fibrous proteins such as wool, hair, quill, horn, muscle, etc., all of which are essentially polypeptides and can be broken down into their constituent amino-acids on hydrolysis. In most cases, however, these acids are far more complex than the simple acids from which fibroin is formed, and this increased complexity results in important differences in the structure which may be conveniently illustrated by considering particularly that of wool.

The essential constituent of wool (Astbury and Street, 1931; Astbury and Woods, 1933) is the polypeptide keratin, which may be represented:

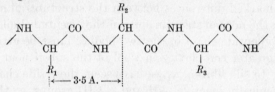

where R_1, R_2, etc., are various univalent side chains of considerable complexity. This arrangement results in a pseudo-repeat period of 3·5 A. immediately comparable with that in silk, but in no true repeat period since an indefinite number of different side chains may follow each other in irregular sequence. Such a polypeptide chain is not, however, found in normal wool, but only in wool which has been stretched in water or steam, under which circumstances the remarkable elastic properties enable a reversible extension to almost exactly double the length to be achieved. In the unstretched state wool shows an entirely different repeat period of 5·1 A., and this can be explained if it is assumed that normally the keratin chain exists not in a straight but in a folded form:

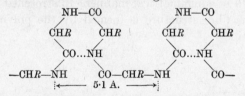

in which a weak binding between the CO and NH groups probably occurs.

In terms of this picture not only the observed repeat distances in the extended and contracted forms may be explained,* but also the limit of the possible extension, for the material covered by a length 5·1 A. in the normal form is extended to $3 \times 3·5 = 10·5$ A. in the straight chain and an extension of about 100 per cent is therefore to be expected. This extension, although completely reversible, differs profoundly from the normal elastic extension of most bodies in that it involves an entire molecular rearrangement, which can, however, take place owing to the flexibility of the molecule and the possibility of free rotation about all the single bonds.

The marked differences between the structures of silk and wool in the normal state, in spite of the essential similarity of the polypeptide chain in the two bodies, must be attributed to the greater complexity in wool of the substituent R side chains. In silk fibroin, as we have seen, these side chains are the chemically inactive —H and —CH_3 groups, so that the lateral binding between the main chains must be largely by residual forces. In wool, however, the principal constituents of the keratin chain are far more complex, and the R groups are sufficiently active to form strong lateral binding between adjacent chains. These bonds may either be salt linkages between basic and acidic side chains, peptide links, links through double amino-acids which form part of two chains, or others of greater complexity. We can thus regard the keratin structure as a series of chains bound together sideways into a coherent grid by the attraction of the side groups, and in fact the regularity of the structure in the normal folded form must be attributed to these lateral bonds, which constrain the main chains to fold in a symmetrical manner. In stretched rubber an analogous fibre structure is formed by the polymerized isoprene chain:

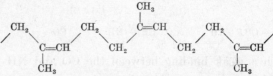

* The chain has not, of course, the flat structure suggested by the above formula. Even so, it seems to be necessary to assume interatomic distances

but the absence of any strong lateral binding results in a completely irregular arrangement of the crumpled chains in the contracted state. In both the normal and extended forms of wool the lateral spacing is closely the same, indicating that the molecular folding must take place in a plane perpendicular to the side chains.

In addition to the characteristic spacing, usually of the order of 10 A., due to the side-chain linkages, there is also observed in the stretched form of keratin a second lateral spacing of 4·65 A. which may be attributed to interaction between the =CO and =NH groups of neighbouring chains. This binding must be considered to be in a plane at right angles to that of the active side chains, so that the idealized structure of keratin in its extended form may be represented thus:

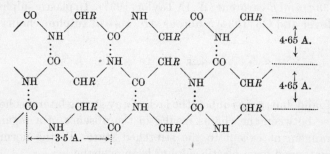

The side chains are in this structure normal to the plane of the paper, but the folding on contraction takes place in this plane, so that in the unstretched form the spacings 3·5 and 4·65 A. disappear while that of about 10 A., representing the side chains, is preserved. Astbury and Sisson (1935) have in fact shown that the extended keratin chains in a number of different natural fibres can by suitable 'working' be made to approximate very closely to this idealized structure, for when squeezed laterally in the presence of steam or hot water the keratin crystallites assume a preferred orientation with the side chains normal to the plane of flattening. No preferential

and interbond angles somewhat different from the usual values to give the repeat distance of 5·1 A.

orientation, however, can be imposed on the keratin chain in its folded form.

Numerous other fibrous proteins of biological importance have recently been studied by X-ray methods, but here it is impossible to give an adequate discussion of this work, of which several reviews, with references, are readily available (Astbury, 1936, 1937; Crowfoot, 1936, 1937). Detailed accounts of the earlier work on fibre structures have been published by Astbury (1932, 1933 *a, b, c, d*).

Other compounds. Other bodies containing long molecules which have been studied include the polyoxymethylenes (Staudinger and Singer, 1929), the diphenylpolyenes (Hengstenberg, 1930), certain natural amino-acids (Bernal, 1931*b*), quinhydrone (Foz and Palacios, 1932; Palacios and Foz, 1935), substances forming liquid crystals (Bernal and Crowfoot, 1933*a*) and β-carotene (W. H. Taylor, 1937). In plastic sulphur (Meyer and Go, 1934) a fibrous structure of sulphur chains

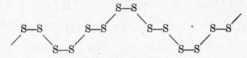

is found, but, as in rubber, the lack of any strong lateral coherence between the chains results in the absence of a regular arrangement except in the stretched state. In the normal unextended form plastic sulphur is amorphous.

Compounds with flat molecules.

Among compounds with flat molecules of which a general X-ray study has been made, the sugars and a number of complex bodies of biological importance, related to the sterols, have been investigated in most detail.

The sugars. For several practical reasons the X-ray determination of the structures of the sugars is a problem of especial difficulty. The physical properties, lacking in any marked anisotropy, throw little light on the molecular arrangement, while morphotropic relationships are rarely informative, since in the carbohydrates the shape and size of the molecules play a less dominating part in determining the structure than in most organic compounds. The hardness, high densities and high melting points of the sugars imply that in these bodies interaction between hydroxyl groups is largely responsible for the coherence of the crystal, so that in substituted derivatives a complete rearrangement of the intermolecular binding, and therefore of the structure itself, often ensues. On the other hand, from the purely chemical point of view the sugars have been the subject of much work as a result of which the general molecular configuration has in many cases been established beyond reasonable doubt: even so, one chemical structure may be consistent with several alternative geometrical arrangements between which only X-ray analysis can distinguish.

The X-ray studies of the sugars have been confined almost entirely to determinations of the dimensions and symmetry of the unit cell, but in favourable cases even this limited information is sufficient to suggest the form of the molecule and the general features of the molecular arrangement.

An extensive series of sugars and their methyl derivatives containing the pyranose and furanose rings has been studied by Cox, Goodwin and Wagstaff (1935 a, b). The exact configuration of the pyranose ring has long been in dispute, and several alternative arrangements have been advanced. In Fig. 112 b, c, p. 360, two 'strainless' forms, proposed by Sachse, in which the usual interbond angles for the carbon valencies are preserved, are represented, while in Fig. 112 a an arrangement of the ring is shown in which all five carbon atoms lie in a plane but in which the oxygen atom of the ring is raised out of this plane. The essential distinction between the Sachse models, on the one hand, and the 'flat' structure, on the other, is in the thickness of the molecule, for of the pyranoses based on a strainless ring some, at least, must have hydroxyl groups projecting considerably from the plane of the carbon atoms. Thus the structure of β-glucose, Fig. 113 a, p. 360, based on the Sachse ring shown in Fig. 112 b, is nearly flat, but in that of galactose, Fig. 113 b, such an arrangement is not possible and one hydroxyl group must be displaced about 1·5 A. from the plane of the molecule. The X-ray observations, however, do not confirm any such distinction between pyranoses with thick and thin molecules, for in a

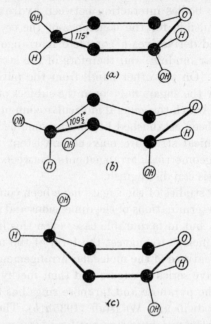

Fig. 112. Possible configurations of the pyranose ring:
(a) 'flat' form; (b) and (c) 'strainless' Sachse forms.

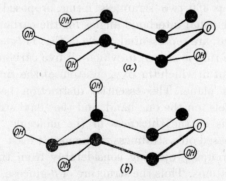

Fig. 113. Configurations of (a) β-glucose and (b) galactose based on a 'strainless' form of the pyranose ring.

whole series of such sugars and their derivatives one cell dimension of about 4·5 A. is consistently observed. This distance is too small to correspond to anything but the thickness of the molecule and can be reconciled only with a structure based on the flat form of the pyranose ring shown in Fig. 112a. The same conclusion is supported by observations on the furanose sugars in which the four carbon atoms of the furanose ring are also found to be coplanar.

In certain isolated sugars there is still more direct evidence of flat structures for the pyranose and furanose rings. Thus in β-l-arabinose (Cox, 1931, 1933) the observed X-ray intensities indicate such a structure for the pyranose ring, while observations on β-mannose (Marwick, 1931; McCrea, 1932) and on α- and β-methylxyloside (Cox, 1932 a, b) lead to similar conclusions. α-Methylmannoside (Cox and Goodwin, 1932) is dimorphous and exists in pyranose and furanose forms:

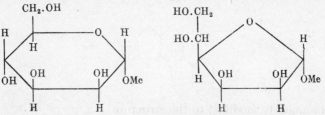

in both of which a planar configuration of the ring carbon atoms is found. These structures are of especial interest since they confirm the arrangement deduced from chemical evidence by Haworth but criticized on the grounds that the process of methylation might be accompanied by changes in ring structure.

The sterols and related substances. The application of X-ray methods of analysis to the sterols and their derivatives has led to significant developments in the understanding of the chemical nature of these biologically important compounds. In the case of bodies of such complexity, of which the molecular configuration and even the chemical composition is often unknown, X-ray analysis cannot as yet indicate the detailed structure, but it can often suggest probable molecular arrangements and often definitely exclude others which have been proposed. The earliest investigations on substances of this type were those of Bernal (1932 c, d, e) on ergosterol, calciferol and other compounds related to vitamin D, which showed that the cell dimensions of the crystals could not be reconciled with either of the previously accepted sterol carbon skeletons

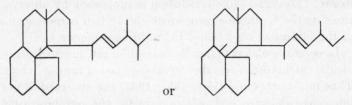

or

and led to the proposition by Rosenheim and King (1932) of a new chrysenoid structure

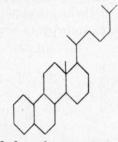

subsequently modified to the structure

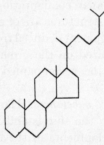

which is now generally accepted. More recent work on calciferol (Bernal and Crowfoot, 1935a) and on some hydrocarbons related to the sterols (Bernal and Crowfoot, 1935b) tends to confirm this arrangement, while X-ray observations (Bernal, 1932f, 1933; Bernal and Crowfoot, 1936) on oestrone and a number of other sex hormones, also closely related to the sterols, have enabled the probable molecular configurations of many of these bodies to be readily deduced from data on cell dimensions, intensities of reflection, and optical and other physical properties.

Other substances of biological importance which have been studied by X-ray methods include vitamin C (Cox, 1932c) and vitamin B_1 (Bernal and Crowfoot, 1933b). We cannot, however, here give any further account of this work, for we have sufficiently emphasized the important part which X-ray observations can play in the determination of the molecular configuration of even the most complex bodies, while any more comprehensive discussion must necessarily take account of the vast mass of purely chemical material on the subject. It is still unfortunately true that the great majority of chemists and biochemists pay little heed to the results of X-ray analysis, and even appear ignorant of the existence of such a method of attack, and certainly few are inclined to regard these methods, rather than indirect arguments of a chemical nature, as the first and most natural approach to an unknown structure.

Compounds with three-dimensional molecules: 'globular' proteins.

Very few substances containing complex three-dimensional molecules have been studied, and the investigations in this field are practically confined to a few isolated observations on the proteins pepsin and insulin. The lack of adequate knowledge of the chemical composition of these bodies necessarily renders structure analysis difficult, while the physical properties can give little assistance on account of the roughly spherical form of the molecule and its consequent lack of marked anisotropy.

The observations on crystals of insulin (Crowfoot, 1935, 1938a) show that the unit cell is very large and contains a single, roughly spherical molecule of radius about 20 A. and molecular weight 37,600, while the less detailed observations on pepsin (Bernal and Crowfoot, 1934b) similarly indicate an approximately spherical molecule of about the same molecular weight. In each case the molecular weight is in very satisfactory agreement with that deduced independently by quite different methods by Svedberg. Any knowledge of the exact structure of the individual molecules, however, must at present be regarded as little more than speculative. There is no doubt that the 'globular' proteins are closely related to the fibrous proteins already described, and, in fact, on denaturation the former pass into the latter (Astbury and Lomax, 1934; Astbury, Dickinson and Bailey, 1935; Astbury, 1936). Similarly, both are polypeptides formed by the condensation of α-amino-acids. These observations have led to the suggestion (Astbury, Dickinson and Bailey, 1935) that in the globular proteins polypeptide chains occur coiled in spiral forms or folded in layers, while Wrinch (1936 a, b, c, 1937 a) has more recently proposed as the basis of the structure of these proteins a polypeptide chain folded to give a closed, as opposed to an open, molecule such as

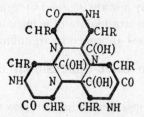

Here the molecule is to be imagined as stabilized in this form by a binding between contiguous $=CO$ and $=NH$ groups resulting from the transformation

$$\text{\Large$>$}C=O \quad H-N\text{\Large$<$} \quad \rightarrow \quad \text{\Large$>$}C(OH)-N\text{\Large$<$}$$

Similar closed molecules can also exist containing more than six amino-acid residues, and quite generally an hexagonal net of indefinite extent can be formed. When, however, it is desired to construct a three-dimensional molecule by the folding of such a net, certain geometrical conditions have to be satisfied, and Wrinch (1937 b, c, d, e) has shown that the only nets which can be folded in a way consistent with the usual interbond angles are those containing 72, 288, ..., $72n^2$, ... amino-acid residues. Of these only that with 288 residues can give a molecular weight of the order of 36,000, and this picture does, therefore, suggest an explanation of this particular molecular weight, and also of the fact that so many proteins appear to have molecules of very nearly the same size. Many more observations, however, are necessary before the accuracy of this or of any other picture can be directly verified, but already preliminary results of work on other proteins are available (Bernal, Fankuchen and Perutz, 1938; Crowfoot and Fankuchen, 1938; Crowfoot and Riley, 1938). For the purely chemical aspects of the problem the reader is referred to the papers quoted and to the work of Astbury (1936).

This concludes our discussion of the crystal chemistry of molecular compounds. We would again emphasize that no attempt has been made to review all the structures studied, but only to give a general account of the structural basis of molecular chemistry. A complete list of all bodies, of every kind, investigated by X-ray methods is to be found in the volumes of the *Strukturbericht*, while recent work is reviewed periodically in the crystallography section of the *Annual Reports on the Progress of Chemistry*.

CONCLUSION

We have now come to the end of our study of systematic crystal chemistry, and in reviewing the field as a whole we see what a large part of the whole realm of chemical science falls within its scope. In many directions the application of X-ray analysis is as yet very limited, but in almost every branch it has been sufficiently widely applied to indicate the broad outlines of the results to be expected and to establish beyond doubt its value as the most powerful tool yet available for the investigation of the solid state of matter. The results of X-ray analysis provide a welcome co-ordination between physical and chemical concepts, for on the one hand they afford a structural basis in terms of which observed physical properties may be explained, while on the other they furnish the chemist with a more rational scheme for the classification of his compounds, based on the physical nature of the forces responsible for their coherence. Indeed, a clear recognition of the different types of chemical binding and of their physical origin, together with an appreciation of the essentially geometrical basis of crystal architecture, are the most important general conclusions which have emerged from the systematic application of X-ray structure analysis.

On the purely theoretical side the results of crystal structure analysis have had no less important applications, and it is only necessary to refer back to our earlier chapters to appreciate that the recent developments of the quantum mechanics as applied to problems of chemical combination have very largely had their origin in the material made available by X-ray analysis. It is not unreasonable to expect that in the future no less than in the past continuous and rapid progress will attend the co-operation of the chemist, the theoretical physicist and the X-ray crystallographer.

BIBLIOGRAPHY

PART I

HISTORICAL (Chapter I)

SPENCER, L. J. Encyclopaedia Britannica, **6**, 809. 14th edit. London and New York, 1929.

LATTICE THEORY (Chapters II and III)

BLOCH, F. Elektronentheorie der Metalle. Akademische Verlagsgesellschaft, Leipzig, 1933.

BORN, M. Dynamik der Kristallgitter. Teubner, Leipzig and Berlin, 1915.
—— Die Gittertheorie des festen Zustandes. Springer, Berlin, 1926.
—— Probleme der Atomdynamik. Springer, Berlin, 1926.
—— Atomic Physics. Blackie, London, 1935.

BRILLOUIN, L. "Die Quantenstatistik." Struktur der Materie in Einzeldarstellung, **13**. Springer, Berlin, 1931.

CLARK, C. H. D. The Electronic Structure and Properties of Matter. Chapman and Hall, London, 1934.

EPHRAIM, F. Chemische Valenz- und Bindungslehre. Akademische Verlagsgesellschaft, Leipzig, 1928.

EUCKEN, A. Lehrbuch der chemischen Physik. Akademische Verlagsgesellschaft, Leipzig, 1930.

FRÖHLICH, H. "Elektronentheorie der Metalle." Struktur und Eigenschaften der Materie, **18**. Springer, Berlin, 1936.

HUME-ROTHERY, W. The Metallic State. Clarendon Press, Oxford, 1931.

LEWIS, G. N. Valence and the Structure of Atoms and Molecules. Chemical Catalog Co., New York, 1923.

MOTT, N. F. and JONES, H. The Properties of Metals and Alloys. Clarendon Press, Oxford, 1936.

PAULING, L. and WILSON, E. B. Introduction to Quantum Mechanics. McGraw Hill, New York and London, 1935.

PENNEY, W. G. The Quantum Theory of Valency. Methuen, London, 1935.

SIDGWICK, N. V. The Electronic Theory of Valency. Clarendon Press, Oxford, 1927.
—— The Covalent Link in Chemistry. University Press, Cornell, 1933.

SMITH, J. D. M. Chemistry and Atomic Structure. Benn, London, 1924.

SPEAKMAN, J. C. An Introduction to the Modern Theory of Valency. Arnold, London, 1935.

VAN ARKEL, A. E. and DE BOER, J. H. Chemische Bindung als elektrostatische Erscheinung. Hirzel, Leipzig, 1931.

WILSON, A. H. The Theory of Metals. University Press, Cambridge, 1936.

PART II

GENERAL CRYSTAL CHEMISTRY

DESCRIPTIVE

EWALD, P. P. and HERMANN, C. Strukturbericht **I**. 1913–28. Akademische Verlagsgesellschaft, Leipzig, 1931.

HERMANN, C., LOHRMANN, O. and PHILIPP, H. Strukturbericht **II**. 1928–32. Akademische Verlagsgesellschaft, Leipzig, 1937.

GOTTFRIED, C. and SCHOSSBERGER, F. Strukturbericht **III**. 1933–35. Akademische Verlagsgesellschaft, Leipzig, 1937.

GOTTFRIED, C. Strukturbericht **IV**. 1936. Akademische Verlagsgesellschaft, Leipzig, 1938.

WYCKOFF, R. W. G. The Structure of Crystals. 1912–30. Chemical Catalog Co., New York, 1931.

—— The Structure of Crystals. (Supplement for 1930–34.) Reinhold Publishing Corporation, New York, 1935.

SYSTEMATIC

Annual Reports on the Progress of Chemistry. The Chemical Society, London.

BRAGG, W. H. An Introduction to Crystal Analysis. Bell, London, 1928.

BRAGG, W. L. The Crystalline State: A General Survey. Bell, London, 1933.

—— Atomic Structure of Minerals. University Press, Oxford, 1937.

CLARK, C. H. D. The Fine Structure of Matter. Chapman and Hall, London, 1937.

EWALD, P. P. Kristalle und Röntgenstrahlen. Springer, Berlin, 1923.

HASSEL, O. Crystal Chemistry. Heinemann, London, 1935.

MAUGUIN, C. La Structure des Cristaux. Presses Universitaires, Paris, 1924.

NEUBURGER, M. C. Kristallchemie. Enke, Stuttgart, 1933.

STILLWELL, C. W. Crystal Chemistry. McGraw Hill, New York and London, 1938.

WOLFF, F. Einführung in die Kristallstrukturlehre. Quelle und Meyer, Leipzig, 1928.

METALS (CHAPTERS IV AND V)

DESCH, C. H. The Chemistry of Solids. University Press, Cornell, 1934.

HANSEN, M. Der Aufbau der Zweistofflegierungen. Springer, Berlin, 1936.

HUME-ROTHERY, W. The Metallic State. Clarendon Press, Oxford, 1931.

—— The Structure of Metals and Alloys. The Institute of Metals, London, 1936.

NEUBURGER, M. C. Röntgenographie der Metalle und ihrer Legierungen. Enke, Stuttgart, 1929.

—— Die Allotropie der chemischen Elemente und die Ergebnisse der Röntgenographie. Enke, Stuttgart, 1936.

IONIC COMPOUNDS (Chapters VII–X)

RANDALL, J. T. The Diffraction of X-Rays and Electrons by Amorphous Solids, Liquids and Gases. Chapman and Hall, London, 1934.

MOLECULAR COMPOUNDS (Chapter XI)

ASTBURY, W. T. Fundamentals of Fibre Structure. University Press, Oxford, 1933.

MARK, H. Physik und Chemie der Cellulose. Springer, Berlin, 1932.

MEYER, K. H. and MARK, H. Der Aufbau der hochpolymeren organischen Naturstoffe. Akademische Verlagsgesellschaft, Leipzig, 1930.

REFERENCES

ANDRADE, E. N. DA C. (1927). The Structure of the Atom. Bell, London.

ANDRESS, K. R. and CARPENTER, C. (1934). Z. Krystallogr. **87**, 446.

ANDRESS, K. R. and GUNDERMANN, J. (1934). Z. Krystallogr. **87**, 345.

ARRHENIUS, S. (1887). Z. phys. Chem. **1**, 637.

ASTBURY, W. T. (1932). Rep. Progr. Chem. **28**, 322.

—— (1933a). Fundamentals of Fibre Structure. University Press, Oxford.

—— (1933b). Sci. Progr. Twent. Cent. **28**, 210.

—— (1933c). Trans. Faraday Soc. **29**, 193.

—— (1933d). J. Soc. Dy. Col., Bradford, 169.

—— (1936). Nature, Lond., **137**, 803.

—— (1937). Trans. Faraday Soc. **34**, 378.

ASTBURY, W. T., DICKINSON, S. and BAILEY, K. (1935). Biochem. J. **29**, 2351.

ASTBURY, W. T. and LOMAX, R. (1934). Nature, Lond., **133**, 795.

ASTBURY, W. T. and SISSON, W. A. (1935). Proc. roy. Soc. A, **150**, 533.

ASTBURY, W. T. and STREET, A. (1931). Philos. Trans. A, **230**, 75.

ASTBURY, W. T. and WOODS, H. J. (1933). Philos. Trans. A, **232**, 333.

BANNISTER, F. A. (1932). Miner. Mag. **23**, 188.

BARLOW, W. and POPE, W. J. (1906). J. chem. Soc. **89**, 1675.

—— —— (1907). J. chem. Soc. **91**, 1150.

BARNES, W. H. (1929). Proc. roy. Soc. A, **125**, 670.

BARTH, T. F. W. (1932). Fortschr. Min. **17**, 25.

BARTH, T. F. W. and LUNDE, G. (1926). Norsk geol. Tidsskr. **8**, 293.

BARTH, T. F. W. and POSNJAK, E. (1931). J. Wash. Acad. Sci. **21**, 255.

—— —— (1932). Z. Krystallogr. **82**, 325.

BAWDEN, F. C., PIRIE, N. W., BERNAL, J. D. and FANKUCHEN, I. (1936). Nature, Lond., **138**, 1051.

BECKER, K. (1933). Phys. Z. **34**, 185.

BEEVERS, C. A. and LIPSON, H. (1932a). Z. Krystallogr. **83**, 123.

—— —— (1932b). Z. Krystallogr. **82**, 297.

—— —— (1934). Proc. roy. Soc. A, **146**, 570.

BEEVERS, C. A. and SCHWARTZ, C. M. (1935). Z. Krystallogr. **91**, 157.

BERMAN, H. (1937). Amer. Min. **22**, 342.

BERMAN, H. and LARSEN, E. S. (1931). Amer. Min. **16**, 140.

BERNAL, J. D. (1924). Proc. roy. Soc. A, **106**, 749.

—— (1929). Trans. Faraday Soc. **25**, 367.

—— (1931a). Ergebn. tech. Röntgenk. **2**, 200.

—— (1931b). Z. Krystallogr. **78**, 363.

—— (1932a). Nature, Lond., **129**, 870.

—— (1932b). Z. Krystallogr. **83**, 153.

—— (1932c). Nature, Lond., **129**, 277.

—— (1932d). Nature, Lond., **129**, 721.

—— (1932e). J. Soc. chem. Ind., Lond., **51**, 466.

—— (1932f). J. Soc. chem. Ind., Lond., **51**, 259.

BERNAL, J. D. (1933). *J. Soc. chem. Ind., Lond.*, **52**, 288.

—— (1937). *Trans. Faraday Soc.* **33**, 27.

BERNAL, J. D. and CROWFOOT, D. M. (1933a). *Trans. Faraday Soc.* **29**, 1032.

—— —— (1933b). *Nature, Lond.*, **131**, 911.

—— —— (1934a). *Rep. Progr. Chem.* **30**, 379.

—— —— (1934b). *Nature, Lond.*, **133**, 794.

—— —— (1935a). *J. Soc. chem. Ind., Lond.*, **54**, 701.

—— —— (1935b). *J. chem. Soc.* 93.

—— —— (1936). *Z. Krystallogr.* **93**, 464.

BERNAL, J. D., DJATLOWA, E., KASARNOWSKY, I., REICHSTEIN, S. and WARD, A. G. (1935). *Z. Krystallogr.* **92**, 344.

BERNAL, J. D., FANKUCHEN, I. and PERUTZ, M. (1938). *Nature, Lond.*, **141**, 523.

BERNAL, J. D. and FOWLER, R. H. (1933). *J. chem. Phys.* **1**, 515.

BERNAL, J. D. and MEGAW, H. D. (1935). *Proc. roy. Soc.* A, **151**, 384.

BERNAL, J. D. and WOOSTER, W. A. (1932). *Rep. Progr. Chem.* **28**, 262.

BETHE, H. A. (1935). *Proc. roy. Soc.* A, **150**, 552.

—— (1938). *J. appl. Phys.* **9**, 244.

BIJVOET, J. M. and NIEUWENKAMP, W. (1933). *Z. Krystallogr.* **86**, 466.

BILTZ, W. (1924). *Z. anorg. Chem.* **133**, 312.

BILTZ, W. and KLEMM, W. (1924). *Z. phys. Chem.* **110**, 318.

—— —— (1926). *Z. anorg. Chem.* **152**, 267.

BLOCH, F. (1929). *Z. Phys.* **52**, 555.

BOLLNOW, O. F. (1925). *Z. Phys.* **33**, 741.

BORELIUS, G. (1934a). *Ann. Phys., Lpz.*, **20**, 57.

—— (1934b). *Ann. Phys., Lpz.*, **20**, 650.

—— (1935a). *Handb. Metallphys.* **1** (i), 185.

—— (1935b). *Ann. Phys., Lpz.*, **24**, 489.

BORELIUS, G., JOHANSSON, C. H. and LINDE, J. O. (1928). *Ann. Phys., Lpz.*, **86**, 291.

BORN, M. (1919a). *Verh. dtsch. phys. Ges.* **21**, 679.

—— (1919b). *Verh. dtsch. phys. Ges.* **21**, 533.

—— (1926). Probleme der Atomdynamik. Springer, Berlin.

—— (1931). *Ergebn. exakt. Naturw.* **10**, 387.

—— (1935). Atomic Physics. Blackie, London.

BORN, M. and BOLLNOW, O. F. (1927). *Handb. Phys.* **24**, 370.

BORN, M. and GÖPPERT-MAYER, M. (1933). *Handb. Phys.* **24** (ii), 623.

BORN, M. and HEISENBERG, W. (1924). *Z. Phys.* **23**, 388.

BORN, M. and LANDÉ, A. (1918). *Verh. dtsch. phys. Ges.* **20**, 210.

BORN, M. and MAYER, J. E. (1932). *Z. Phys.* **75**, 1.

BOSCOVICH, R. J. (1763). Theoria Philosophiae naturalis redacta ad unicam legem virium. Venice.

BRADLEY, A. J. and GREGORY, C. H. (1931). *Phil. Mag.* **12**, 143.

BRADLEY, A. J. and JAY, A. H. (1932a). *Proc. roy. Soc.* A, **136**, 210.

—— —— (1932b). *J. Iron Steel Inst.* **125**, 339.

BRADLEY, A. J. and THEWLIS, J. (1928). *Proc. roy. Soc.* A, **112**, 678.

BRAGG, W. H. (1922). *Proc. phys. Soc., Lond.*, **34**, 98.

BRAGG, W. H. and BRAGG, W. L. (1913). *Proc. roy. Soc.* A, **88**, 428.

BRAGG, W. L. (1913). *Proc. roy. Soc.* A, **89**, 248.

—— (1920). *Phil. Mag.* **40**, 169.

—— (1924a). *Proc. roy. Soc.* A, **105**, 370.

BRAGG, W. L. (1924b). *Proc. roy. Soc.* A, **106**, 346.

—— (1930). *Z. Krystallogr.* **74**, 237.

—— (1933a). The Crystalline State. Bell, London.

—— (1933b). *Nature, Lond.*, **131**, 749.

—— (1935). *J. Inst. Met.* **56**, 275.

—— (1937). Atomic Structure of Minerals. University Press, Oxford.

BRAGG, W. L. and BROWN, G. B. (1926). *Z. Krystallogr.* **63**, 538.

BRAGG, W. L. and CHAPMAN, S. (1924). *Proc. roy. Soc.* A, **106**, 369.

BRAGG, W. L. and WEST, J. (1926). *Proc. roy. Soc.* A, **111**, 691.

BRAGG, W. L. and WILLIAMS, E. J. (1934). *Proc. roy. Soc.* A, **145**, 699.

—— —— (1935). *Proc. roy. Soc.* A, **151**, 540.

BRAGG, W. L. and ZACHARIASEN, W. H. (1930). *Z. Krystallogr.* **72**, 518.

BRÜCK, H. (1928). *Z. Phys.* **51**, 707.

BUBECK, W. and MACHATSCHKI, F. (1935). *Z. Krystallogr.* **90**, 44.

BURTON, E. F. and OLIVER, W. F. (1936). *Proc. roy. Soc.* A, **153**, 166.

CHAPMAN, S., TOPPING, J. and MORRALL, J. (1926). *Proc. roy. Soc.* A, **111**, 25.

CLARK, C. H. D. (1934). The Electronic Structure and Properties of Matter. Chapman and Hall, London.

CLEWS, C. J. B. and LONSDALE, K. (1937). *Proc. roy. Soc.* A, **161**, 493.

COX, E. G. (1931). *J. chem. Soc.* 2313.

—— (1932a). *J. chem. Soc.* 2535.

—— (1932b). *J. chem. Soc.* 138.

—— (1932c). *Nature, Lond.*, **130**, 205.

—— (1932d). *Proc. roy. Soc.* A, **135**, 491.

—— (1933). *Z. Krystallogr.* **84**, 45.

—— (1938). *Rep. Progr. Chem.* **34**, 176.

COX, E. G. and GOODWIN, T. H. (1932). *J. chem. Soc.* 1844.

COX, E. G., GOODWIN, T. H. and WAGSTAFF, A. I. (1935a). *J. chem. Soc.* 978.

—— —— —— (1935b). *J. chem. Soc.* 1495.

CROWFOOT, D. M. (1935). *Nature, Lond.*, **135**, 591.

—— (1936). *Rep. Progr. Chem.* **32**, 223.

—— (1937). *Rep. Progr. Chem.* **33**, 214.

—— (1938a). *Proc. roy. Soc.* A, **164**, 580.

CROWFOOT, D. M. and FANKUCHEN, I. (1938). *Nature, Lond.*, **141**, 522.

CROWFOOT, D. M. and RILEY, D. P. (1938). *Nature, Lond.*, **141**, 521.

DARWIN, C. G. (1914a). *Phil. Mag.* **27**, 315.

—— (1914b). *Phil. Mag.* **27**, 675.

DEBYE, P. (1920). *Phys. Z.* **21**, 178.

DEBYE, P. and SCHERRER, P. (1916). *Phys. Z.* **17**, 277.

DEHLINGER, U. (1931a). *Z. Phys.* **68**, 535.

—— (1931b). *Ergebn. exakt. Naturw.* **10**, 325.

—— (1932a). *Z. Phys.* **74**, 267.

—— (1932b). *Z. Phys.* **79**, 550.

—— (1932c). *Z. Elektrochem.* **38**, 148.

—— (1933). *Z. Phys.* **83**, 832.

—— (1934). *Z. phys. Chem.* B, **26**, 343.

—— (1935a). *Z. Phys.* **94**, 231.

—— (1935b). *Handb. Metallphys.* **1** (i), **1**.

—— (1935c). *Z. Elektrochem.* **41**, 344.

—— (1937). *Z. Phys.* **105**, 21.

DEHLINGER, U. and GRAF, L. (1930). *Z. Phys.* **64**, 359.

DE L'ISLE, R. (1783). Crystallographie ou Description des Formes propre à tous les Corps du Règne minéral. Paris.

DEPARTMENT OF SCIENTIFIC AND INDUSTRIAL RESEARCH (1931). The Application of X-Ray Crystal Analysis to Industrial Problems. H.M. Stat. Office, London.

—— (1934). The Industrial Application of X-Ray Crystal Analysis. Dept. of Scientific and Industrial Research, London.

DESCH, C. H. (1934). The Chemistry of Solids. University Press, Cornell.

DHAR, J. (1932). *Indian J. Phys.* **7**, 43.

DICKINSON, R. G. and BILICKE, C. (1930). *J. Amer. chem. Soc.* **50**, 764.

DICKINSON, R. G. and RAYMOND, A. L. (1923). *J. Amer. chem. Soc.* **45**, 22.

DUSHMAN, S. and SEITZ, F. (1937). *J. phys. Chem.* **41**, 233.

EISENSCHITZ, R. and LONDON, F. (1930). *Z. Phys.* **60**, 491.

EKMAN, W. (1931). *Z. phys. Chem.* B, **12**, 57.

EPHRAIM, F. (1928). Chemische Valenz- und Bindungslehre. Akademische Verlagsgesellschaft, Leipzig.

—— (1931). *Ergebn. Physiol.* **32**, 1.

EUCKEN, A. (1930). Lehrbuch der chemischen Physik. Akademische Verlagsgesellschaft, Leipzig.

EVANS, R. C. (1935). *Chem. Age, Lond.*, **33**, 559.

—— (1936). *Rep. Progr. Chem.* **32**, 181.

EWALD, P. P. (1918). *Ann. Phys., Lpz.*, **54**, 519.

—— (1921). *Ann. Phys., Lpz.*, **64**, 253.

EWING, D. H. and SEITZ, F. (1936). *Phys. Rev.* **50**, 760.

FAJANS, K. (1923). *Phys. Z.* **11**, 165.

—— (1925). *Z. Krystallogr.* **61**, 18.

—— (1928a). *Z. Krystallogr.* **66**, 321.

—— (1928b). *Z. Elektrochem.* **34**, 502.

FAJANS, K. and JOOS, G. (1924). *Z. Phys.* **23**, 1.

FANKUCHEN, I. (1935). *Z. Krystallogr.* **91**, 473.

—— (1936). *Z. Krystallogr.* **94**, 212.

FOWLER, R. H. (1935a). *Proc. roy. Soc.* A, **149**, 1.

—— (1935b). *Proc. roy. Soc.* A, **151**, 1.

FOWLER, R. H. and BERNAL, J. D. (1933). *Trans. Faraday Soc.* **29**, 1049.

FOZ, O. R. and PALACIOS, J. (1932). *An. Soc. esp. Fís. Quím.* **30**, 421.

FRANCIS, F., PIPER, S. H. and MALKIN, T. (1930). *Proc. roy. Soc.* A, **128**, 214.

FRANCK, J. and KUHN, H. (1927). *Z. Phys.* **43**, 164.

FRIEDEL, G. and FRIEDEL, E., and others (1931). *Z. Krystallogr.* **79**, 1.

FRIEDRICH, W., KNIPPING, P. and LAUE, M. (1912). *S.B. bayer. Akad. Wiss.* 303.

FUCHS, K. (1935). *Proc. roy. Soc.* A, **151**, 585.

—— (1936a). *Proc. roy. Soc.* A, **153**, 622.

—— (1936b). *Proc. roy. Soc.* A, **157**, 444.

GASKELL, T. F. (1937). *Z. Krystallogr.* **96**, 203.

GILLETTE, R. H. and SHERMAN, A. (1936). *J. Amer. chem. Soc.* **58**, 1135.

GOLDSCHMIDT, V. M. (1926a). *Skr. norske VidenskAkad.* Kl. 1926, No. 2.

—— (1926b). *Skr. norske VidenskAkad.* Kl. 1926, No. 8.

—— (1926c). *Naturwissenschaften*, **14**, 477.

—— (1927a). *Ber. dtsch. chem. Ges.* **60**, 1286.

GOLDSCHMIDT, V. M. (1927b). Z. tech. Phys. **8**, 251.

—— (1928a). Z. Elektrochem. 34, 453.

—— (1928b). Z. phys. Chem. 133, 397.

—— (1931a). Fortschr. Min. 15, 73.

—— (1931b). Nachr. Ges. Wiss. Göttingen, 184.

GOLDSCHMIDT, V. M., BARTH, T. and LUNDE, G. (1925). Skr. norske VidenskAkad. Kl. 1925, No. 7.

GOLDSZTAUB, S. (1935). Bull. Soc. franç. Minér. **58**, 6.

GOMBÁS, P. (1935a). Z. Phys. 94, 473.

—— (1935b). Z. Phys. 95, 687.

—— (1936a). Z. Phys. 99, 729.

—— (1936b). Z. Phys. 100, 599.

—— (1936c). Z. Phys. 104, 81.

GORSKY, W. (1928). Z. Phys. 50, 64.

—— (1934). Phys. Z. Sowjet. 6, 69.

GRIMM, H. G. (1927). Handb. Phys. 24, 466.

—— (1928). Z. Elektrochem. 34, 430.

GRIMM, H. G. and HERZFELD, K. F. (1923). Z. Phys. 19, 141.

GRIMM, H. G. and SOMMERFELD, A. (1926). Z. Phys. 36, 36.

GRIMM, H. G. and WOLFF, H. (1933). Handb. Phys. 24 (ii), 923.

GROTH, P. (1906–19). Chemische Krystallographie. Engelmann, Leipzig.

GUDDEN, B. and POHL, R. (1923). Z. Phys. 16, 42.

HABER, F. (1919). Verh. dtsch. phys. Ges. 21, 750.

HÄGG, G. (1929). Z. phys. Chem. B, 6, 221.

—— (1930a). Z. phys. Chem. B, 7, 339.

—— (1930b). Z. phys. Chem. B, 8, 445.

—— (1931). Z. phys. Chem. B, 12, 33.

—— (1935a). Z. phys. Chem. B, 29, 192.

—— (1935b). Z. phys. Chem. B, 29, 95.

—— (1935c). Z. Krystallogr. 91, 114.

HÄGG, G. and SÖDERHOLM, G. (1935). Z. phys. Chem. B, 29, 88.

HÄGG, G. and SUCKSDORFF, J. (1933). Z. phys. Chem. B, 22, 444.

HASSEL, O. (1928). Norsk. geol. Tidsskr. 10, 33.

—— (1931). Z. Elektrochem. 37, 540.

—— (1935). Crystal Chemistry. Heinemann, London.

HASSEL, O. and KRINGSTAD, H. (1930). Tidsskr. Kemi Bergv. 10, 128.

HASSEL, O. and MARK, H. (1924). Z. Phys. 25, 317.

HAÜY, R. J. (1784). Essai d'une Théorie sur la structure des Crystaux. Paris.

—— (1801). Traité de Minéralogie. Paris.

HECKMANN, G. (1925). Ergebn. exakt. Naturw. 4, 100.

HEITLER, W. (1930). Phys. Z. 31, 185.

HEITLER, W. and LONDON, F. (1927). Z. Phys. 44, 455.

HELMHOLZ, H. and MAYER, J. E. (1934). J. chem. Phys. 2, 245.

HENDRICKS, S. B. (1928a). Z. Krystallogr. 67, 106.

—— (1928b). Z. Krystallogr. 67, 475.

—— (1928c). Z. Krystallogr. 68, 189.

—— (1928d). J. Amer. chem. Soc. 50, 2455.

—— (1930a). Z. Krystallogr. 74, 29.

—— (1930b). Nature, Lond., 126, 167.

HENDRICKS, S. B. (1935). *Z. Krystallogr.* 91, 48.

HENDRICKS, S. B., and JEFFERSON, M. E. (1936). *J. chem. Phys.* 4, 102.

HENDRICKS, S. B., POSNJAK, E. and KRACEK, F. C. (1932). *J. Amer. chem. Soc.* 54, 2766.

HENGSTENBERG, J. (1930). *Z. Krystallogr.* 75, 301.

HERRMANN, K. (1936). *Phys. in regelmäss. Ber.* 4, 1.

HERZFELD, K. F. (1928). *Handb. expt. Phys.* 7 (ii), 325.

—— (1937). *J. appl. Phys.* 8, 319.

HESS, K. and TROGUS, C. (1934). *Ergebn. tech. Röntgenk.* 4, 21.

HEY, J. S. and TAYLOR, W. H. (1931). *Z. Krystallogr.* 80, 428.

HIRSCHFELDER, J., STEVENSON, D. and EYRING, H. (1937). *J. chem. Phys.* 5, 896.

HUGGINS, M. L. (1937). *J. chem. Phys.* 5, 143.

HULL, A. W. (1917). *Phys. Rev.* 10, 661.

HUME-ROTHERY, W. (1926). *J. Inst. Met.* 35, 295.

—— (1928). *Phil. Mag.* 5, 173.

—— (1930). *Phil. Mag.* 10, 217.

—— (1931). The Metallic State. Clarendon Press, Oxford.

—— (1936). The Structure of Metals and Alloys. The Institute of Metals, London.

HUME-ROTHERY, W., MABBOTT, G. W. and CHANNEL-EVANS, K. M. (1934a). *Philos. Trans.* A, 233, 1.

—— —— —— (1934b). *Philos. Trans.* A, 233, 44.

HUME-ROTHERY, W. and POWELL, H. M. (1935). *Z. Krystallogr.* 91, 23.

HUND, F. (1925). *Z. Phys.* 34, 833.

IBALL, J. (1934). *Proc. roy. Soc.* A, 146, 140.

ITO, T. and WEST, J. (1932). *Z. Krystallogr.* 83, 1.

JACKSON, W. W. and WEST, J. (1930). *Z. Krystallogr.* 76, 211.

—— —— (1933). *Z. Krystallogr.* 85, 160.

JAMES, R. W., KING, G. and HORROCKS, H. (1935). *Proc. roy. Soc.* A, 153, 225.

JENSEN, H. (1936). *Z. Phys.* 101, 164.

JOHANSSON, C. H. and LINDE, J. O. (1925). *Ann. Phys., Lpz.*, 78, 439.

JONES, H. (1934a). *Proc. roy. Soc.* A, 144, 225.

—— (1934b). *Proc. roy. Soc.* A, 147, 396.

KETELAAR, J. A. A. (1934a). *Z. Krystallogr.* 88, 26.

—— (1934b). *Z. Krystallogr.* 87, 436.

KIMBALL, G. E. (1935). *J. chem. Phys.* 3, 560.

KITAIGORODSKI, A. (1936). *Acta physicochim. U.S.S.R.* 5, 749.

KLEMM, W. (1928). *Z. Elektrochem.* 34, 523.

KNAGGS, I. E. (1935). *Proc. roy. Soc.* A, 150, 576.

KORDES, E. (1935a). *Z. Krystallogr.* 91, 193.

—— (1935b). *Z. Krystallogr.* 92, 139.

KOSSEL, W. (1916). *Ann. Phys., Lpz.*, 44, 229.

KRACEK, F. C. (1931). *J. Amer. chem. Soc.* 53, 2609.

KRACEK, F. C. and POSNJAK, E. (1931). *J. Amer. chem. Soc.* 53, 1183.

KRACEK, F. C., POSNJAK, E. and HENDRICKS, S. B. (1931). *J. Amer. chem. Soc.* 53, 3339.

KRISHNAN, K. S. and BANERJEE, S. (1935). *Philos. Trans.* A, 234, 265.

KRISHNAN, K. S., GUHA, B. C. and BANERJEE, S. (1933). *Philos. Trans.* A, 231, 235.

KRUTTER, H. M. (1935). *Phys. Rev.* **48**, 664.

KURNAKOW, N., ZEMCZUZNY, S. and ZASEDATELEV, M. (1916). *J. Inst. Met.* **155**, 305.

LANDÉ, A. (1920*a*). *Z. Phys.* **1**, 191.

—— (1920*b*). *Z. Phys.* **2**, 87.

LASSETTRE, E. N. (1937). *Chem. Rev.* **20**, 259.

LATIMER, W. M. and RODEBUSH, W. H. (1920). *J. Amer. chem. Soc.* **42**, 1419.

LAVES, F. (1930). *Z. Krystallogr.* **73**, 202.

LENGYEL, B. (1932). *Z. Phys.* **77**, 133.

LENNARD-JONES, J. E. (1925). *Proc. roy. Soc.* A, **109**, 584.

—— (1931*a*). *J. Lond. math. Soc.* **6**, 290.

—— (1931*b*). *Proc. phys. Soc., Lond.*, **43**, 461.

LENNARD-JONES, J. E. and DENT, B. M. (1926). *Proc. roy. Soc.* A, **112**, 230.

LENNARD-JONES, J. E. and TAYLOR, P. A. (1925). *Proc. roy. Soc.* A, **109**, 476.

LEWIS, G. N. (1916). *J. Amer. chem. Soc.* **38**, 762.

—— (1923). Valence and the Structure of Atoms and Molecules. Chemical Catalog Co., New York.

LIPSON, H. (1935). *Proc. roy. Soc.* A, **151**, 347.

LIPSON, H. and BEEVERS, C. A. (1935). *Proc. roy. Soc.* A, **148**, 664.

LLEWELLYN, F. J., COX, E. G. and GOODWIN, T. H. (1937). *J. chem. Soc.* 883.

LONDON, F. (1928). *Leipzig. Vorträge*, 59.

—— (1929). *Naturwissenschaften*, **17**, 516.

—— (1930*a*). *Z. Phys.* **63**, 245.

—— (1930*b*). *Z. phys. Chem.* B, **11**, 222.

—— (1937). *Trans. Faraday Soc.* **33**, 8.

LONSDALE, K. (1928). *Nature, Lond.*, **122**, 810.

—— (1929*a*). *Proc. roy. Soc.* A, **123**, 494.

—— (1929*b*). *Trans. Faraday Soc.* **25**, 352.

—— (1937). *Z. Krystallogr.* **97**, 91.

LONSDALE, K. and KRISHNAN, K. S. (1936). *Proc. roy. Soc.* A, **156**, 597.

MCCREA, G. W. (1932). *Proc. roy. Soc. Edinb.* **51**, 190.

MCFARLAN, R. L. (1936*a*). *J. chem. Phys.* **4**, 60.

—— (1936*b*). *J. chem. Phys.* **4**, 253.

MACHATSCHKI, F. (1928). *Zbl. Min. Geol. Paläont.* A, 97.

—— (1932). *Geol. Fören. Stockh. Förh.* **54**, 447.

—— (1938*a*). *Naturwissenschaften*, **26**, 67.

—— (1938*b*). *Naturwissenschaften*, **26**, 86.

MADELUNG, E. (1918). *Phys. Z.* **19**, 524.

MAGNUS, A. (1922). *Z. anorg. Chem.* **124**, 289.

MALKIN, T. (1930). *J. Amer. chem. Soc.* **52**, 3739.

MARK, H. (1932). Physik und Chemie der Cellulose. Springer, Berlin.

MARK, H. and SCHOSSBERGER, F. (1937). *Ergebn. exakt. Naturw.* **16**, 183.

MARWICK, T. C. (1931). *Proc. roy. Soc.* A, **131**, 621.

MAYER, J. E. (1930). *Z. Phys.* **61**, 798.

—— (1933*a*). *J. chem. Phys.* **1**, 270.

—— (1933*b*). *J. chem. Phys.* **1**, 327.

MAYER, J. E. and HELMHOLZ, L. (1932). *Z. Phys.* **75**, 19.

MAYER, J. E. and LEVY, R. B. (1933). *J. chem. Phys.* **1**, 647.

MAYER, J. E. and MALTBIE, M. M. (1932). *Z. Phys.* **75**, 748.

MEGAW, H. D. (1933). *Proc. roy. Soc.* A, **142**, 198.

—— (1934). *Z. Krystallogr.* **87**, 185.

MEISENHEIMER, J. (1921). *J. phys. Chem.* **97**, 304.

MELLOR, J. W. (1924). A comprehensive Treatise on Inorganic and Theoretical Chemistry, vol. v. Longmans, Green and Co., London.

MEYER, K. H. and GO, Y. (1934). *Helv. chim. Acta*, **17**, 1081.

MEYER, K. H. and MARK, H. (1928). *Ber. dtsch. chem. Ges.* **61**, 593.

—— —— (1930). Der Aufbau der hochpolymeren organischen Naturstoffe. Akademische Verlagsgesellschaft, Leipzig.

MILLMAN, J. (1935). *Phys. Rev.* **47**, 286.

MOTT, N. F. (1935). *Proc. phys. Soc., Lond.*, **47**, 571.

—— (1937). *Sci. Prog. Twent. Cent.* **31**, 414.

MOTT, N. F. and JONES, H. (1936). The Properties of Metals and Alloys. Clarendon Press, Oxford.

MÜLLER, A. (1927). *Proc. roy. Soc.* A, **114**, 542.

—— (1928). *Proc. roy. Soc.* A, **120**, 437.

—— (1930). *Proc. roy. Soc.* A, **127**, 417.

—— (1932). *Proc. roy. Soc.* A, **138**, 514.

—— (1933). *Helv. chim. Acta*, **16**, 155.

—— (1937). *Proc. roy. Soc.* A, **158**, 403.

MULLIKEN, R. S. (1931). *Chem. Rev.* **9**, 347.

—— (1932). *Phys. Rev.* **41**, 49.

NIX, F. C. (1937). *J. appl. Phys.* **8**, 783.

NIX, F. C. and SHOCKLEY, W. (1938). *Rev. mod. Phys.* **10**, 1.

NORTON, J. T. (1937). *J. appl. Phys.* **8**, 307.

NOYES, W. A. (1935). *Chem. Rev.* **17**, 1.

ORELKIN, B. and LONSDALE, K. (1934). *Proc. roy. Soc.* A, **144**, 630.

OSEEN, C. W., and others (1933). *Trans. Faraday Soc.* **29**, 883.

OWEN, E. A. and PICKUP, L. (1933). *Proc. roy. Soc.* A, **139**, 526.

PALACIOS, J. and FOZ, O. R. (1935). *An. Soc. esp. Fis. Quim.* **33**, 627.

PANETH, F. (1926). *Handb. Phys.* **22**, 520.

PAULING, L. (1924). *J. Amer. chem. Soc.* **46**, 2738.

—— (1927). *J. Amer. chem. Soc.* **49**, 765.

—— (1928a). *Z. Krystallogr.* **67**, 377.

—— (1928b). *Chem. Rev.* **5**, 173.

—— (1929). *J. Amer. chem. Soc.* **51**, 1010.

—— (1930a). *Phys. Rev.* **36**, 430.

—— (1930b). *Z. Krystallogr.* **72**, 482.

—— (1931a). *J. Amer. chem. Soc.* **53**, 1367.

—— (1931b). *J. Amer. chem. Soc.* **53**, 3225.

—— (1932a). *J. Amer. chem. Soc.* **54**, 988.

—— (1932b). *J. Amer. chem. Soc.* **54**, 3570.

—— (1933). *Z. Krystallogr.* **85**, 380.

PAULING, L. and BROCKWAY, L. O. (1934). *Proc. nat. Acad. Sci., Wash.*, **20**, 336.

PAULING, L. and HUGGINS, M. L. (1934). *Z. Krystallogr.* **87**, 205.

PAULING, L. and SHERMAN, J. (1933a). *J. chem. Phys.* **1**, 606.

—— —— (1933b). *J. chem. Phys.* **1**, 679.

—— —— (1934). *Proc. nat. Acad. Sci., Wash.*, **20**, 340.

PAULING, L. and WHELAND, G. W. (1933). *J. chem. Phys.* **1**, 362.

PEIERLS, R. (1936). *Proc. roy. Soc.* A, **154**, 207.

PENNEY, W. G. and KYNCH, G. J. (1938). *Proc. roy. Soc.* A, **164**, 409.

PICKETT, L. W. (1933). *Proc. roy. Soc.* A, **142**, 333.

—— (1936). *J. Amer. chem. Soc.* **58**, 2299.

PIPER, S. H., MALKIN, T. and AUSTIN, H. E. (1926). *J. chem. Soc.* 2310.

POLANYI, M. (1921). *Naturwissenschaften*, **9**, 337.

POSNJAK, E. and BARTH, T. F. W. (1931). *Phys. Rev.* **38**, 2234.

RANDALL, J. T. (1934). The Diffraction of X-rays and Electrons by Amorphous Solids, Liquids, and Gases. Chapman and Hall, London.

—— (1938). *Rep. Progr. Chem.* **34**, 169.

REIS, A. (1920). *Z. Phys.* **1**, 204.

ROBERTSON, J. M. (1933*a*). *Proc. roy. Soc.* A, **142**, 674.

—— (1933*b*). *Proc. roy. Soc.* A, **140**, 79.

—— (1933*c*). *Proc. roy. Soc.* A, **141**, 594.

—— (1933*d*). *Proc. roy. Soc.* A, **142**, 659.

—— (1934). *Proc. roy. Soc.* A, **146**, 473.

—— (1935*a*). *Proc. roy. Soc.* A, **150**, 348.

—— (1935*b*). *J. chem. Soc.* 615.

—— (1935*c*). *Proc. roy. Soc.* A, **150**, 106.

—— (1936*a*). *J. chem. Soc.* 1195.

—— (1936*b*). *Proc. roy. Soc.* A, **157**, 79.

—— (1937). *Sci. Progr. Twent. Cent.* **32**, 246.

—— (1938 *a*). *Rep. Progr. Phys.* **4**, 332.

—— (1938 *b*). *J. chem. Soc.* 131.

ROBERTSON, J. M., PRASAD, M. and WOODWARD, I. (1936). *Proc. roy. Soc.* A, **154**, 187.

ROBERTSON, J. M. and WOODWARD, I. (1936). *J. chem. Soc.* 1817.

—— —— (1937*a*). *Proc. roy. Soc.* A, **162**, 568.

—— —— (1937*b*). *J. chem. Soc.* 219.

—— —— (1938). *Proc. roy. Soc.* A, **164**, 436.

RODEBUSCH, W. H. (1928). *Chem. Rev.* **5**, 509.

ROSENHEIM, O. and KING, H. (1932). *J. Soc. chem. Ind., Lond.*, **51**, 464.

SACHS, G. and WEERTS, J. (1931). *Z. Phys.* **67**, 507.

SAVILLE, W. B. and SHEARER, G. (1925). *J. chem. Soc.* 591.

SCHIEBOLD, E. (1923). *Z. Krystallogr.* **57**, 579.

—— (1932). *Ergebn. exakt. Naturw.* **11**, 352.

—— (1933). *Ergebn. exakt. Naturw.* **12**, 219.

SEEMAN, H. (1919). *Phys. Z.* **20**, 169.

SEITZ, F. (1935). *Phys. Rev.* **47**, 400.

SEITZ, F. and JOHNSON, R. P. (1937*a*). *J. appl. Phys.* **8**, 84.

—— —— (1937*b*). *J. appl. Phys.* **8**, 186.

—— —— (1937*c*). *J. appl. Phys.* **8**, 246.

SHERMAN, J. (1932). *Chem. Rev.* **11**, 93.

SHOCKLEY, W. (1936). *Phys. Rev.* **50**, 754.

SIDGWICK, N. V. (1927). The Electronic Theory of Valency. Clarendon Press, Oxford.

—— (1933). The Covalent Link in Chemistry. University Press, Cornell.

—— (1934). *Trans. Faraday Soc.* **30**, 801.

—— (1936). *J. chem. Soc.* 533.

SIDGWICK, N. V. (1937). *J. chem. Soc.* 694.

SKINNER, E. W. (1930). *Phys. Rev.* 36, 1625.

SLATER, J. C. (1924). *Phys. Rev.* 23, 488.

—— (1931a). *Phys. Rev.* 37, 481.

—— (1931b). *Phys. Rev.* 38, 325.

—— (1931c). *Phys. Rev.* 38, 1109.

—— (1934a). *Rev. mod. Phys.* 6, 209.

—— (1934b). *Phys. Rev.* 45, 794.

—— (1937). *J. appl. Phys.* 8, 385.

SLATER, J. C. and KIRKWOOD, J. G. (1931). *Phys. Rev.* 37, 682.

SOMMERFELD, A. (1928a). *Z. angew. Chem.* 41, 1.

—— (1928b). *Z. Phys.* 47, 1.

SOUTHARD, J. C., MILNER, R. T. and HENDRICKS, S. B. (1932). *J. chem. Phys.* 1, 95.

SPANGENBERG, K. (1923). *Z. Krystallogr.* 57, 494.

SPEAKMAN, J. C. (1935). An Introduction to the Modern Theory of Valency. Arnold, London.

STAUDINGER, H. and SINGER, R. (1929). *Z. Krystallogr.* 70, 193.

STEWART, G. W. (1929). *Chem. Rev.* 6, 483.

—— (1930). *Rev. mod. Phys.* 2, 116.

—— (1931). *Phys. Rev.* 37, 9.

STROCK, L. W. (1934). *Z. phys. Chem.* B, 25, 441.

—— (1935). *Z. phys. Chem.* B, 31, 132.

—— (1936). *Z. Krystallogr.* 93, 285.

SYKES, C. (1935). *Proc. roy. Soc.* A, 148, 422.

TAMMANN, G. (1919). *Z. anorg. Chem.* 107, 1.

TARASOV, L. P. and WARREN, B. E. (1936). *J. chem. Phys.* 4, 236.

TAYLOR, N. W. and COLE, S. S. (1934). *J. Amer. chem. Soc.* 56, 1648.

TAYLOR, W. H. (1930). *Z. Krystallogr.* 74, 1.

—— (1933). *Z. Krystallogr.* 85, 425.

—— (1934). *Proc. roy. Soc.* A, 145, 80.

—— (1935a). *J. Soc. chem. Ind., Lond.*, 54, 732.

—— (1935b). *Z. Krystallogr.* 91, 450.

—— (1937). *Z. Krystallogr.* 96, 150.

TAYLOR, W. H., DARBYSHIRE, J. A. and STRUNZ, H. (1934). *Z. Krystallogr.* 87, 464.

TAYLOR, W. H. and NÁRAY-SZABÓ, ST. (1931). *Z. Krystallogr.* 77, 146.

TAYLOR, W. H. and WEST, J. (1928). *Proc. roy. Soc.* A, 117, 517.

—— —— (1929). *Z. Krystallogr.* 70, 461.

UNSÖLD, A. (1927). *Z. Phys.* 43, 563.

VAN ARKEL, A. E. and DE BOER, J. H. (1931). Chemische Bindung als elektrostatische Erscheinung. Hirzel, Leipzig.

VAN DER WAALS, J. D. (1873). Die Kontinuität des gasförmigen und flüssigen Zustandes. Leiden.

VAN HORN, K. R. (1935). *Metal Progr.* 28, 22.

VAN VLECK, J. H. and SHERMAN, A. (1935). *Rev. mod. Phys.* 7, 167.

VEGARD, L. (1921). *Z. Phys.* 5, 17.

—— (1928). *Z. Krystallogr.* 67, 239.

VEGARD, L. and DALE, H. (1928). *Z. Krystallogr.* 67, 148.

VEGARD, L. and KLOSTER, A. (1934). *Z. Krystallogr.* 89, 560.

VERWEY, E. J. W. (1935). *Z. Krystallogr.* **91**, 65.

VON HEVESY, G. (1928). *Z. Elektrochem.* **34**, 463.

VON STACKELBERG, M. (1934). *Z. phys. Chem.* B, **27**, 53.

WAGNER, C. and SCHOTTKY, W. (1930). *Z. phys. Chem.* B, **11**, 163.

WALLER, J. (1925). *Uppsala Univ. Årsskr.*

WARREN, B. E. (1933). *Z. Krystallogr.* **86**, 349.

—— (1934). *Phys. Rev.* **45**, 657.

—— (1937). *J. appl. Phys.* **8**, 645.

WARREN, B. E. and BRAGG, W. L. (1928). *Z. Krystallogr.* **69**, 168.

WARREN, B. E. and BURWELL, J. T. (1935). *J. chem. Phys.* **3**, 6.

WARREN, B. E. and HILL, C. F. (1934). *Z. Krystallogr.* **89**, 481.

WARREN, B. E. and MODELL, D. I. (1931). *Z. Krystallogr.* **78**, 422.

WASASTJERNA, J. A. (1923). *Comment. phys.-math., Helsingf.*, **1**, 38.

WEST, J. (1930). *Z. Krystallogr.* **74**, 306.

WESTGREN, A. (1931). *J. Franklin Inst.* **212**, 577.

—— (1932a). *Trans. Amer. Soc. Steel Treat.* **20**, 507.

—— (1932b). *Z. angew. Chem.* **45**, 33.

WESTGREN, A. and ALMIN, A. (1929). *Z. phys. Chem.* B, **5**, 14.

WESTGREN, A. and EKMAN, W. (1930). *Ark. Kemi Min. Geol.* **10** B, No. 11.

WESTGREN, A. and PHRAGMÉN, G. (1925). *Kolloidzschr.* **36**, 86.

—— —— (1928). *Metallwirtschaft*, **7**, 700.

WIGNER, E. and SEITZ, F. (1933). *Phys. Rev.* **43**, 804.

—— —— (1934). *Phys. Rev.* **46**, 509.

WILLIAMS, E. J. (1935). *Proc. roy. Soc.* A, **152**, 231.

—— (1937). *Sci. Progr. Twent. Cent.* **32**, 15.

WILSON, A. H. (1936). The Theory of Metals. University Press, Cambridge.

WILSON, D. A. and OTT, E. (1934). *J. chem. Phys.* **2**, 231.

WOLFF, F. (1928). Einführung in die Kristallstrukturlehre. Quelle und Meyer, Leipzig.

WOOSTER, W. A. (1931). *Z. Krystallogr.* **80**, 495.

—— (1936). *Z. Krystallogr.* **94**, 375.

WRINCH, D. M. (1936a). *Nature, Lond.*, **137**, 411.

—— (1936b). *Nature, Lond.*, **138**, 241.

—— (1936c). *Nature, Lond.*, **138**, 651.

—— (1937a). *Proc. roy. Soc.* A, **160**, 59.

—— (1937b). *Nature, Lond.*, **139**, 972.

—— (1937c). *Science*, **85**, 566.

—— (1937d). *Trans. Faraday Soc.* **33**, 1368.

—— (1937e). *Proc. roy. Soc.* A, **161**, 505.

WYCKOFF, R. W. G. (1928). *Z. Krystallogr.* **67**, 91.

—— (1931). The Structure of Crystals. Chemical Catalog Co., New York.

—— (1935). The Structure of Crystals (Supplement for 1930–34). Reinhold Publishing Corporation, New York.

WYCKOFF, R. W. G. and COREY, R. B. (1932). *Z. Krystallogr.* **81**, 386.

—— —— (1934). *Z. Krystallogr.* **89**, 462.

YANNAQUIS, N. (1933). *C.R. Acad. Sci., Paris*, **196**, 784.

ZACHARIASEN, W. H. (1928a). *Skr. norske VidenskAkad.* Kl. 1928, No. 4.

—— (1928b). *Norsk. geol. Tidsskr.* **10**, 14.

—— (1929a). *Z. Krystallogr.* **71**, 517.

—— (1929b). *Z. Krystallogr.* **71**, 501.

ZACHARIASEN, W. H. (1930a). *Z. Krystallogr.* **73**, 1.

—— (1930b). *Z. Krystallogr.* **74**, 139.

—— (1930c). *Z. Krystallogr.* **73**, 141.

—— (1931a). *Z. Krystallogr.* **80**, 137.

—— (1931b). *Z. Krystallogr.* **76**, 289.

—— (1931c). *Phys. Rev.* **37**, 775.

—— (1931d). *J. Amer. chem. Soc.* **53**, 2123.

—— (1932). *J. Amer. chem. Soc.* **54**, 3841.

—— (1933). *J. chem. Phys.* **1**, 634.

—— (1934a). *Z. chem. Phys.* **2**, 109.

—— (1934b). *Z. Krystallogr.* **89**, 529.

—— (1934c). *Z. Krystallogr.* **88**, 150.

—— (1934d). *Z. Krystallogr.* **89**, 442.

—— (1935). *J. chem. Phys.* **3**, 158.

—— (1937). *J. chem. Phys.* **5**, 919.

ZACHARIASEN, W. H. and BARTA, F. A. (1931). *Phys. Rev.* **37**, 1626.

ZACHARIASEN, W. H. and BUCKLEY, H. E. (1931). *Phys. Rev.* **37**, 1295.

ZACHARIASEN, W. H. and MOONEY, R. C. L. (1934a). *Z. Krystallogr.* **88**, 63.

—— —— (1934b). *J. chem. Phys.* **2**, 34.

ZACHARIASEN, W. H. and ZIEGLER, G. E. (1932). *Z. Krystallogr.* **83**, 354.

ZDANOW, V., ERSCHOW, A. and GALACHOW, G. (1935). *Z. Phys.* **94**, 241.

ZIEGLER, G. E. (1934). *Z. Krystallogr.* **89**, 456.

ZINTL, E. and BRAUER, G. (1933). *Z. phys. Chem.* B, **20**, 245.

ZINTL, E. and DULLENKOPF, W. (1932). *Z. phys. Chem.* B, **16**, 195.

ZINTL, E. and HARDER, A. (1931). *Z. phys. Chem.* B, **14**, 265.

ZINTL, E. and KAISER, H. (1933). *Z. anorg. Chem.* **211**, 113.

INDEX

ABO_3 compounds, 258
ABX_4 compounds, 69, 258, 264
A_2BX_4 compounds, 258–260
—, morphotropy of, 262–264
Aliphatic alcohols, 329–330
Aliphatic ketones, 330
Alkali halides, interatomic distances in, 5–6
—, lattice energies of, 49, 57
—, lattice theory of, 44–50, 55–58, 85
—, polarization in, 182–183
Alkyl-ammonium halides, 331–332
Alloy systems, 106–156
—, chemistry of, 153–156
—, classification of, 108, 143
—, —, table, 143
—: electron compounds, 123–133
—, general features of, 144–145
—: interstitial structures, 145–153
—, of a true metal and a B sub-group element, 122–141
—, of two B sub-group elements, 141–143
—, of two true metals, 109–115
—, order-disorder transformation in, 116–122
Aluminium, 99–100
Aluminium hydroxide, 293
Aluminium-iron system, 111–114
Aluminium-magnesium system, 139–140
Alums, 3, 282
Amphiboles, 230–234
Anatase, 49, 187, 216
—, lattice theory of, 49–50
Anhydrite, 258–259
Anions, complex, 247–254
—, —, structures containing, 255–265
—, radii, 169–175
—, —, table, 171
Anisodesmic structures, 246–286
—, chemistry of, 265–267
—, definition of, 166
Anthracene, 337–338
—, magnetic properties of, 351
Anti-isomorphism, 200
Antimony, 97–98
Aragonite, 256

Arsenic, 97–98
Atomic radii, 7, 101–105
—, tables, 104, 171
AX compounds, 177, 182–186
AX_2 compounds, 186–193
A_mX_n compounds, 194

Barium peroxide, 248
Barium sulphate, 258
Basic beryllium acetate, 318–319
Benzene, 69–70, 335–337
Benzoquinone, 346–347
Beryl, 229–230
Bismuth, 97–98
Bloch theory of metals, 74–84
Bohr atom, 11–13
Bond lengths in molecular compounds, table, 313
Borates, 220–223
Boric acid, 295–296
Born-Haber cycle, 46–48
—, applied to oxides and sulphides, 59
Born-Landé lattice theory of ionic crystals, 44–50
Born-Mayer lattice theory of ionic crystals, 55–60
Bragg-Williams theory of order-disorder transformation, 118–122
Brookite, 187, 216
B sub-group elements, 91, 96–101, 103
BX_3 ions, 249–250
—, structures containing, 255–258
BX_4 ions, 250–252
—, structures containing, 258–262
BX_6 ions, 252
—, structures containing, 265

Cadmium, 99
Cadmium chloride, 190–193
Cadmium iodide, 190–193
Cadmium-silver system, 123–128
Caesium chloride, 20, 63
— structure in alloy systems, 137–139
Calcite, 3, 255–256, 265–266, 272
Carboxylic acids, 330–331
—, resonance in, 71
Cations, complex, 255
—, —, structures containing, 265

Cations, radii of, 169–175
—, —, table, 171
Cellulose, 353–354
Chemical binding and lattice theory, 63–65
Chemical combination, definition of, 155
Chemical laws, 87
Chondrodite, 227
Chrysene, 338–339
Classification, of alloy systems, 108, 123
—, of crystal structures, 41–43
—, —, table, 43
—, of 'defect' structures, 210–211
—, of hydrates, 276
—, of interstitial structures, 147–148
—, of ionic compounds, 165–168
—, of molecular compounds, 314–316
—, of silicates, 225
Close-packed structures, 91–94
Commensurable structures, definition of, 7
Complex co-ordination compounds, 284–286
Complex ions, 247–255
—, structures containing, 255–265
Conductivity, see Electrical properties
Contrapolarization in A_2BX_4 structures, 263–264
Co-ordinate bond, see Homopolar bond
Copper-gold system, 109–111, 116–117
Copper sulphate pentahydrate, 280–281
Cristobalite, 187–188
Crystal chemistry, aim of, 89
—, definition of, 5
—, early history of, 5–8
Crystal structure and morphology, 196–202
Cuprite, 160–161
Cuprous halides, binding in, 64
—, lattice energies of, 64
Cyanuric triazide, 345–346
Cycloparaffins, 328–329
γ-phases, 125–129, 131, 132, 156

'Defect' structures, 209–214
—, in zeolites, 241
Diamond, 28–29, 157–158
—, zone theory of, 85–86

Diatomic ions, 247–248
Dibenzyl, 342
Diffraction of X-rays, discovery of, 3
p-Dinitrobenzene, 347
Diopside, 230, 233
Diphenyl, 339–340
o-Diphenylbenzene, 340
p-Diphenylbenzene, 339–340
—, magnetic properties of, 351
p-Diphenyldiphenyl, 339–340
—, magnetic properties of, 351
Directed valency, 67–69

Electrical conductivity, see Electrical properties
Electrical properties, of homopolar crystals, 30–31
—, of ionic crystals, 23–24
—, of metallic crystals, 34–35
—, —, Bloch theory of, 78–80
—, of molecular crystals, 39–40
Electron compounds, 123–133
—, chemical significance of, 155–156
Electronic structure of the elements, 13–18
Electrostatic valency, definition of, 165
— principle, 218–219
Electrovalent bond, see Ionic bond
Enantiomorphism of tartaric acid, 2
Exclusion principle, 75

Fatty acids, 330–331
Felspars, 239–240
Fibre structures, 353–358
Fluorides, 195
Fluorite, 3, 186–187, 189
— structure in alloy systems, 140
Furanose ring, 361

Gallium, 98–99
General theory of the solid state, 84–87
Geometrical basis of morphotropy, 19–20, 175–178
Germanates, 245
Germanium, 98
Glasses, 306–309
'Globular' proteins, 363–365
Gold-copper system, 109–111
Goniometer, invention of, 1
Graphite, 333–335
Grimm-Sommerfeld rule, 141–142, 158–159
Gypsum, 284

Hardness, *see* Physical properties
Heats of formation of hypothetical compounds, 62
Heterodesmic structures, classification of, 41–42
—, definition of, 8
—, stability of, 61
Heteropolar bond, *see* Ionic bond
Hexamethylbenzene, 335–336
Hexamethylenetetramine, 320
Historical survey, 1–5
Homodesmic structures, definition of, 8
Homopolar bond, *see also* Homopolar compounds
—, elementary theory of, 26–27
—, quantum theory of, 65–74
—, transition to metallic bond, 100–101
Homopolar compounds, 157–163; *see also* Homopolar bond
—, atomic radii in, 162–163
—, physical properties of, 30–32, 73, 100, 267–274
—, structural characteristics of, 27–30
—, zone theory of, 85–86
Hume-Rothery's rule, 129–133
Hydrated compounds, 274–284
Hydrogen bond, 287–291
—, in ammonium hydrogen fluoride, 291
—, in oxalic acid, 324
—, in phthalocyanine, 345
—, in potassium dihydrogen phosphate, 289–290
—, in resorcinol, 348
—, in sodium bicarbonate, 290
Hydrogen molecule, theory of, 66
Hydroxides, 196, 291–294
Hydroxyl bond, 291–301
—, in aluminium hydroxide, 293
—, in boric acid, 295–296
—, in ice, 298–301
—, in lepidocrocite, 296
—, in oxalic acid, 324
—, in pentaerythritol, 322
—, in resorcinol, 348
Hypothetical compounds, stability of, 61–62

Ice, 298–301
Indium, 98–99
Inert gases, 317
Insulin, 363–364
Interatomic binding forces, 9–43

Interatomic distances, in alkali halides, 5–6
—, in molecular compounds, 313
Intermetallic systems, *see* Alloy systems
Intermolecular binding, types of, 312–314
Internal mixed crystals, 211
Interstitial structures, 145–153
Iodine, 96
Ionic bond, *see also* Ionic compounds
—, theory of, 18–19, 44–50, 55–60
Ionic compounds, 164–309; *see also* Ionic bond
—: anisodesmic structures, 246–286
—, as polyhedra of anions, 215–218
—, classification of, 165–168
—, containing hydrogen, 287–301
—, geometrical basis of, 19–20, 175–178
—, ionic radii in, 169–175
—, —, table, 171
—: isodesmic structures, 164–214
—: mesodesmic structures, 215–245
—, physical properties of, 21–25, 49–50, 267–274
—, structural characteristics of, 19–21
Ionic radii, 7, 169–175
—, table, 171
Iron, dimorphism of, 96
Iron-aluminium system, 111–114
Isodesmic structures, chemistry of, 194–196
—, definition of, 166
—, multiple, 203–209
—, simple, 168–196
Isomorphism, discovery of, 2
—, structural basis of, 197–201

Keratin, 355–358

Lanthanide contraction, 105
Lattice energies, of AX structures, 177–178
—, of alkali halides, 48–49, 57
—, of molecular crystals, 54–55
—, of oxides and sulphides, 58
Lattice theory, of homopolar crystals, 65–74
—, of ionic crystals, 44–50, 55–60
—, of metallic crystals, 74–84
—, of molecular crystals, 50–55
—, of the solid state, 84–87
—, structural significance of, 60–65
Law of rational indices, 1, 3

Laws of chemistry, 87
Layer lattices, 136–137, 190–193
Lead, 99–100
Lepidocrocite, 296
Liquid crystals, 304–306
Liquids, 301–304
London theory of van der Waals bond, 50–55

Magnesium-aluminium system, 139–140
Magnetic properties, of *B* sub-group elements, 100
—, of homopolar crystals, 100
—, of ionic crystals, 24–25
—, of molecular crystals, 350–352
Mechanical properties, of homopolar crystals, 30
—, of ionic crystals, 21–23
—, of metallic crystals, 35–36, 95–96
—, of molecular crystals, 38–39
Melting point, *see* Physical properties
Mercury, 99
Mesodesmic structures, 215–245
—, definition of, 166
Metaborates, 222
Metallic bond, *see also* Metallic elements
—, theory of, 32, 74–84
—, transition to homopolar bond, 100–101
Metallic elements, 89–105
—, atomic radii of, 101–105
—, —, table, 104
—: *B* sub-group metals, 96–101
—, classification of, 91–92
—, physical properties of, 34–36, 95–96, 100, 267–274
—, structural characteristics of, 33–34
—: true metals, 91–96
Metallic state, theory of, 74–84
Metallic systems, *see* Alloy systems
Methylene blue halides, 349
Micas, 234–238
Mixed crystals, 194, 198–199
—, internal, 211
Model structures, 200–201
—, of silicates, 243–244
Molecular compounds, 310–366; *see also* van der Waals bond
—, bond lengths in, table, 313
—, classification of, 314–316
—, magnetic properties of, 350–352

Molecular compounds, physical properties of, 38–40, 267–274
—, structural characteristics of, 37–38
Molecule, significance of, 87
Molybdenum sulphide, 136
Morphology and crystal structure, 196–202
—, table, 202
Morphotropy, and lattice theory, 62–63
—, definition of, 60
—, geometrical basis of, 175–178

Naphthalene, 337–338
—, magnetic properties of, 351
Nickel arsenide, 134–135
Nickel sulphate heptahydrate, 276–279

Olivine, 225–227, 262–264
One-electron bond, 72–73
Optical properties, and structure, 270–274
—, —, table, 273
—, of homopolar crystals, 31–32
—, of ionic crystals, 24–25
—, of metallic crystals, 34–35
—, of molecular crystals, 39–40
Order-disorder transformation, 116–122
Orthoborates, 222
Orthosilicates, 225–228
Oxalic acid, 322–325
Oxides, 195
—, lattice energies of, 58
Oxygen co-ordination of cations, 195–196

Palladium sulphide, 161–162
Paraffins, 326–328
Pauling-Slater theory of homopolar bond, 67–74
Pauling's rules, 218–220
Pentaerythritol, 320–322
Pepsin, 363–364
Periodic classification, 13–18
—, table, 12
—, after Bohr, table, 17
Perovskite, 204–206
Phenacite, 227–228, 263–264
Phthalocyanine, 343–345
Physical properties, of crystals, 267–274
—, —, tables, 40, 273
—, of homopolar crystals, 30–32, 73, 100

Physical properties, of ionic crystals, 21–25, 49–50
—, of metallic crystals, 34–36, 95–96, 100
—, of molecular crystals, 38–40, 350–352
Plastic sulphur, 358
Platinum sulphide, 161–162
Polar bond, see Ionic bond
Polarizability of ions, 179–181
Polarization, 64
—, in anisodesmic structures, 263–264
—, influence on ionic radii, 173–174
—, in isodesmic structures, 178–185, 188–193
—, in mesodesmic structures, 242
Polarizing power of ions, 179–181
Polymeric isomorphism, 200
Polymorphism, 201
Polynuclear complex anions, 252–254
Potassium chlorate, 257–258
Potassium chloroplatinite, 262
Potassium dihydrogen phosphate, 289–290
Potassium sulphate, 260, 262–264
Principle of parsimony, 219–220
Proteins, fibrous, 354–358
—, 'globular', 363–365
Pyranose ring, 359–361
Pyrites, 135–136, 137
Pyroxenes, 230–234
Pyrrhotite, 212

Quantum theory of homopolar bond, 65–74

Radii, 7
—, atomic, 101–105
—, —, table, 104
—, ionic, 169–175
—, —, table, 171
—, 'tetrahedral', 162–163
—, univalent, 174–175
Radius ratios, critical values of, 176
Rare earths, 16–17
Rate of attainment of equilibrium in order-disorder transformation, 120–122
Reflecting goniometer, 1
Refractivity, see Optical properties
Relative valency effect, 145
Repulsive forces between atoms, 53–54

Residual bond, see van der Waals bond
Resonance, 66, 69–71
—, between homopolar and ionic structures, 71–72
—, between metallic and homopolar structures, 100–101
—, in benzene, 69–70, 337
—, in carboxylic acids, 71
—, in cyanuric triazide, 346
—, in oxalic acid, 323
—, in phthalocyanine, 344–345
—, in silicates, 72
—, in stilbene, 343
—, in urea, 320
Resorcinol, 347–348
Rotation of molecules and ions, 249, 267–270
—, Fowler's theory, 270
—, in paraffins, 328
Rubber, 356–357
Rutile, 187, 216–217
—, lattice theory of, 49–50

Scheelite, 261
Selenium, 96–97
Silicates, 223–245
—, binding in, 72, 242
—: chain structures, 230–234
—, classification of, 225, 241, 244
—, crystal chemistry of, 224–225, 231–234, 242–244
—: framework structures, 239–242
—: orthosilicates, 225–228
—: ring structures, 229–230
—: sheet structures, 234–238
Silk, 354
Silver-cadmium system, 123–128
Silver halides, binding in, 64
Silver iodide, 'defect' structure of, 213
SiO_4 group, binding in, 242–243
Sodium bicarbonate, 290–291
Sodium chloride, 4, 20, 63, 176–178, 216–217
—, Born-Haber cycle applied to, 47–48
— structure in alloy systems, 140
Sodium sulphate, 258, 260, 262–264
Sodium sulphite, 257
Sodium thallide, 138–139
Solid solution, 194, 198–199
—, definition of, 155
Solid state, general theory of, 84–87
Spinel, 206–209, 216–217, 263–264
Stability of a crystal structure, 60–63
Steel, 150–153

Sterols, 361–362
Stibnite, 142–143
Stilbene, 342–343
Structural properties, of crystals, table, 40
—, of homopolar crystals, 27–30
—, of ionic crystals, 19–21
—, of metallic crystals, 33–34
—, —, Bloch theory of, 80–83
—, of molecular crystals, 37–38
Structural significance of lattice theory, 60–65
Sugars, 358–361
Sulphides, lattice energies of, 58
Sulphur, orthorhombic, 333–334
—, plastic, 358
Superlattices, 111
—, stability of, 114–115

Tartaric acid, enantiomorphism of, 2
Tellurium, 96–97
'Tetrahedral' radii, 162–163
1.2.4.5-Tetramethylbenzene, 341–342
Thallium, 99–100
Thermal expansion, see Physical properties
Thiourea, 319–320
Three-electron bond, 72–73
Tin, 98
Tobacco mosaic virus, 304–305
Tolane, 343
Transition metals, 14–18, 91
Triatomic ions, 248–249
1.3.5-Triphenylbenzene, 341
True metals, 91–96

Univalent radii, 174–175
Urea, 319–320

Valency, 87
—, directed, 67–69
van der Waals bond, elementary theory of, 36–37
—, physical properties of, 38–40
—, quantum theory of, 50–55
—, structural characteristics of, 37–38
van der Waals lattice energy, 52
Vegard's law, 109, 144–145

Water, 302–304
—, function of, in hydrates, 274–276
—— molecule, constitution of, 299–300
Wolframite, 261
Wool, 355–358
Wurtzite, 158–160
— structure in alloy systems, 141–142

X-ray diffraction theory, 4
X-ray spectrometer, 4

Yttrium fluoride, 194

Zachariasen's rule, 250
Zeolites, 240–241, 283
Zinc, 99
Zincblende, 29–30, 157–160
— structure in alloy systems, 141–142
$(8 - n)$ rule, 27, 96, 97, 98, 99